AN INTRODUCTION TO CRYSTAL OPTICS

AN INTRODUCTION TO CRYSTAL OPTICS

P. GAY, M.A., Ph.D.

Fellow and Tutor of Downing College, Cambridge,
University Lecturer in Mineralogy and Petrology

LONGMANS

LONGMANS, GREEN AND CO LTD
48 Grosvenor Street, London W.1
Associated companies, branches and representatives throughout the world

First published 1967

Set in 10 on 12 point Times New Roman and printed in Great Britain by Jarrold & Sons Ltd, Norwich

CONTENTS

PREFACE

SINCE the last war there has been a growing interest in all aspects of solid state studies; inevitably this has stimulated the teaching of crystallography and the physical properties of crystalline solids as a part of courses covering a wide range of academic disciplines and technological interests. At Cambridge the teaching of natural sciences has always emphasised the necessity for undergraduates to acquire a broad scientific education before any subsequent specialisation, and for many years the Department of Mineralogy and Petrology was exclusively responsible for the basic instruction in most aspects of the crystalline state. Over these years considerable experience has been gained in the presentation of this subject material to students of differing backgrounds and interests; my indebtedness to my colleagues in the Department, past and present, must be recorded, for I have drawn upon this common pool of experience in the preparation of this book.

An introduction to the optical properties of transparent crystalline solids can have theoretical and practical emphases. Both developments are complementary, and the courses on which this book is based have aimed at the preservation of a satisfactory balance. In an elementary textbook there must be a limitation of the subject matter; theoretical treatments cannot always be made in the strictest terms, nor can descriptions of sophisticated practical techniques be undertaken in any depth. The present book aims to provide a firm elementary foundation from which excursions into more advanced topics can be made as experience and inclination demand.

The text has been written with the assumption that the reader has a sound knowledge of the essentials of geometrical crystallography; all studies of the crystalline state are firmly rooted in this, and rather than attempt a brief and necessarily incomplete synopsis here, it is preferable that the reader should get this basic groundwork from one of the books devoted exclusively to elementary crystallography. We are concerned with optical crystallography and this is developed assuming only some acquaintance with elementary geometrical and physical isotropic optics; in the chapters of the book mathematical treatment is minimised, though more detailed but simple analyses are to be found in appendices. Most chapters are illustrated by exercises that are both practical and theoretical, emphasising that the student gains in experience and understanding from both aspects of his work. The materials used in the practical work are generally mineralogical specimens which are commonly available, though they can always be substituted by other similar crystalline substances if these are more readily available.

The greater part of the preparation of the text of this book was carried out during a period of leave of absence from duties in Cambridge, and I am most grateful to the General Board of the University and the Governing Body of Downing College for this opportunity. I must record my thanks to my colleague, Dr N. F. M. Henry, whose detailed advice and comments on the manuscript at all stages helped to formulate the completed text. I am also indebted to Mr H. C. Waddams for the skill with which he has translated rough diagrams into the final text figures. Finally I must record my thanks to my wife for her invaluable assistance, both in the preparation of the manuscript and in the many other tasks which arise when an original manuscript is transformed into this book.

Cambridge
1966

P. GAY

CHAPTER 1

INTRODUCTION

1.1 Types of wave motion

IN discussions of physical properties, we often have to use the concept of wave motion, in which the meaning of the word 'wave' is taken to indicate movement to and fro in a regular manner. There are, however, many different types of wave motion underlying various physical phenomena. Probably the most familiar is that which takes place on the surface of a pool of water when a stone is dropped in. The energy imparted by the stone is seen to be transmitted outwards along the water surface in a series of waves which lap on the edge of the pool; a cork on the water bobs up and down in a rhythmic manner as each wave passes, but does not change its position laterally. Movements of the water as the motion passes are perpendicular to the direction of travel of the waves; these disturbances are a simple example of a transverse motion in which a particle of matter is caused to vibrate at right-angles to the direction of the wave. Other wave motions in matter can be described as longitudinal and cause particles to vibrate along the direction of travel of the disturbance; shock waves due to earthquakes can be both transverse and longitudinal. There are also the familiar sound waves by which we hear, in which the material is alternately compressed and extended as the wave passes through it.

It has long been recognised that light waves are transverse like the waves on the pool, and we can pursue this well-known example to demonstrate some of the characteristic features of this kind of motion. As the cork at a particular position on the pool oscillates vertically, the maximum displacement from its undisturbed, or mean, position defines the amplitude of the wave; this must be an important characteristic of the motion for it is clearly a measure of the energy carried by the disturbance. As successive ripples cross the pool, the wavelength is the distance between successive crests (or troughs); the velocity of motion is measured by the advance of a particular crest or trough in unit time. Nevertheless although velocity and wavelength are important in defining a particular disturbance, in some ways a more fundamental characteristic of the motion is its frequency, or the number of complete oscillations made by the cork in unit time; this is invariant for a particular disturbance whatever the medium of propagation and is determined by the source. The relationships between these and other constants of transverse wave motion are more fully discussed in 2.1. In our simple illustration, the energy imparted by the stone will be spent after a time, and the surface of the pool will become calm again. The whole series of waves from the first to the last one discernible comprise a wave train, in this case, of finite extent. Strictly an infinite wave train would require an indefinitely vibrating source continuously radiating energy, though some trains are so long relative to the wavelength of the motion that we can think of them as being infinite (see 2.3).

These water waves and most of the other familiar examples of wave motions may be called 'matter waves', in the sense that they are only capable of being transmitted through some form of matter. But light waves, with which we are concerned, are of a different kind, and can be called 'non-matter waves', in that they can also be transmitted through free space. The presence of matter is not essential in allowing them to carry energy in the form of electro-magnetic fields, and they form a small part of a wide spectrum of electro-magnetic radiation.

1.2 Electro-magnetic radiation

The idea that light is a form of electro-magnetic radiation arose from theoretical developments by Maxwell. Previously there had been many proponents of a wave theory, but they had always been opposed by supporters of the corpuscular theory due to Newton. The theoretical work showed that energy could be transmitted as radiation in the form of rapidly alternating mutually perpendicular electric and magnetic fields transverse to the direction of propagation of the waves. Shortly afterwards experimental confirmation of Maxwell's theory came with the production of invisible radio waves, and it soon became recognised that light represented a small part of a vast spectrum of electro-magnetic radiation (Fig. 1.1). The range of this effectively continuous spectrum extends roughly from wavelengths of 10^{-10} cm for cosmic γ-rays, etc. to 10^6 cm for long radio waves, and increases as our methods of detecting extreme wavelengths improve. All radiation within this spectrum owes its origin to matter, but can travel independently of matter; the properties of waves arising from their interaction with matter change greatly from one end of this spectrum to the other, but the essential electro-magnetic character persists throughout.

Light is that part of the spectrum to which our eyes are sensitive; it is quite small, covering a wavelength range from about $4-8\times10^{-5}$ cm.

At the short wavelength end, the sensation caused by the interaction with the retina of the observer is what we call a violet colour. With increasing wavelength this colour changes gradually to blue, green, yellow, orange and red, before passing the threshold of visible perception; the exact colour sensation of particular wavelengths varies

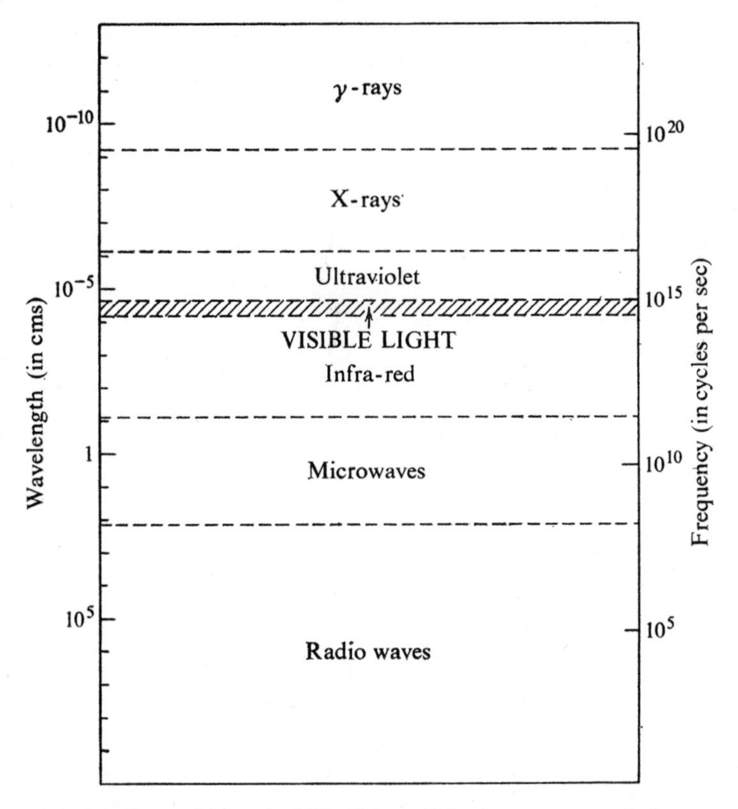

Fig. 1.1 The position of visible light within the spectrum of electro-magnetic radiation. The free space wavelengths and frequencies are plotted on a logarithmic scale.

slightly with individual observers. While the wavelength (or strictly, the frequency) causes the sensation of colour, the amplitude of the electro-magnetic fields is responsible for the strength or intensity of the colour detected by the observer.

Some time after the acceptance of the electro-magnetic wave theory of light, it became clear that a wave nature is inadequate to explain certain optical phenomena; light can behave rather as the particles of a corpuscular theory, and in certain contexts the concept of light quanta (or photons) is essential. This duality of light (and other forms of radiation) is now a firmly established physical principle, and the reconciliation of a particle and wave nature of light presents no fundamental difficulties. From the viewpoint of those interactions with matter with which we are concerned in this treatment of crystal optics, it is convenient to emphasise the wave nature, and to describe light as a form of the electro-magnetic radiation predicted by Maxwell.

1.3 Nature of matter

Each of the atoms constituting matter is most simply thought of as having a nucleus with 'planetary' electrons, each of which has its own electro-magnetic field. The nucleus is very small, and takes no part in any interaction with light waves; the number and arrangement of extranuclear electrons depends on the element, whose atomic size is effectively determined by the radii of the outermost electronic orbits. In any state of aggregation, atoms of a particular element retain most of the characteristics of the electronic distribution of a free atom, though details of their configuration depend on the arrangement of neighbouring atoms; these changes in electron distribution can be most important in determining the physical properties of a collection of atoms.

In a gas, the unit particles (atoms or molecular atomic groups) move independently of each other apart from occasional collisions; on the average, the units are relatively distant from one another, and behave as if they were free. In a liquid, the units are all more or less in contact, although there is no regular arrangement which persists beyond nearest neighbours; the atoms vibrate with thermal energies, which can be large enough to break any temporary attachments between neighbouring units and prevent the formation of any long-range regularity. We may contrast this with the arrangement of atoms which is produced on solidification as the thermal energy is decreased by lowering the temperature. For the majority of solids, the atoms vibrate about fixed mean positions as permanent bonds are formed between neighbouring atoms; the forces of these bonds impose a periodic (but not necessarily the most compact) arrangement upon the atoms, in which there is a long-range regularity. The structure of crystalline matter can be regarded as a characteristic pattern of atoms regularly repeated in three dimensions rather as a basic design motif is repeated on a wallpaper in two dimensions; the rules which govern the repetition of the atomic pattern form the basis of crystallography. There is, however, another category of solid matter, the amorphous state, which is best described as a 'frozen' liquid structure; the atoms vibrate about fixed mean positions, but there is no regularity beyond the nearest neighbours. Although stable amorphous solids are relatively rare, we are apt to think of them as being more common than they are for they have many uses in everyday life; in particular, glass, an important component of much optical equipment, has this kind of atomic arrangement.

Our concern is with the interaction of light waves and solid matter—mainly with crystalline matter, and only indirectly with amorphous glasses. Optical properties result from the modification of the electromagnetic fields of the light waves by the particular electric and magnetic fields within the solid which have arisen from its atomic structure. The detailed theoretical treatment of optics on an atomic scale is still at a very early stage of development, mainly due to our inability to characterise the atomic fields inside solids. For the present we must be content with a more *ad hoc* approach on a macroscopic scale, but it is important to recognise the fundamental origin of the phenomena which we describe.

1.4 Scope of the present book

Crystal optics embraces all aspects of the interaction of light with crystalline matter. When light waves travel within a crystalline solid they have certain characteristics (velocity, vibration direction, etc.) which can depend both on the nature of the solid and the direction o propagation; but in every case there is a decrease, to a greater or lesser extent, in intensity as the light progresses through the crystal. This suggests that we must make a distinction between transparent crystals, on the one hand, and opaque crystals on the other. An ideally transparent crystal is one in which there is no absorption and an ideally opaque crystal is one in which there is no transmission. Of course, real crystals do not conform to these ideals but are intermediate in properties.

The proportion of the incident light energy transmitted through a particular crystalline solid depends on the optical path length. With those materials which we call transparent, the reduction is quite small even for quite thick sections, although some incident energy is reflected, especially if the surface is polished. Substances with lower degrees o transparency allow a significant amount of light to pass only if the thickness is reduced and are often called translucent. Finally there are those crystals which are said to be opaque, though we are unlikely to find any which accord strictly with the ideal definition; for example, even gold can be beaten so thin as to transmit light. In opaque substances, the light is absorbed (and converted into other forms of energy, mainly heat) within the first few layers of atoms, though much of the energy of the incident light is reflected back from the surface of the crystal.

In this book we shall be concerned only with the nature and properties of the light transmitted through crystals; essentially we shall regard all crystalline matter as ideally transparent, and neglect the effects of absorption (except in so far as they affect optical phenomena in a qualitative way to give colours, etc. as described in Chapter 5). Although this restricted approach is clearly a special case of the general interaction of light and crystalline matter, it may be legitimately applied to the vast majority of substances, where the neglect of absorption produces little or no quantitative effect on optical properties. However, we must always bear in mind that for highly absorbing substances our descriptions of transmitted light optics may have to be modified; they cannot necessarily be carried over unchanged into other fields of crystal optics (for example, the study of opaque substances by means of the reflection of light).

CHAPTER 2

THE REPRESENTATION OF LIGHT AS A WAVE MOTION

2.1 The description and properties of simple waves

THE description which we shall give in this section is a purely geometric representation which can be applied to several quite different physical phenomena having only their wave nature in common. Let us imagine a wave emitted by a source along some particular direction and see what effect the passage of the wave will have in this direction. Of course, as the wave advances, the condition imposed by the motion upon a given point in space varies rhythmically during a certain period. In terms of a cork oscillating on a disturbed water surface, the displacement of the cork as the waves pass increases to a maximum positive value, then decreases through the mean position to a maximum negative value and thence back to zero before repeating positive displacements again. This oscillatory displacement of the given point on the water marked by the cork is repeated each period so long as the wave lasts.

We can look at this motion in rather a different way by taking a 'photograph' of the moving wave. At a particular instant we shall see the relative amplitudes of the displacements due to the wave motion at all points along the chosen direction (Fig. 2.1). This figure shows the simplest form of amplitude variation along a given direction, a sine curve. This representation of a *simple sinusoidal wave* shows what is meant by its wavelength (λ) and its amplitude (a), but to characterise our wave further we must also specify its velocity (v); the velocity of propagation is the speed of advance of a wave crest (or any other point). Other methods of defining the motion can be used. These involve the period (T), which is the time taken for a particular point to execute a complete cycle of displacement, and the frequency (ν), which is the number of wave crests to pass a given point in unit time. It is clear that these constants of the motion must be interrelated, i.e. that the wavelength must be the product of velocity and the period, so that

$$v=\lambda/T, \text{ and } \nu=1/T=v/\lambda.$$

We notice, too, that the wave motion is *transverse* in that the displacements are perpendicular to the direction of propagation. Furthermore, for this simple wave motion, the displacements (as defined by the relative amplitudes) are all parallel to the same direction, and so this motion may be said to be *linearly polarised* parallel to this direction. Sometimes in the past the term 'plane polarised' has been used, denoting the fact that the displacements all lie in a single plane containing the direction of propagation; this term is not so relevant in that it does not relate linear polarisation to the more complex circular and elliptical polarisations so clearly, and will not generally be used here.

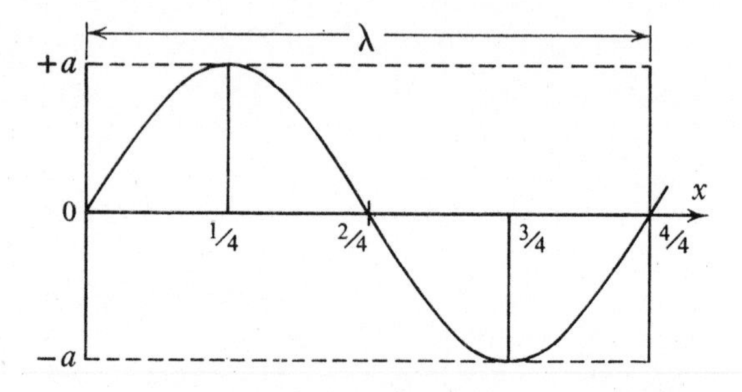

Fig. 2.1 Geometrical representation of sinusoidal wave motion, linearly polarised, of amplitude a and wavelength λ, travelling in direction x.

In this way the simplest wave motion can be described, but of course, in practice we shall never be able to obtain the single, isolated wave train that we have described. A stone dropped into the pool produces wave trains travelling in all directions, and so any small source dissipates its energy in all directions. If a photograph is now taken, it would be seen that the locus of particular equal displacements in space would be the surface of a sphere surrounding the source. Such surfaces form wave fronts, so that at all points on the wave fronts the same condition has been imposed on the waves diverging in all directions from the source. A small source generates spherical waves, with the source at the centre of the spherical wave fronts, but effectively plane wave fronts can be obtained by selecting a small area of the spherical front, by some form of aperture, when the front is relatively distant from the source, so that the radius of curvature is large. In this context, then, we can speak of plane wave fronts advancing in a direction perpendicular to the front, the *wave normal direction*.

The simple transverse wave motion that has been described can lead to planar wave fronts passing through a medium. The complete specification of the motion involves a knowledge of (*a*) the wave normal direction, (*b*) the velocity of propagation, (*c*) the amplitude (whose square gives a measure of the intensity), (*d*) the wavelength (or frequency), and (*e*) the direction of polarisation. An analytical treatment of these simple waves is given in Appendix B.

2.2 Combination of waves

If we drop two stones simultaneously into a pool of water at different places, two sets of waves spread across its surface. In the region of the pool where the two sets of waves cross, we should see complex disturbances affecting the water. These complex disturbances can be analysed quite simply if it is realised that the motion of the cork placed in this region is due to the sum of the vertical displacements it would have from each wave independently. It is reasonable that the problem should be treated in this way for we should see that each independent wave train when passing out of the region of crossing is completely unchanged; all the characteristics of each wave motion are just the same as if they had crossed the undisturbed surface of the pool. All the familiar experience of our vision suggests that the principle of superposition is applicable to light waves as well as water waves.

One of the simplest problems to consider is when there are two simple, linearly polarised sine waves of equal amplitude, velocity and wavelength travelling in the same direction. If the two waves had started at the same instant of time, obviously the resultant wave would also be a sine wave with twice the amplitude of one of the single waves; at all points along the direction of travel the displacements due to the individual waves have been added to give the new wave form (Fig. 2.2*a*). If the two vibrations had started at different instants of time they would be out of step with one another; at a particular instant of time, corresponding displacements would be separated in space. When the effects of the two waves are added together, we see that the overall disturbance has the same wavelength as the original waves but has a different amplitude and in general is out of step with both of them (Fig. 2.2*b*). A rather more convenient method of finding the effects of two or more similar wave motions along the same direction is obtained by a simple geometrical construction. If in Fig. 2.3*a* a point on the circumference of the circle moves around it at a fixed angular velocity, the motion of the projection of this point on to a diameter of the circle is exactly the same as the displacement imposed on a particular point by the passage of the simple wave motion. Viewed end on to the circle, the point would complete its

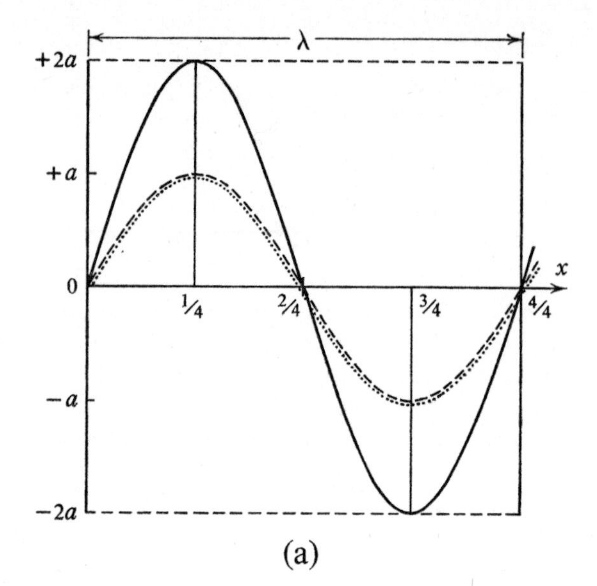

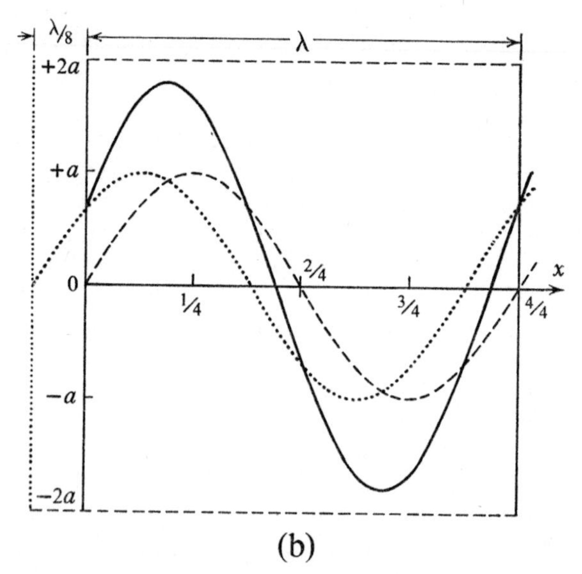

Fig. 2.2 Superposition of sinusoidal wave motions.
a. Equal amplitudes, in phase, i.e. no path difference.
b. Equal amplitudes, out of phase by 45°, i.e. path difference $\lambda/8$.
In both diagrams, the constituent motions are represented by dotted and dashed lines; the resultant wave motion is shown as a heavy line.

cycle of oscillation while the front of the wave advanced through one complete wavelength. We can use this representation in finding out the resultant of two or more wave motions moving along the same line. Each of the two wave motions is represented by a vector, a line with both magnitude and direction. The magnitude of the lines represents the amplitudes of the vibrations, and the angle between them represents the lag of one behind the other. Now the lag of one motion behind the other

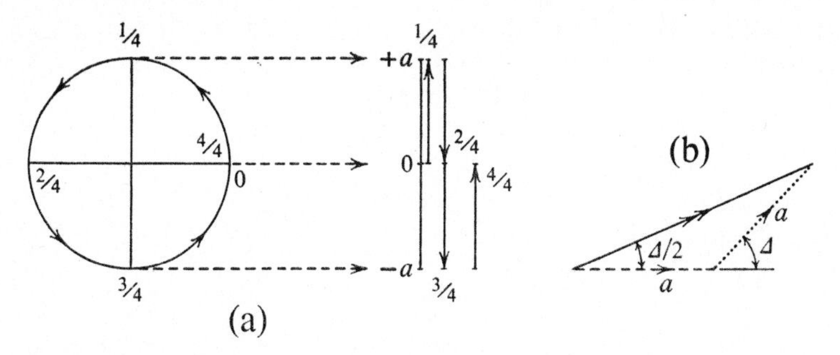

Fig. 2.3 Vector representation of sinusoidal wave motion.
a. The projection of a point on the circumference of a circle radius a, on to a diameter in the same plane. This represents the displacement imposed upon a given point by the passage of a sinusoidal wave.
b. Vectorial representation of the superposition of wave motions of Fig. 2.2*b*. The combination of the two wave motions (dotted and dashed) of equal amplitude with a phase angle of $\Delta(=45°)$ to give a resultant wave whose amplitude and phase is represented by the vector with a double arrow.

can be specified in different ways. Probably the most obvious is in terms of the *path difference*, the separation between corresponding crests of the two waves; path differences are usually expressed as a fraction of the wavelength of the motion, so that in Fig. 2.2*b* the path difference between the two wave motions is $\lambda/8$. We saw just now that in terms of the movement of a point around the circumference of a circle, one revolution was completed as the wave advanced through one wavelength. Thus, if one wave has a certain path difference relative to another, we can express this as a fraction of the whole revolution associated with one wavelength, so that we get the *phase* (*angle*) *difference* (in radians) between the two waves as $2\pi/\lambda$ times the path difference. A path difference of $\lambda/8$ as in Fig. 2.2*b* corresponds to a phase (angle) difference of $2\pi/8$ radians$=45°$. We can now represent the two waves of this example, for we know both the magnitudes and the relative angular orientation of the associated vectors. The amplitude and phase of the resultant wave motion is then obtained by finding the sum of these two vectors. This can conveniently be done graphically for the vector sum is represented by the line which closes the triangle whose first two sides are formed by the original pair of vectors (Fig. 2.3*b*); the length of this new resultant vector represents the amplitude of the new wave motion, while its orientation is a measure of the phase, which is different from those of the original waves. This figure is called a *phase-amplitude diagram*, and more detailed explanation of its use is given in Appendix B. It can deal with any number of wave motions of similar or different amplitudes with phase differences between them, provided only that their displacements are co-planar and that they have the same frequency.

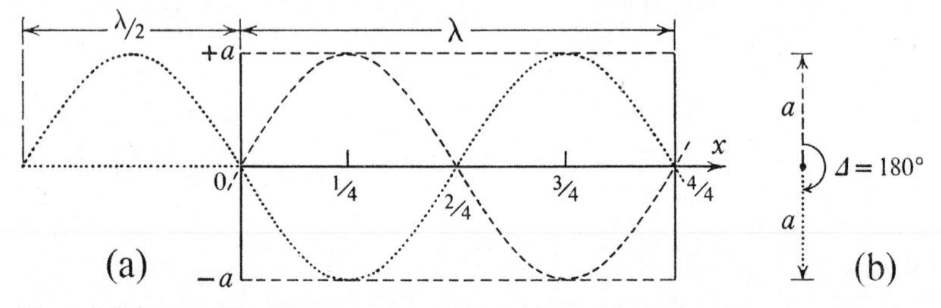

Fig. 2.4 Superposition of two wave motions exactly out of phase.
a. Geometrical representation of two wave motions, linearly polarised, of amplitude a and wavelength λ, with path difference $\lambda/2$. There is no resultant disturbance at any point along the direction of travel, x.
b. Vector representation of the same wave motions, equal amplitudes but with phase angle $\Delta(=180°)$.

In the simplest original example with no path difference between the two waves, they are exactly in phase; the phase-amplitude diagram shows a resultant vector whose amplitude is twice that of either of the original waves and whose phase is unchanged. Physically such complete reinforcement means that there is a transmission of energy in this direction of propagation four times greater than that associated with either of the original waves. We have also seen above in the second example a case of partial interference which produced a new wave with different amplitude and phase from either of the original waves. Another interesting case occurs when the phase angle is 180°, so that the two waves are said to be exactly out of phase and annul each other (Fig. 2.4). Physically such *total destructive interference* means that there is no transmission of energy along this direction of propagation. It is important to realise that we cannot learn from the phase-amplitude diagram what happens to the original energy save that none of it is transmitted along the original direction. If we were considering the particular case of light waves, we would have to assume that the original energy is dissipated perhaps by being diverted to another direction or perhaps by being released as thermal energy.

2.3 Light waves

It is now important to consider whether the simple, linearly polarised sinusoidal waves of the previous two sections provide an adequate model of light waves. In the electro-magnetic theory, the transmitted radiation can be of this form; there is no physical displacement of an element of the material of the medium of transmission, only the periodic waxing and waning of the electric and magnetic fields at the element. The physiological effect of electro-magnetic radiation within a particular band of frequencies on the eye is to produce the sensation of intensity and colour. The intensity is a measure of the energy implied by the amplitude of the electric (or magnetic) vector; the colour seen by the eye is determined by the wavelength (or more strictly the frequency, for, as will be seen in the next chapter, this is invariant while the wavelength and velocity vary with the transmitting medium).

Now the light sources usually employed in optical work are incandescent (such as the filament of an electric lamp) or vapour discharge. Such sources produce radiation which differs from that described by the simple sinusoidal waves in a number of ways. First, many sources emit white light which contains a continuous or semi-continuous range of wavelengths. This presents no great difficulty for we can treat the wave trains of different wavelengths independently; alternatively we can approach the ideal single wavelength by using a single spectral line as the source or by passing the white light through a filter of narrow band width. Second, the light emitted by optical sources is unpolarised. The nature of unpolarised light will be discussed more fully in this section, but for the moment it is enough to realise that the waves of a more or less precise wavelength, produced by, say, a line of an emission spectrum are not linearly polarised. This again presents no great difficulty for there are polarising devices, such as those described in Chapter 6, which ensure that the transmitted light has its displacement vectors parallel to only one direction. A much more fundamental difficulty arises from the physical processes within the source which give the electro-magnetic radiation. Essentially the radiation is produced when the extranuclear electrons of the atoms of the source move from one fixed energy state to another; excess energy is radiated away. The energy levels whose difference determine this excess energy are a characteristic of the atoms of the emitter and their state of aggregation. The general nature of this mechanism suggests that the emission of light is a discontinuous process, i.e. that the wave trains are emitted in short bursts rather than in effectively infinite trains. The finite character of the group of waves in a

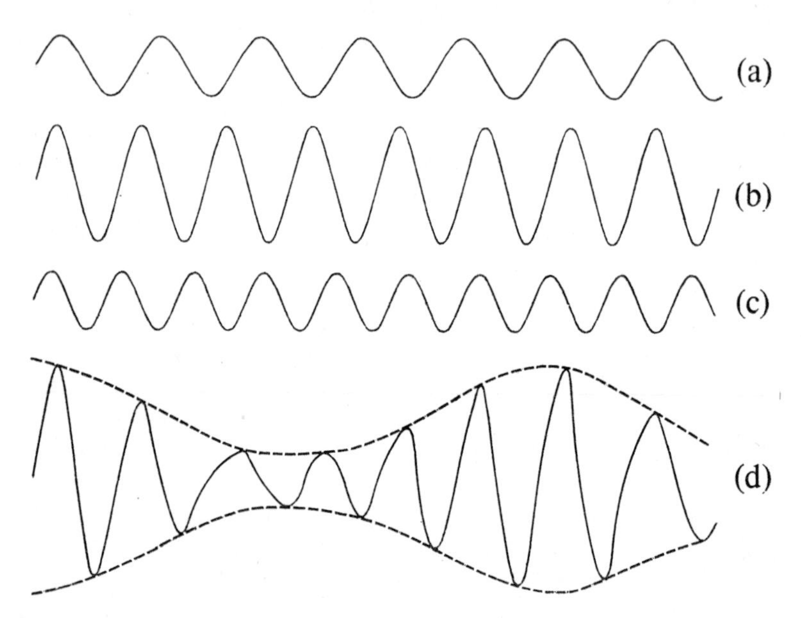

Fig. 2.5 The production of a complex waveform by the addition of simple sinusoidal waves.
a. is a sinusoidal wave of amplitude a and wavelength $7\lambda/6$;
b. is a sinusoidal wave of amplitude $2a$ and wavelength λ;
c. is a sinusoidal wave of amplitude a and wavelength $5\lambda/6$;
d. is the complex waveform produced by the summation of a, b and c; the dashed envelope shows the pulsating nature of the resultant.

pulse presents a difficulty in that to produce the ideal sinusoidal wave it is necessary for the source to emit continuously. A group of waves of finite extent does not have the simple form that our model requires, though a way around this problem is possible when it is realised that any complex wave form can be analysed into a large number of simple components by the correct arrangement of amplitudes and wavelengths. A simple illustration of this general principle is given in Fig. 2.5. Three waves of related amplitude but slightly different wavelengths are summed to produce a complex wave form; even with this crude example the pulsed nature of the resultant is beginning to become apparent. In this way we can regard the light which is emitted in bursts as being made up of simple waves with a distribution of wavelengths about a mean value; while there is a maximum intensity at a particular wavelength some of the energy of the wave train is carried in other wavelengths. Clearly the more complete cycles there are in a group, the closer we approach the ideal of a single wavelength, and the smaller the spread of wavelengths on either side of the position of maximum intensity. An estimate of the extent of the wave train in a pulse from an optical source can be made from the energy lost by an electron of the source in producing this pulse. For example, the energy change which causes the emission of a spectral line of sodium of wavelength 5800×10^{-8} cm leads to a frequency of 5×10^{14} cycles per second. If the duration of the pulse is a hundred millionth of a second, there will be 5×10^{6} waves in the pulse. So that the light pulses always contain millions of waves suggesting that the variation of wavelengths about a mean value is very small. Nevertheless we must be prepared for the implications of this pulsed nature of light in our experiments.

One obvious consequence of the intermittent character of the wave motion is that in any dispersive medium, i.e. one in which the velocity of travel depends on wavelength, an individual wave crest may move with a speed different from the train as a whole. This can often be seen when watching waves on a pond; ripples appear which move through the group of waves to die away at the front and reappear at the back. There are then two velocities to be considered, one, the *wave (or phase) velocity* representing the speed of the individual wave crests and the other, *the group velocity*, which is a measure of the speed of the pulse as a whole. Of course the wave and group velocities are the same if the light is travelling in a medium for which there is no dispersion. This is certainly true in a vacuum but is not generally so in matter. The velocity of light in free space is directly determined as about 3×10^{10} cm per second, which is the fundamental physical constant usually denoted by the symbol c. For air the change in the velocity is so slight that it can be neglected in all ordinary work. We obtain our information about the velocity of propagation in most other materials indirectly by measurement of their refractive indices; since these materials are dispersive to a greater or lesser extent it is important to be clear that such measurements depend on the wave (or phase) velocity (see 3.1). In transparent media, such as we are primarily concerned with in this book, this wave velocity is always less than c. For gases the change is slight (reduction factor for air at normal temperatures and pressures, 1/1·0003), while for liquids, the highest values (reduction factor about 1/1·33) are for water and methyl alcohol. For solids the range is considerable; the highest values (1/1·31) are found for glasses, going down to diamond (1/2·4), with still lower values for absorbing substances such as sulphide ore minerals. The nature of the dispersion is such that the wave velocity is always greater than the group velocity. Thus in a strongly dispersive liquid such as carbon disulphide direct determination of the velocity shows that the group velocity is $c/1{\cdot}76$, whereas the determination of the phase velocity by refractive index measurement gives a value of $c/1{\cdot}64$.

Another consequence of the intermittent emission of light concerns the polarisation of the radiation. A single pulse will be linearly polarised with the direction of the electric (or magnetic) displacement vectors parallel to a particular direction, but each pulse can have a different direction of polarisation. Thus, as light is radiated by the source, a succession of pulses will follow one another at random intervals, linearly polarised in random directions. This is what is implied by the term *unpolarised light*, and we can only obtain linearly polarised light by passing the unpolarised light from the source through some device which will constrain the vibration planes of the electric and magnetic vectors. This conception of the nature of light explains why interference effects of the kind described in the previous section are only observed experimentally for light if the two interfering wave trains are coherent and come from the same source. If it were possible to arrange that identical pulses were simultaneously emitted by two sources and a predetermined phase lag was imposed upon one of them, a particular interference effect could be observed for an infinitesimal interval of time. Even if the polarisation of the next pulses was the same, they would not be emitted at the same instant of time by the two sources. This will impose an additional phase lag over and above that predetermined by the experimental conditions, so that a different interference effect would be observed for an infinitesimal time; the same would hold for all subsequent pulses vibrating in the same plane. Thus, whenever interference can occur, effects of different kinds succeed one another extremely rapidly in a random manner; to an observer these average to give no visible effects of interference whatsoever. For light, in order to see the effects of interference, the wave trains must be derived from the same light source, because for a given source the difference in phase between any pair of points on the source is constant, so that the only factor which determines the delay which one wave train suffers relative to another is imposed by the external experimental arrangement. In this way the interference effect will be the same for all pulses of light and will be observable.

Finally for this electro-magnetic radiation we must consider how the plane of polarisation, or preferably, the direction of polarisation, is to be defined. The electro-magnetic character of light is such that as the wave front advances, the magnetic and electrical displacements, which are in phase with each other, wax and wane in directions perpendicular to each other but both in the plane of the wave front. With a mechanical wave, there is not this duality of direction for the displacement vector, and the plane of polarisation is simply defined as containing both the displacement vector (or vibration direction) and the wave normal direction. For light, it must be decided which of the two possible displacement vectors, electric or magnetic, shall be taken as the vibration direction (in the sense that it has been used for a mechanical wave). In many ways this must be an arbitrary choice because in most optical phenomena, the electric waves influence each other in the same way as do the magnetic waves. It has been shown experimentally that it is the electric vector which produces an effect upon a photographic emulsion, which causes fluorescence, and which is responsible for photoelectric effects. It is a reasonable assumption from this experimental data that it is the electric vector to which the retina of the eye is sensitive. And so, we may regard the electric wave as being responsible for the many effects which can be seen with light waves, with the magnetic wave, which must co-exist with it, being of less importance. Whenever, for linearly polarised light, we speak of the *vibration direction* of the light vector, it is the electric vector that is referred to; the plane of polarisation is therefore the plane containing the wave normal and the electric vector.

CHAPTER 3

LIGHT WAVES IN ISOTROPIC AND ANISOTROPIC MEDIA

3.1 Light waves in isotropic media

IN the previous chapter we established the characteristics of light as a wave motion. One of the most important of these is that its velocity of propagation depends on the medium in which it is travelling, though it was also pointed out that many media were dispersive in the sense that the velocity depends on the wavelength. We shall see shortly that there is a further complexity in that in many materials the velocity of propagation also depends on the vibration direction of the light vector, but for the moment this will be neglected. We shall consider only those media, which are said to be *isotropic* (equal directions), in which the speed of travel is the same in all directions and for all vibration directions. Substances which are isotropic in their optical properties embrace gases, liquids and amorphous solids (in particular, glasses), but only a small part of crystalline matter, that belonging to the cubic symmetry system.

Let us start with the simplest problem in which light waves travelling in a general direction in one isotropic medium strike a boundary with a second isotropic medium into which they are transmitted with exactly the same velocity. To find out how the light waves are propagated in the second medium after passing through the boundary, the construction proposed by Huyghens to explain the rectilinear propagation of light can be used. In this, each point on the boundary on which the incident light falls, acts as a source from which secondary disturbances radiate into the second medium. Fig. 3.1 illustrates the construction. Plane wave fronts follow one another through the first material to strike the boundary surface at an angle i. In the diagram wave fronts are drawn at unit intervals of time, t, during which they travel a distance, vt. It is clear that the velocity, v, is the wave (or phase) velocity, since this construction is concerned with the movement of wave fronts (which are the loci of identical phase). The figure shows the position at the instant of arrival of the wave front marked zero at the point O on the boundary. From this point, the secondary spherical wave (produced by the arrival of the previous wave front marked +1) has just spread out to a radius vt, since a unit of time t elapses between the impact of successive wave fronts; at the point marked 1/2 on the boundary, only half a time unit has passed since the arrival of the +1 wave front, and so the secondary spherical wave has a radius $vt/2$. Obviously the location of the +1 wave front in the second medium is the envelope of all the secondary

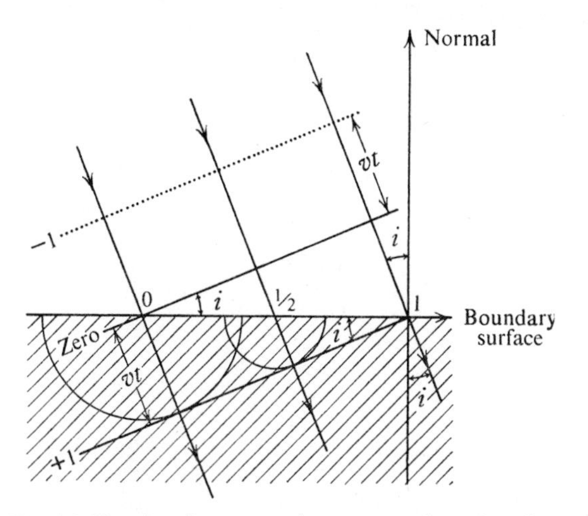

Fig. 3.1 Huyghens's construction across a boundary between two isotropic media in both of which light travels with the same speed.

disturbances radiating from points along the boundary; this will be the common tangent to all these semicircles for which those in the diagram are representative. The geometry of this simple example shows that the light is transmitted unchanged through the boundary; the wave normals in both media are inclined at the same angle, i, to the normal to the surface.

Now let us examine in the same way what happens when the velocity of propagation is different in the two media across the boundary. We will suppose that the velocity in the first material (v_1) is greater than that in the second material (v_2). Fig. 3.2 shows a similar situation to the previous diagram except that in unit time the semicircles in the second medium have a smaller radius (v_2t) than they do in the first medium (v_1t). As a consequence of this, the direction of the wave fronts is changed; the wave normal is bent, or refracted, towards the normal to the boundary when the waves enter the second medium. If i and r respectively define the incident and refracted angles, then

$$\sin i/\sin r = v_1/v_2$$

Refraction is controlled by the relative velocities in the two media, and their ratio for transparent materials is called the *refractive index* (${}_1n_2$) for the boundary. If the first medium is free space (or air) the ratio becomes

$$c/v_2 = n$$

where n is a constant known as the refractive index of the medium. In the form $n = \sin i/\sin r$, the relationship is known as Snell's law,

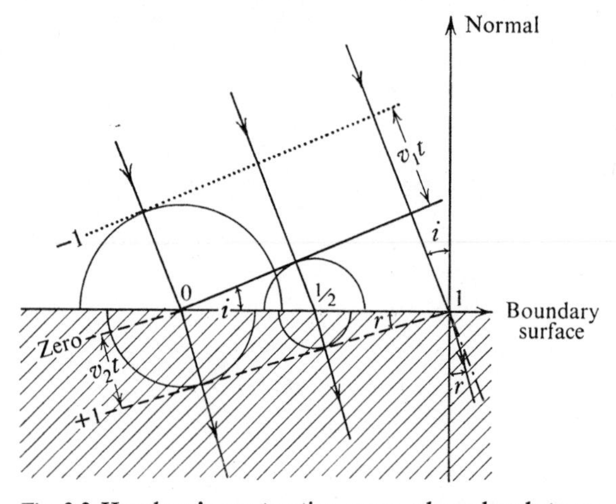

Fig. 3.2 Huyghens's construction across a boundary between two isotropic media in which light travels with different speeds.

which can be used for the experimental determination of n. For transparent substances, the values of n are always greater than unity, showing that the velocity of light in these media is always less than c. In general there is always a reduction in velocity when light crosses a boundary between a less dense medium of lower refractive index and a more dense medium of higher refractive index. Fig. 3.2 also shows that the separation of the wave fronts is reduced in the same way so that

$$\lambda_1/\lambda_2 = v_1/v_2$$

The simultaneous changes in both wavelength and velocity on entering different media imply that the invariant characteristic of the wave motion is its frequency (see 2.1).

The refractive index of an isotropic substance is clearly an important physical constant. When expressed in the form of Snell's law it is of practical use in predicting the changes in wave normal directions for light passing through different media, but it must be stressed that it is essentially a reciprocal wave velocity constant; the ratio of sines becomes meaningless at normal incidence when both i and r are 0°. Let us examine briefly the effect of increasing i from zero, as the wave fronts enter a

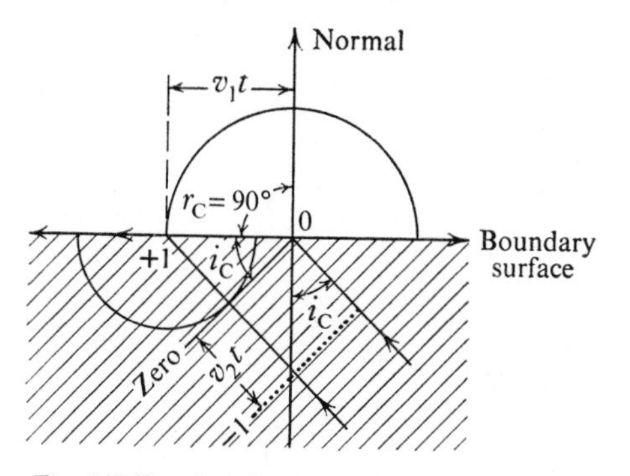

Fig. 3.3 Huyghens's construction at the critical angle for total internal reflection; light incident on the boundary from the medium in which it travels slowest.

more dense medium. As ${}_1n_2 > 1$, the value of r will always be less than i, and the limit will be reached when $i = 90°$; the maximum angle of refraction will be given by $\sin r = 1/{}_1n_2$. But this provides us with a convenient starting-point to consider what happens when light passes across a boundary from a more dense medium into a less dense medium. Clearly all we have to do is to reverse the direction of travel of the wave fronts in Fig. 3.2. The value of the angle of incidence is less than that of the angle of refraction, and the refractive index for the boundary ${}_2n_1$ $(= 1/{}_1n_2)$ is less than unity. Now as the inclination of the incident wave normal is increased from zero, a point will be reached when $r = 90°$ beyond which it will no longer be possible to draw transmitted wave fronts. This limiting case is shown in Fig. 3.3. The angle of incidence at which this occurs is called the *critical angle* (i_c), and is given by $\sin i_c = v_2/v_1 = {}_2n_1 = 1/{}_1n_2$; if the light is emerging into free space (or air) $\sin i_c = 1/n$. For larger values of i total internal reflection back into the medium occurs at the boundary, and light is not transmitted through the interface. Of course this last statement cannot be strictly true, and a more complete analysis shows that the depth of penetration of the electro-magnetic radiation through the boundary is very limited and not detectable in ordinary optical experiments.

The reflection of light at an interface does not only take place under total internal reflection conditions. Whenever light waves strike a boundary, some of their energy goes into the refracted waves but some proportion of the energy is always reflected back at the same angle as

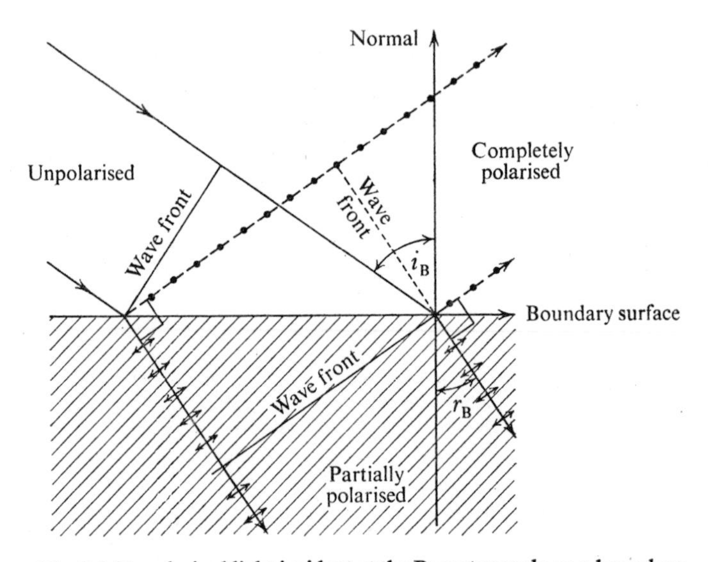

Fig. 3.4 Unpolarised light incident at the Brewster angle on a boundary between two different isotropic media. The reflected waves (dashed) are completely polarised; the refracted waves (full line) are partially polarised. Vibration directions in plane of diagram marked with short arrows; vibration directions perpendicular to plane of diagram marked with dots.

waves within the original medium. Moreover, unpolarised light reflected at the surface of a transparent substance is partially polarised. This degree of polarisation varies with the angle of incidence for a particular material, and Brewster found that the reflected waves were effectively linearly polarised when the wave normals of the refracted and reflected waves are exactly perpendicular (Fig. 3.4). For a particular material, the angle of incidence at which this occurs, the Brewster angle (i_B), is such that

$$i_B + r_B = 90°; \tan i_B = {}_1n_2.$$

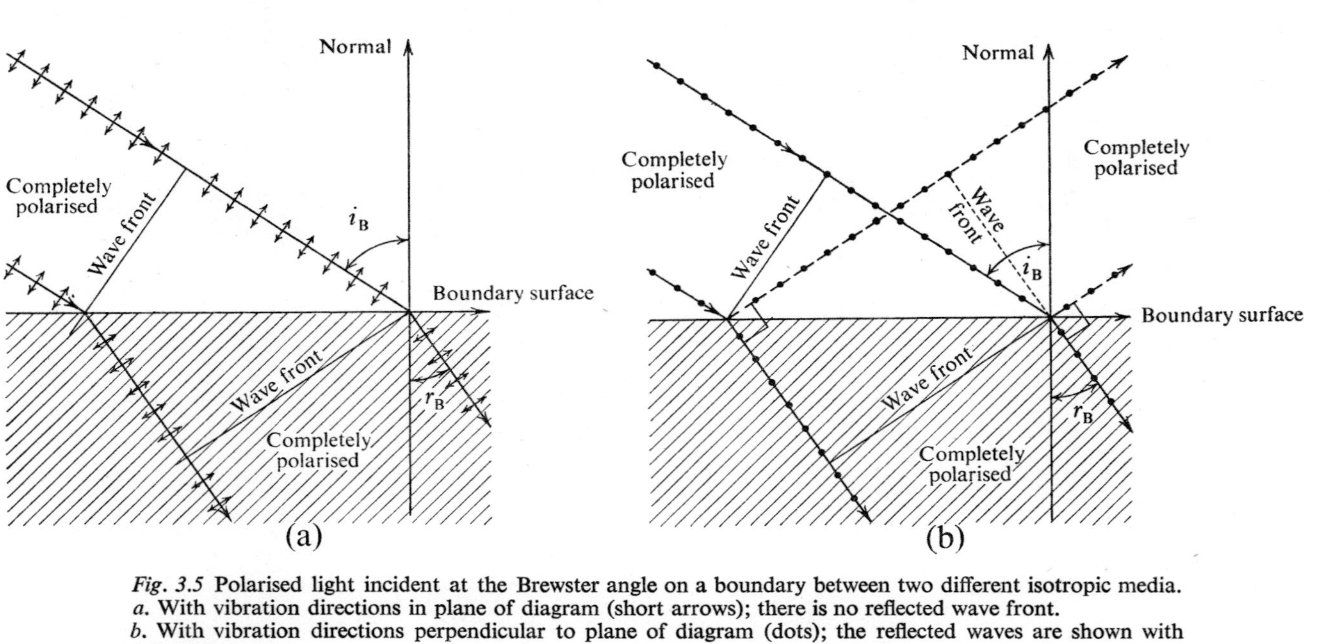

Fig. 3.5 Polarised light incident at the Brewster angle on a boundary between two different isotropic media.
a. With vibration directions in plane of diagram (short arrows); there is no reflected wave front.
b. With vibration directions perpendicular to plane of diagram (dots); the reflected waves are shown with dashed lines.

The vibration direction of the polarised reflected light is normal to the plane of incidence. At the same time, it is found that the refracted light is partially polarised in a perpendicular direction; with unpolarised incident light, the refracted waves are never completely polarised, but they have a maximum linearly polarised component at the Brewster angle (Fig. 3.4). Although waves reflected at the Brewster angle are effectively polarised, they do not provide an adequate source of polarised light both because the Brewster angle varies with wavelength if the medium is dispersive and, more importantly, because most of the energy of the incident waves goes into the transmitted refracted waves. As a corollary of these observations, we realise that if light incident at the Brewster angle is linearly polarised with its vibration direction in the plane of incidence, it will be transmitted without partial reflection and will remain completely polarised in the same plane (Fig. 3.5*a*). Similarly if its vibration direction is normal to the plane of incidence, linearly polarised light which strikes the boundary at the Brewster angle is partly reflected and partly refracted, but remains totally polarised in the same direction (Fig. 3.5*b*).

3.2 Optical anisotropy and uniaxial crystals

The simple laws of refraction, reflection, etc. described in the previous section are valid for isotropic materials such as glass and crystals with cubic symmetry. The vast mass of crystalline material has non-cubic symmetry, and is said to be optically *anisotropic*; this implies that the optical properties are dependent on the direction of propagation of light in the medium. One of the more obvious manifestations of optical anisotropy is shown in the well known experiments with a rhombohedron of calcite, one of the crystalline forms of $CaCO_3$. If a dot on a piece of paper is viewed through an isotropic substance, we see a single image of the dot with an apparent change in depth due to the refractive index of the material; if the same dot is viewed through a pair of opposite faces of the calcite rhombohedron, two images are seen. Not only are the apparent depths of the images different, but one is undisplaced while the other is displaced laterally. This formation of two images is an example of *double refraction*, a phenomenon characteristic of optically anisotropic crystals. Furthermore it can be easily demonstrated that the light waves forming each of the images are linearly polarised but with mutually perpendicular vibration directions, again a characteristic of optically anisotropic crystals. The effects displayed by calcite are easily observed because the size of the double refraction shown by this material is large. It is worth while to examine these experiments in more detail to see what implications they have about the propagation of light waves in this medium. To do this we must assume that we have some device for analysing the vibration direction of linearly polarised light (such as a polar described in Chapter 6) and that we are able to determine the refractive index for any vibration direction.

The rhombohedron of calcite can be regarded as a cube compressed along a body diagonal (Fig. 3.6). This direction in the rhomb is unique, and is the direction of a threefold inversion axis of symmetry; this triad, then, emerges from one of the corners of the rhombohedron and makes equal angles with the three faces which meet at this corner. We shall now try to describe our simple experiments with regard to this important crystallographic reference direction. As we know, when the block is lying flat upon the paper there is double refraction and two images of a dot are seen. The position of the displaced image is such that the plane which contains it and the undisplaced image is always parallel to the triad axis; thus as the crystal is rotated on the paper, the displaced image revolves around the undisplaced dot following the movement of the axis (Fig. 3.7). If we now tilt the rhomb so that the angle of incidence is changed, in general two images are still observed; although the amount of their separation depends on the amount of tilt, the plane containing the dots remains parallel to the triad axis. As we tilt the rhomb so that the light travels more nearly along the triad axis, so the separation becomes smaller, until when we are viewing exactly parallel to the triad axis there is only one single image of the dot. In practice, faces would have to be cut on the rhomb perpendicular to the axis, and the effect is perhaps easier to see using a section of a prismatic crystal of calcite cut parallel to the base of the prism (Fig. 3.8). It will also be found that we apparently see a single image in directions perpendicular to the triad axis, i.e. looking through one of the prism faces; however, as we shall see shortly, there is double refraction for such directions but

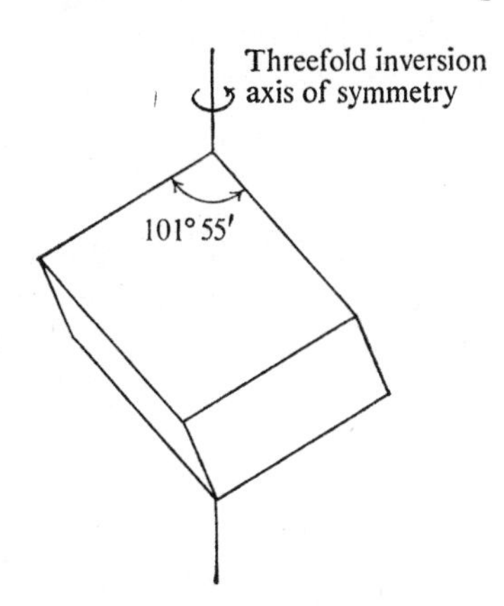

Fig. 3.6 The cleavage $\{10\bar{1}1\}$ rhombohedron of calcite (class $\bar{3}$m).

the two images are superposed and a single dot is apparently observed. The unique direction for which there is truly no double refraction is known as the optic axis. In any anisotropic medium, an *optic axis direction* is one for which there is no double refraction; in calcite and many other crystalline substances there is only one direction of this kind in the crystal; hence such crystals are said to be optically *uniaxial*.

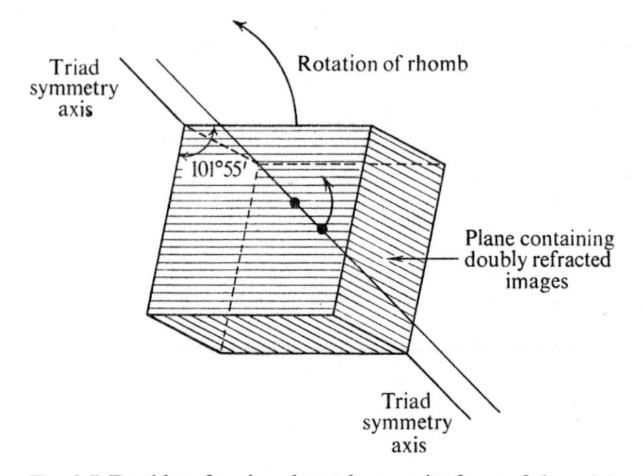

Fig. 3.7 Double refraction through opposite faces of the calcite rhomb. The plane containing the undisplaced and displaced images is parallel to the triad axis; with rotation of the rhomb there is corresponding rotation of this plane.

Now let us consider the vibration directions of the light transmitted through the calcite crystals. To do this we use a polar which only permits the transmission of light linearly polarised parallel to one fixed direction; thus if the vibration direction of incident linearly polarised light is perpendicular to that permitted by the polar, no light is transmitted. Using such a device above the rhomb lying flat upon the paper, the undisplaced image is not observed through the polar when the vibration plane of the polar is parallel to the plane containing the two images. This must mean that the vibration direction for the undisplaced image is perpendicular to that of the polar. The light transmitted by the crystal to form this image is linearly polarised with its vibration direction perpendicular to a principal section of the crystal, i.e. a section which contains the direction of the triad (or optic) axis. When the polar is rotated through 90°, the undisplaced image reappears but the displaced dot is not seen. This confirms that the light transmitted by the crystal to form the two images is linearly polarised with perpendicular vibrations, so that the waves forming the displaced image have their vibration direction parallel to a principal section. We should find that such relationships between the vibration directions hold for all general directions of light propagation in calcite.

Summarising the position so far, in all but one direction in the calcite

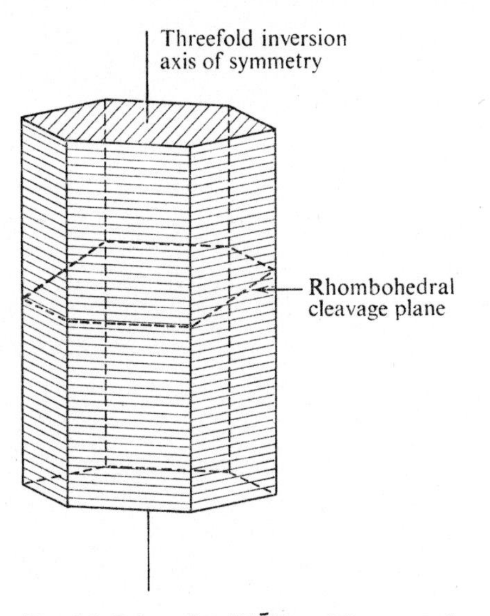

Fig. 3.8 Prismatic $\{10\bar{1}0\}$ calcite crystal (class $\bar{3}$m), with basal $\{0001\}$ pinacoid. The trace of one rhombohedral cleavage $(10\bar{1}1)$ is also shown.

there is double refraction. By this we mean that unpolarised light from the object is transmitted through the crystal as two plane polarised disturbances, one vibrating in a principal section and the other perpendicular to a principal section. In addition, the amount of double refraction as indicated by the relative displacement of the images depends on the direction of propagation in the crystal; for one direction, the optic axis direction parallel to the principal crystallographic symmetry axis, there is no double refraction. It is instructive at this point to analyse our calcite experiments with rhomb and polar in terms of the resolution of the light vector permitted by the phase-amplitude treatment of 2.2. Fig. 3.9 shows the two images observed through the rhomb; the arrows attached to the dots represent the amplitudes and vibration directions of the linearly polarised waves. In the next diagram of the set, the addition of the polar is shown schematically by the superposition of the vibration direction which it allows to be transmitted to the observer. Only the undisplaced spot is seen because the vibration

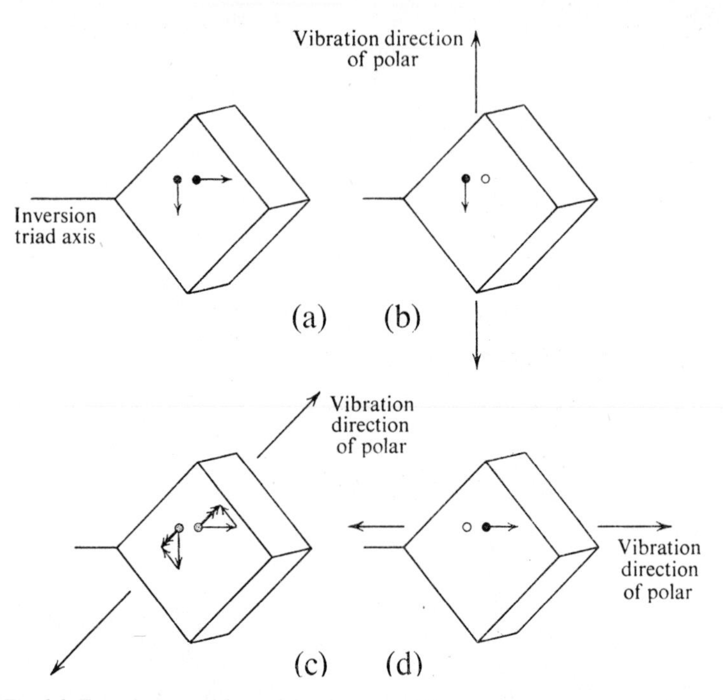

Fig. 3.9 Experiments with a calcite rhomb and linearly polarised incident light. The undisplaced image is on the left; the intensities of the images are indicated as maximum, heavy dot; intermediate, light dot; zero, open circle.
a. Unpolarised incident light; the amplitudes and vibration directions are shown by the lengths and directions of the arrows.
b. Linearly polarised light, vibration direction perpendicular to principal section.
c. Linearly polarised light, vibration direction at 45° to principal plane.
d. Linearly polarised light, vibration direction parallel to principal section.

direction of the displaced wave trains is perpendicular to that of the polar and so the light vector has zero resolved component parallel to the polar. The next figure shows the position after the polar has been rotated through 45°. Both spots are visible with equal but diminished intensity, for both the undisplaced and displaced vibrations have equal but reduced components when resolved parallel to the vibration direction of the polar. As we turn on from this position, the intensity of the ordinary image will decrease since its resolved amplitude components get smaller, while the displaced image gets stronger as its resolved amplitude components get larger; finally only the displaced image is visible after 90° rotation. Simple analyses of this kind involving resolution of the light vector are valid in considering many of the optical phenomena that we shall refer to, and such treatment is quite informative.

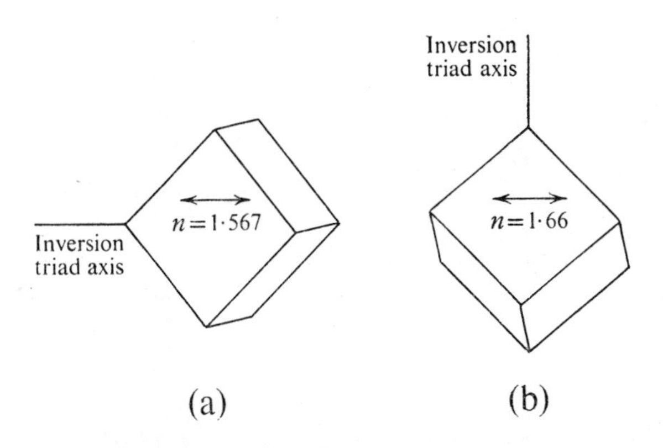

Fig. 3.10 Refractive index values for the calcite rhomb.
a. Light transmitted vibrating parallel to principal plane; only displaced image visible.
b. Light transmitted vibrating perpendicular to principal plane; only undisplaced image visible.

We have so far neglected the different apparent depths of the two dots seen through the rhomb. These must reflect different speeds of travel, i.e. different refractive indices, for the light waves forming the two images. We can determine the refractive indices appropriate to the two images by constraining the incident light (by means of a polar) to be plane polarised first parallel to the principal section and then perpendicular to it; we shall see first only the displaced image and then only the undisplaced image. We find that when the incident vibration plane is parallel to the short diagonal of the rhomb face (i.e. the principal plane) the value of n is 1·567, while when it is perpendicular n is 1·66 (Fig. 3.10). If the rhomb is tilted slightly a value of n of 1·66 is still recorded for light transmitted by the crystal vibrating perpendicular to a principal plane, whereas the value of n for light vibrating in a principal plane is slightly greater or less than 1·567 depending on the direction of tilt. Next we can examine the prismatic crystals. It will be recalled that only one image was visible through a pair of prism faces, but it was suggested that this was due to the superposition of the two doubly refracted images. We can now confirm this, for if there is double refraction, one linearly polarised vibration within the crystal will be parallel to the length of the prism (in a principal plane) and the other will be vibrating in a plane perpendicular to the optic axis. With the vibration plane of the polar perpendicular to the length of the prism n is found to be 1·66; with the polar rotated through 90°, n is only 1·48 (Fig. 3.11). This behaviour is to be contrasted with measurements on the basal section for which there is no double refraction, which show $n = 1{\cdot}66$ for any direction of measurement.

These typical measurements for rhombohedral and prismatic calcite crystals can be generalised as follows. Clearly there is one constant value of the refractive index ($n = 1{\cdot}66$) which occurs whenever the transmitted light has a vibration direction perpendicular to a principal section. The basal section, perpendicular to the triad axis, containing all possible directions of this type is isotropic since all these vibration directions are equivalent. When light travels in any general direction, the calcite crystal transmits only those two linearly polarised disturbances, whose perpendicular vibration directions are parallel and at right-angles to a principal plane. One of these, vibrating perpendicular to the principal plane, can be said to behave normally in that its speed of travel (i.e. its refractive index) is constant; this disturbance, corresponding to the undisplaced image seen through the rhomb, is said to be the *ordinary* disturbance. The other (or *extraordinary*) disturbance associated with the displaced image seen through the rhomb, due to light with its vibration plane parallel to a principal section, has a velocity of propagation which is dependent on its direction of travel; we see this from the different refractive indices which are measured for it through the rhomb and through the prism faces. In fact the refractive indices associated with this extraordinary disturbance vary from about 1·48 when the vibration direction is parallel to the optic axis, to a maximum value of about 1·66 when the vibration direction is normal to the optic axis. For vibration directions between these extreme directions the values of n are intermediate (as for the rhomb face).

We can now summarise more completely what these simple experiments demonstrate about the propagation of light in calcite and other uniaxial anisotropic crystals of this type. Unpolarised light from the source is resolved into two linearly polarised components whose vibration directions are perpendicular to each other. This means that for any general direction of wave normal propagation in the calcite,

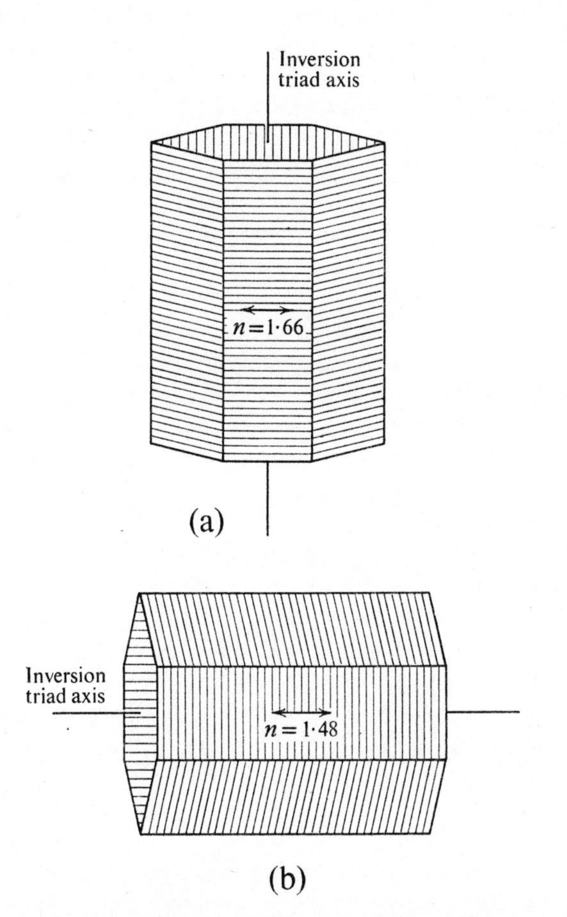

Fig. 3.11 Refractive index values for a prismatic calcite crystal.
a. Light transmitted vibrating perpendicular to a principal plane.
b. Light transmitted vibrating in a principal plane.

there are two permitted vibration directions; the calcite crystal transmits only light which is vibrating parallel to these mutually perpendicular vibration directions. One of the two permitted disturbances, the ordinary, vibrating perpendicular to a principal plane, travels with constant velocity no matter what the direction of travel; the other, the extraordinary, vibrating within a principal plane, has a variable but limited range of velocities dependent on the direction of travel in the crystal. For one direction only, the optic axis direction, there is no double refraction of this kind, and the crystal behaves as if it were an isotropic substance. This means that unpolarised light incident in this direction is transmitted unchanged as unpolarised light, and that the velocity of travel is constant for light vibrating in any direction perpendicular to the optic axis. For light transmitted perpendicular to the optic axis the double refraction is at its greatest with the maximum difference in the speeds of travel of the two polarised disturbances. In a particular substance, the speed of the extraordinary disturbance may be either greater or less than that of the ordinary disturbance. For our example of calcite, the extraordinary waves are always the faster; in other uniaxial materials, for example the common mineral quartz (SiO_2), they always travel slower than the ordinary waves. This leads us to a subdivision of uniaxial crystals into two groups. Quartz with the extraordinary disturbance the slower of the two is said to be optically positive, while calcite, for which the extraordinary vibration is fast, is said to be optically negative; this assignment of *optic sign* to a crystal can be most useful in characterising its optical properties during examination. Further, as we have seen earlier, the velocity of light waves in a medium is inversely proportional to refractive index; thus we can rewrite our definitions of optic sign more practically in terms of refractive indices as:

$$n_e > n_{e'} > n_o \text{ (positive sign); } n_e < n_{e'} < n_o \text{ (negative sign)}$$

where n_o is the ordinary refractive index, n_e is the limiting extraordinary refractive index (vibration direction parallel to optic axis) and $n_{e'}$ is any other value for the extraordinary refractive index in any intermediate direction. n_e and n_o are called the *principal refractive indices* of the crystal.

Such properties as we have described in this section are characteristic of only one kind of optically anisotropic crystalline matter, that in which there is only one direction for which there is no double refraction. Uniaxial optical properties are associated with crystalline substances belonging to the tetragonal, hexagonal and trigonal crystal systems. For each of these systems whatever the subsidiary elements of symmetry, there is always a principal symmetry axis present (the tetrad, hexad and triad respectively); the optic axis direction is always parallel to this principal symmetry axis.

3.3 Optical anisotropy and biaxial crystals

Another large group of crystalline materials show anisotropic optical properties different from those we have just described for calcite and uniaxial materials. If the same simple experiments are carried out with

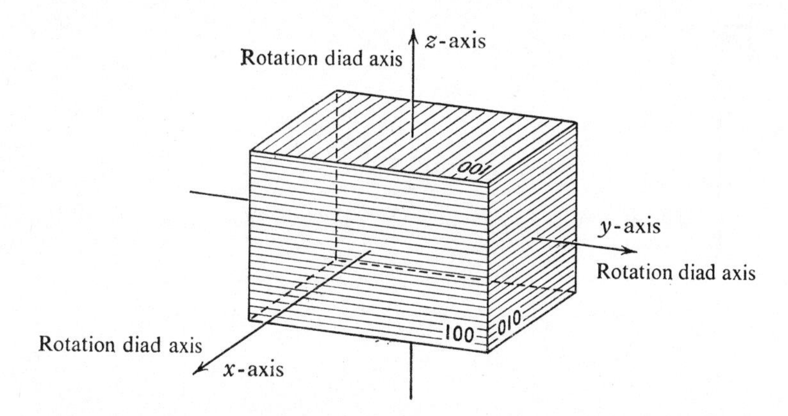

Fig. 3.12 Parallelopiped of anhydrite (class mmm) formed by the pinacoidal cleavages {100}, {010} and {001}.

a crystal of this second group, there are certain similarities and certain dissimilarities compared to uniaxial properties. In general directions, there is double refraction, with the transmission of two linearly polarised waves whose vibration directions are mutually perpendicular; however, both disturbances now have velocities which depend on the direction of propagation through the crystal. We could say that both are 'extraordinary waves', and there is no 'ordinary wave', although this terminology is not used for these materials. It is also found that there are two directions for which there is no double refraction and along which unpolarised light is transmitted unchanged. This means that there are two optic axis directions, which is why we choose to call this group, the optically *biaxial crystals*. Clearly the transmission of light waves in biaxial crystals represents a more general case than for uniaxial crystals.

We can investigate this in more detail with some experiments upon anhydrite, one of the crystalline forms of $CaSO_4$, which has orthorhombic symmetry. Let us suppose that we have a parallelopiped formed by the pinacoidal cleavages {100}, {010} and {001} (Fig. 3.12); the essential symmetry elements, three perpendicular diads normal to the faces, will act as reference directions for the optical measurements. For each pair of opposite faces of the parallelopiped, there is double refraction, with two mutually perpendicular permitted vibration directions for light travelling normal to the faces. As for calcite, we can measure the refractive indices for each of these vibration directions in

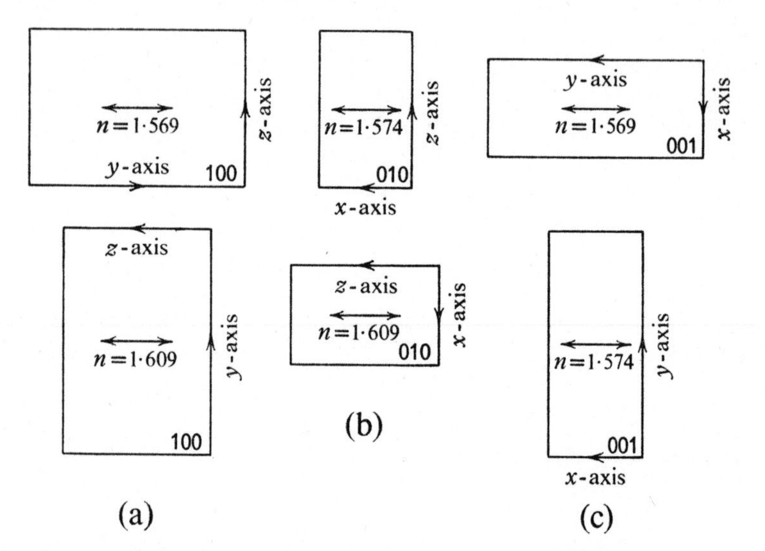

Fig. 3.13 Refractive index values for the anhydrite parallelopiped.
a. Light transmitted through {100} faces; vibration direction parallel to *y*- and *z*-axes.
b. Light transmitted through {010} faces; vibration directions parallel to *x*- and *z*-axes.
c. Light transmitted through {001} faces; vibration directions parallel to *y*- and *x*-axes.

turn, and relate the observations to the crystallographic symmetry elements. First with the light travelling normal to the {100} faces (Fig. 3.13*a*), the permitted vibration directions are parallel to the edges of the face, and are in the direction of the *y*- and *z*-crystallographic axes. Measurements of the refractive indices using linearly polarised incident light then give the values for light vibrating parallel to *y*-axis, n_y (1·569) and parallel to the *z*-axis, n_z (1·609). Similarly for the {010} faces, we measure n_x (1·574) and n_z (1·609) (Fig. 3.13*b*), while the {001} faces give n_x (1·574) and n_y (1·569) (Fig. 3.13*c*). If other more general sections were cut, they too would be doubly refracting, and when the refractive indices are measured for each pair of permitted perpendicular vibration directions the values would vary with the orientation of the section but in every case would lie between the extreme values found for n_y (1·569) and n_z (1·609). We can check this by tilting those sections in Fig. 3.13 showing n_y about an axis normal to the polar and seeing that the refractive index increases from 1·569; if we tilt the sections showing n_z in the same way the refractive index decreases from 1·609.

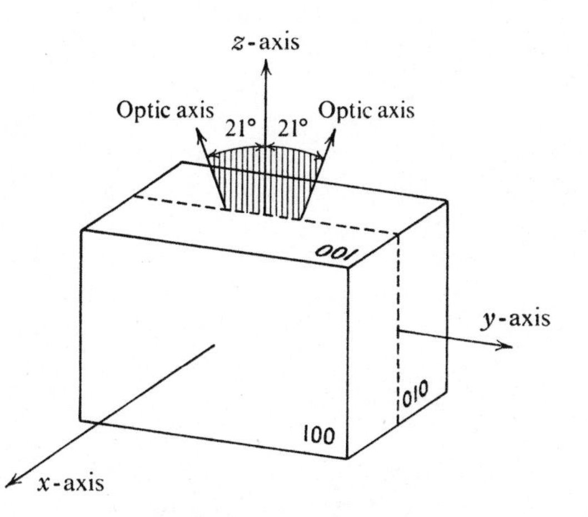

Fig. 3.14 The directions of the optic axes for anhydrite.

The results of the measurements so far suggest that the velocity of propagation of light in anhydrite depends on the vibration direction of the light vector. But there are two optic axis directions for which we observe optically isotropic properties. In anhydrite, as we might expect, these lie in the crystallographic *y–z* plane, symmetrically disposed at about 21° on either side of the *z*-axis (Fig. 3.14); they are not normal to any particular crystallographic planes. The value of the refractive index for light travelling along an optic axis direction is the same as n_x (1·574).

In practice it would be difficult to carry out all these observations on anhydrite in a simple manner, for suitably large cleavage parallelopipeds are not found, but the refractive index measurements can be made on tiny cleavage fragments parallel to the pinacoids using a microscope. The results are typical of optically biaxial crystals, and show that there are three important refractive index values; the greatest is symbolically n_g, or better, n_γ, the least n_p, or better, n_α, and that intermediate value appropriate to light travelling along an optic axis direction, n_m, or better, n_β. For anhydrite $n_\gamma = n_z$, and $n_\alpha = n_y$; moreover $n_\beta = n_x$, showing that the value of n_β is also associated with light vibrating perpendicular to the plane defined by the vibration directions of the greatest and least values. The values n_γ, n_β and n_α are called the *principal refractive indices* of the crystal. The value of n_β, although a constant for a particular crystal, is intermediate between n_γ and n_α but bears no special relationship to them. This implies that the angle between the two optic axis directions, again constant for a particular material, can vary from substance to substance. Related to this will be the possibility of subdividing biaxial crystals, optically positive and negative, just as was done for uniaxial signs. This division, however, is not made by changing the sign when n_β is the mean of n_γ and n_α, and we will defer discussion of it until 4.4.

Biaxial optical properties are associated with matter belonging to the less symmetrical orthorhombic, monoclinic and triclinic crystal systems. We should stress here that the relationship between the principal refractive indices, optic axes, etc. and the crystallographic reference directions that was deduced in the example of anhydrite does not necessarily hold for other optically biaxial materials. It is not always true that $n_\gamma = n_z$, $n_\alpha = n_y$ and $n_\beta = n_x$, nor even that the principal refractive indices shall be measured in the directions corresponding to the crystallographic axes. The problem of the relationship of optical properties to crystallographic reference directions is more complex than for uniaxial crystals, and we will hold over detailed consideration until 4.4.

3.4 Summary

Crystalline materials may be classified into three broad groups with regard to their optical properties; further subdivision will be discussed in later chapters. These groups comprise the isotropic crystals, anisotropic crystals which are uniaxial (like calcite and quartz) and anisotropic crystals which are biaxial (like anhydrite). The general optical characteristics of these three groups that have been established so far are conveniently summarised in Table 3.1.

Table 3.1

Summary of general optical properties of crystalline material

Isotropic	*Anisotropic*	
	Uniaxial	*Biaxial*
No double refraction	In general directions, doubly refracting	In general directions, doubly refracting
In all directions unpolarised light transmitted unchanged; normal laws of optics obeyed	In general directions, unpolarised incident light transmitted as two linearly polarised waves vibrating in mutually perpendicular planes; one wave obeys the normal laws of optics (ordinary), the other does not (extraordinary)	In general directions unpolarised incident light transmitted as two linearly polarised waves vibrating in mutually perpendicular planes; neither wave obeys the normal laws of optics
No optic axes	One optic axis	Two optic axes of variable inclination and orientation
One principal refractive index, n	Two principal refractive indices, n_o and n_e	Three principal refractive indices n_γ, n_β and n_α
Crystals of the cubic system	Crystals of the tetragonal, hexagonal and trigonal systems, with optic axis parallel to main symmetry axis	Crystals of the orthorhombic, monoclinic and triclinic systems. No general relation between optic and crystallographic axes for the three systems

3.5 Exercises

1. Use of Huyghens's construction for isotropic media:

A polished glass plate is attached to the flat surface of a glass hemisphere by a liquid:

(i) Use Huyghens's construction to trace the ray paths through the system for light incident on the curved surface of the hemisphere at an angle of 65° to the normal to the liquid-glass interface. The refractive indices of the glass and liquid are 1·66 and 1·55. What is the wavelength of NaD light (5890×10^{-8} cm) within each of the media?

(ii) For the same conditions of incidence, to what refractive index must the liquid be changed in order that no light is transmitted through the system?

(iii) With this new liquid, at what angle of incidence will the reflected light be completely polarised?

(iv) Check the results of your constructions by computation. (This apparatus is a crude form of Abbé refractometer used to determine refractive indices of liquids, see 8.3.)

2. Experiments with calcite rhombs and a polar:

Place a cleavage rhomb of calcite over a dot on a piece of paper and observe the doubly refracted images:

(i) Carry out the relevant qualitative experiments described in 3.2, noting particularly the effects of rotation, the relationship between the triad and the plane containing the images, the vibration directions of the light forming the two images; decide whether the extraordinary ray direction is refracted towards or away from the optic axis direction. By using a second rhomb, investigate the influence of the thickness of the crystal on the separation of the images.

(ii) Extend these experiments by superposing a second rhomb on the first. Observe the effect of rotating one rhomb relative to the other, noting particularly the mutual disposition of the images formed and the changes in their relative intensities.

(iii) Account for your observations by using diagrams illustrating the resolution of the light vectors in the calcite crystals.

CHAPTER 4

LIGHT WAVES AND THE INDICATRIX

4.1 The ray velocity surface for uniaxial crystals

IN the preceding chapter we have tried to establish by simple experiments some of the more important facts about the transmission of light waves in isotropic and anisotropic crystals. Unpolarised light is not in general transmitted unchanged through anisotropic media, and the two perpendicularly polarised waves into which it is resolved travel with different speeds.

We can visualise some of the essential differences between isotropic and uniaxial anisotropic crystals in the following way. If we could place a point source of light inside an isotropic medium, flash the source for an infinitesimally small interval and then record photographically the locus of all the rays diverging from the source, it is evident that the locus would be spherical in shape since in any direction in the isotropic body the light waves travel with the same speed. Also, although it would not be apparent on our photographic record, the light arriving at any point on the sphere would be unpolarised. If we could now carry out the same experiment with the source placed inside, say, a calcite crystal, the results would be strikingly different. The photographic plate would show two surfaces. One of these, corresponding to the ordinary disturbance, would be spherical in shape since in any direction the ordinary wave travels with the same speed. We should also see for calcite that there was a second surface enclosing the first. This second surface has the form of an ellipsoid of revolution which touches the spherical surface at the opposite ends of one diameter. The ellipsoidal surface represents the locus of the diverging extraordinary rays after an interval of time. The extraordinary disturbance travels with different speeds in different directions. In one direction, the optic axis direction, there is no double refraction; this is represented by the diameter joining the points at which the two surfaces touch. In all other directions the extraordinary is faster than the ordinary disturbance, the form of the variation being elliptical to give the maximum difference in speeds perpendicular to the optic axis. Although not apparent on the photograph, in any given direction each of the disturbances would be linearly polarised.

The surfaces seen on these photographs are known as *ray velocity* (or sometimes *wave*) *surfaces*. For all uniaxial anisotropic crystals, we have a double surface; when the crystal has a positive optic sign (like quartz), the ellipsoid of revolution is enclosed by the sphere, but if the crystal is optically negative (like calcite), the ellipsoid encloses the sphere (Fig. 4.1). The assumption that the form of the variation of velocity for the extraordinary disturbance in uniaxial crystals is ellipsoidal was first

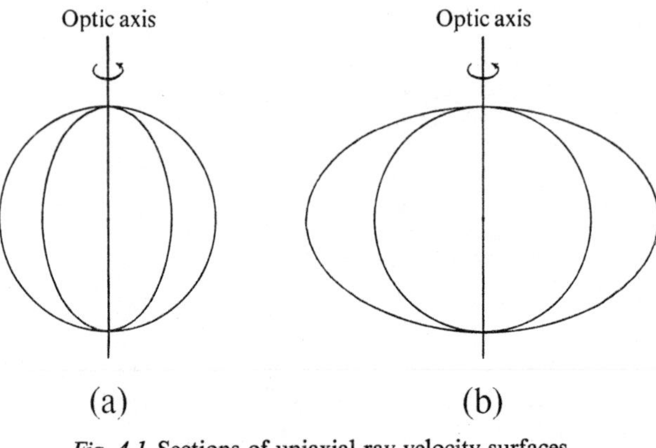

Fig. 4.1 Sections of uniaxial ray velocity surfaces.
a. Optically positive crystal.
b. Optically negative crystal.

made empirically to explain double refraction, etc., but this shape can be justified by detailed investigation of the transmission of electromagnetic waves in this kind of dielectric medium. Once the form of the ray velocity surface is known, it can be used to predict the directions of the wave fronts, etc. within the medium by the methods of 3.1.

4.2 Huyghens's construction for uniaxial crystals

We can illustrate this construction by considering the simple experiment showing the double refraction of an object dot viewed through opposite faces of a calcite rhomb. Let us take a section through the air-crystal interface through which light from the object enters the calcite. In Fig. 4.2 the incident light beam, normal to the interface, is defined by the extreme rays PR and QS; in the Huyghenian construction the points R and S, on the wave front marked zero, act as sources for the secondary disturbances to simultaneously spread within the crystal, as do all intermediate points on the interface. During the interval of time between the wave fronts, the rays diverging from the secondary sources will have spread into the crystal to points on negative uniaxial ray velocity surfaces. The figure shows the section of the two double-surfaced figures arising from the limiting secondary sources R and S, although we must remember that there is an infinite number of such surfaces due to all the sources between R and S. We must now consider the implications of this diagram.

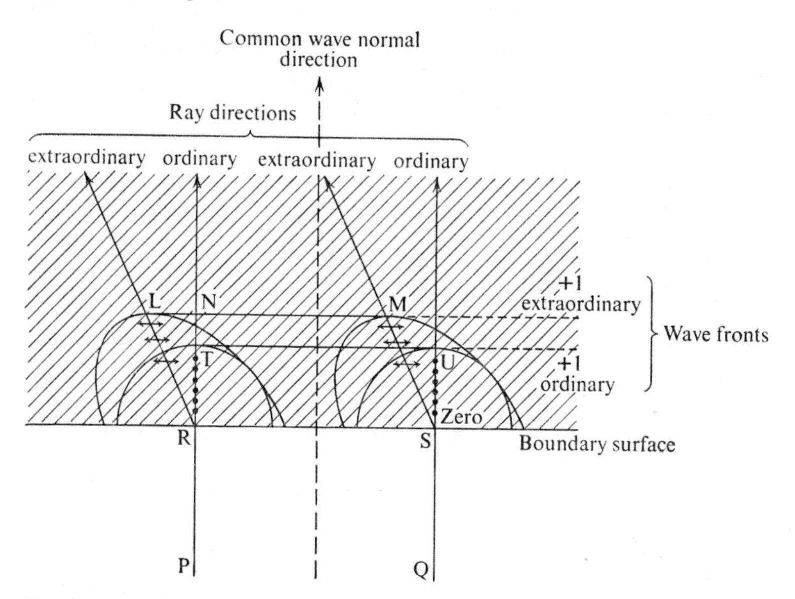

Fig. 4.2 Huyghens's construction for light incident normally on a rhombohedral face of a calcite crystal.

The wave fronts transmitted within the crystal are the envelopes of all the surfaces representing the secondary wavelets; thus the +1 wave fronts in the crystal are given by the common tangents to extreme secondary wavelets. We see from the figure that there are two parallel wave fronts travelling in the crystal represented by TU and LM for the ordinary and extraordinary waves respectively, and that the wave normal direction is common both to them and the incident waves. It is also clear that the two parallel wave fronts travel with different speeds for they are at different positions within the crystal; the extraordinary wave fronts advance faster than the ordinary wave fronts (RN>RT). In order to locate the images of the dot formed by the two waves, we must now consider the direction of advance of a given point on the front; physically this is what is meant by the *ray directions* within the crystal.

Obviously, the ray directions associated with each wave front can be obtained by joining the source of the secondary wavelet to the point at which the surface of the wavelet is touched by the wave front. For ordinary waves, the ray directions are parallel to RT and SU, while the extraordinary ray directions are parallel to RL and SM. We see then that although the two transmitted waves have parallel fronts, i.e. they share a common wave normal direction, the ordinary and extraordinary ray directions diverge to give the double image of the object dot. The ordinary ray directions predict the undisplaced image, while the extraordinary ray directions give rise to the displaced image which rotates as the rhomb is rotated on the paper. The different velocities of the two wave fronts, i.e. different refractive indices, imply that the two images will appear at different apparent depths. Concerning velocities of propagation, it is as well to clarify at this point an apparent dilemma arising from the fact that for the extraordinary disturbances the ray and wave normal directions do not, in general, coincide. This means that the ray velocity is different from the wave velocity (i.e. RL>RN), contrary to the experience of isotropic propagation, exemplified by the ordinary disturbance where they are identical. For the extraordinary waves, there must theoretically be both ray and wave refractive indices due to these different speeds, but in any practical observation we are concerned with the movement of wave fronts and have no means of selecting an individual point on one of them and following its progress. Therefore whenever the term 'refractive index' is used without prefix, it is taken to mean that which is experimentally determined, i.e. the wave refractive index.

It is instructive to pursue the interpretation of the calcite rhomb experiment beyond the simple Huyghenian construction to learn something about the polarisation of the transmitted light. The electromagnetic theory of light requires that the electric vector (representing the vibration direction of the light) shall be contained in the plane of the wave front. Both ordinary and extraordinary vibration directions must be parallel to the plane perpendicular to that of our diagram which contains the interface. We have also seen from the experiments with a polar that the ordinary disturbances vibrate perpendicular to a principal section. The plane of our diagram must be a principal section since it contains the optic axis direction. Therefore the ordinary vibration direction is perpendicular to the plane of the diagram (indicated by dots on the ray path RT, etc.). We know also that the extraordinary disturbance must vibrate in the principal section plane (indicated by the arrows on the ray path RL, etc.). It is apparent from this that the vibration direction for the transmitted extraordinary waves is not generally perpendicular to the ray direction.

We can now summarise the conclusions that have been reached for conditions of normal incidence about the light waves which pass through

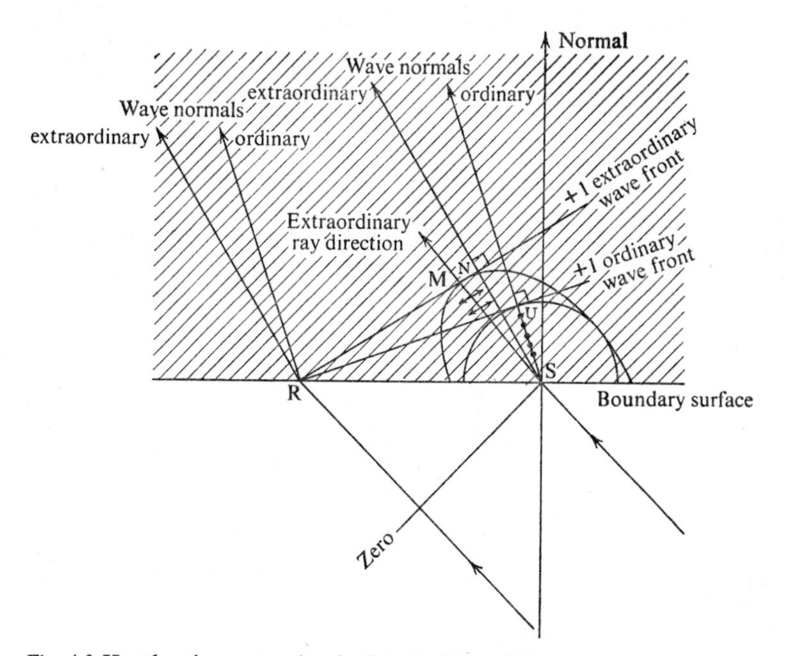

Fig. 4.3 Huyghens's construction for light incident obliquely on a rhombohedral face of a calcite crystal.

a general section of a uniaxial crystal. The two disturbances, ordinary and extraordinary, have parallel wave fronts but their velocities along the common wave normal direction are different; if the optic sign is positive, the ordinary waves travel faster, and vice versa. The two transmitted waves are linearly polarised. For the ordinary disturbance the vibration direction is perpendicular to the principal section containing the common wave normal and the optic axis; it lies in the plane of the wave front and perpendicular to the ray direction. For the extraordinary disturbance the vibration direction lies in the principal section containing the common wave normal and the optic axis; it lies in the plane of the wave front, but is inclined at a general angle to the ray direction.

The condition of normal incidence is that most commonly used in optical experiments, though we will now consider oblique incidence (e.g. tilting the rhomb) briefly to see whether these deductions have to be modified. Fig. 4.3 shows the position when an inclined wave front (marked zero) is just striking the boundary at S. The secondary wavelets spreading from S due to the previous wave front have formed a section of the ray velocity surface centred on S. The positions of the two transmitted wave fronts in the crystal (marked +1) are obtained by drawing the tangents from R to the circle and ellipse, RU and RM respectively. The wave normal directions for the ordinary and extraordinary disturbances, SU and SN respectively, are no longer common, although they are still co-planar with the incident wave normal. The vibration directions have the same characteristics as before, remaining in the plane of the appropriate wave front, vibrating perpendicular and parallel to the principal plane for the ordinary and extraordinary respectively.

Constructions of this kind help us to clarify certain relationships within uniaxial crystals, but they are not particularly convenient for visualising optical properties, which are usually described in terms of refractive indices; we should find even greater difficulty if we were to apply the same treatment to biaxial crystals. And so in the next sections we shall describe a more convenient kind of optical representation surface for both uniaxial and biaxial crystals.

4.3 The uniaxial indicatrix

For optically uniaxial crystals we know that the refractive index values for extraordinary waves are variable over a limited range, with that for ordinary waves fixed at one end of this range. We can link this observation with that concerning the vibration directions for the two waves travelling along a general wave normal direction; the ordinary vibration direction is always perpendicular to the optic axis, while the extraordinary vibration is always in the plane containing the optic axis and wave normal direction. This suggests that we may connect the variation of the refractive index in the crystal with the vibration direction of the light. This concept was used by Lazarus Fletcher who suggested that a convenient representation of anisotropic optical properties could be in the form of a spatial plot of the variation of refractive index as a function of vibration direction. Such a surface is known as the *optical* (or *Fletcher*) *indicatrix*, and for most optical problems it is far superior to other types of representation surfaces that have been proposed.

Its relationship to ray velocity surfaces and the justification of the properties which are given below will be found in Appendix A.

For uniaxial crystals, the optical indicatrix is a single-surfaced ellipsoid of revolution similar in shape to the extraordinary ray velocity surface. To construct the optical indicatrix for a particular example, say calcite, we construct the ellipsoid of revolution so that the radius of

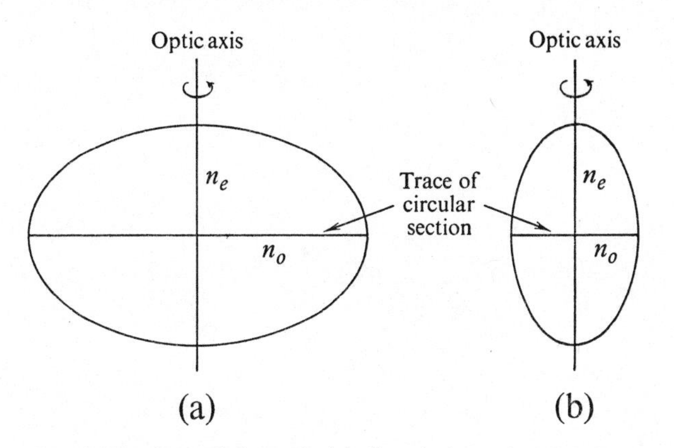

Fig. 4.4 Sections of the optical indicatrix for uniaxial crystals.
a. Optically negative crystal.
b. Optically positive crystal.

its central circular section is directly proportional to the ordinary refractive index, and the length of the unique axis of revolution is directly proportional to the minimum value of the extraordinary refractive index; for this negative crystal, the indicatrix is an oblate ellipsoid (Fig. 4.4*a*). For an optically positive crystal, the radius of the central circular section is again proportional to the ordinary refractive index, while the length of the axis of revolution is proportional to the maximum value of the extraordinary refractive index; the indicatrix is a prolate ellipsoid (Fig. 4.4*b*). In both figures, we notice that the radius vector normal to the circular section is n_e, showing that a maximum (or minimum) refractive index is observed for light with this vibration direction; the axis of revolution must be the optic axis direction. Since the optic axis is perpendicular to the circular section of the indicatrix of radius n_o, light vibrating perpendicular to the optic axis always has this value of the refractive index. For any other radius vector of the figure, i.e. any general vibration direction, the refractive index $n_{e'}$ is intermediate between the two principal values.

We must now consider how the properties of such figures allow us to interpret the transmission of light in any direction in a crystal. Let us imagine that the transmitted waves are travelling within a negative uniaxial crystal at some general inclination to the optic axis, i.e. in the direction of the common wave normal of Fig. 4.5. In order to find the optical properties of the crystal for light travelling in this direction, we cut a central elliptical section of the ellipsoid perpendicular to the wave

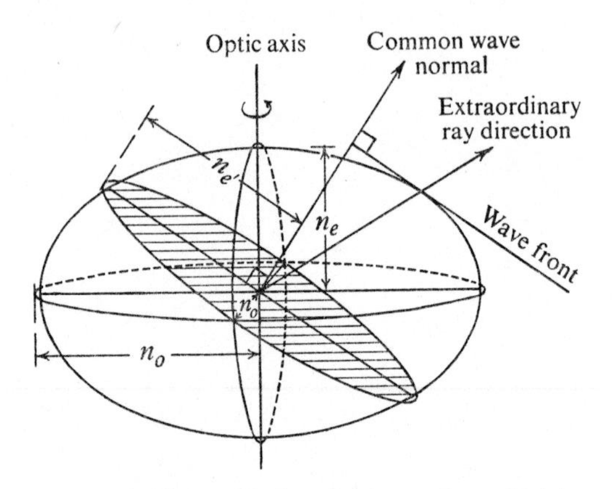

Fig. 4.5 The properties of the negative uniaxial indicatrix.

normal, i.e. we take the central section of the indicatrix cut by the plane of the wave fronts in the crystal. Now, it is shown in Appendix A that the properties of the indicatrix are such that the two axes of this elliptical section define the two mutually perpendicular vibration directions permitted for this wave normal direction, while the length of the semi-axis is, in each case, therefore proportional to the appropriate refractive index (Fig. 4.5). Consideration of the figure shows that every central section of the ellipsoid (except that perpendicular to the axis of revolution) is an ellipse with one of its axes perpendicular to the axis of revolution. One of the axes of the ellipse must always lie in the circular section of the indicatrix; this is the ordinary vibration direction with a corresponding refractive index n_o. The other axis of the ellipse must lie in the principal plane containing the wave normal; this is the extraordinary vibration direction with a corresponding refractive index $n_{e'}$, intermediate between the extreme values of n_e and n_o. For the special case when the wave normal is parallel to the axis of revolution, all vibration directions lie in the circular section of the ellipsoid and have equal values; they are not to be distinguished from each other, and there is only one refractive index value n_o so confirming that the optic axis direction corresponds to the axis of revolution. As the difference between n_e and n_o is reduced towards zero, the shape of the ellipsoid approaches a sphere, which is the indicatrix for an isotropic substance, in which all vibration directions are indistinguishable and there is only one value of the refractive index.

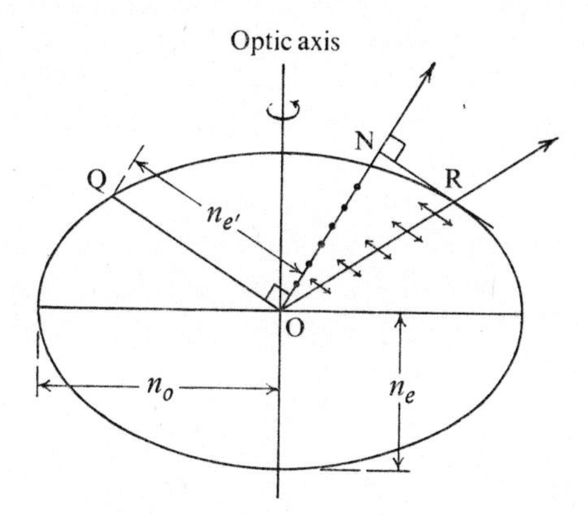

Fig. 4.6 A principal section of the negative uniaxial indicatrix.

After this description of the properties of the indicatrix, we can illustrate them by returning to the calcite rhomb experiment. With normal incidence, there is a common wave normal direction within the calcite inclined to the optic axis at a general angle determined by the geometry of the rhomb. For simplicity Fig. 4.6 shows only that principal section of the negative indicatrix containing the optic axis and the common wave normal (ON). From what we have just said about the properties of the indicatrix, the radius OQ represents by its direction and length the vibration direction and associated refractive index for the extraordinary wave fronts travelling along ON. We know that the extraordinary ray direction is not ON, for in general it does not coincide with the wave normal. To find this ray direction, we can make use of the similarity in shape between the indicatrix and the extraordinary ray velocity surface used in the Huyghenian construction. We may draw the wave front (NR) which is tangent to the indicatrix at R; from this we deduce that OR is the extraordinary ray direction, for we have joined the centre of a secondary wavelet to the point at which it is touched by the wave front. The ordinary wave front is also parallel to NR, and since the ordinary ray direction is perpendicular to the wave front, it is represented by ON. The vibration direction for the two waves are, as we have said, parallel to the axes of the elliptical section of the indicatrix, and are represented on the figure by the arrows for the extraordinary disturbance and the dots for the ordinary disturbance vibrating perpendicular to the plane of the diagram.

From this example, we see how the important features of the transmission of light through a calcite rhomb can be derived from the representation surface. In this way, we can use the optical indicatrix as a very convenient geometrical expression of the relations we have observed in uniaxial crystals. The indicatrix can be visualised, its sections appropriate to the direction of transmission of the light examined so that we may readily deduce the optical properties that we expect to observe, or conversely use our observations to define the indicatrix. Since the indicatrix is to be used in this way, its orientation with respect to crystallographic reference directions must be established; for uniaxial crystals, the relationships have already been implied but they may now be stated formally.

We know that the unique direction of the uniaxial indicatrix is the axis of revolution or optic axis direction; we know also that uniaxial optical properties are shown by crystals with tetragonal, hexagonal or trigonal symmetry, i.e. crystals with characteristic tetrad, hexad or triad symmetry axes respectively. The characteristic symmetry axis is always coincident with the unique optic axis of the indicatrix. Since the indicatrix is an ellipsoid of revolution it does not matter how it is orientated about this axis; there can be no specific orientation with respect to any other directions of crystallographic significance. Thus the three uniaxial crystal systems have generally similar optical properties. As any given property can occur in a similar manner in any one of the systems, the systems cannot be distinguished from one another simply on the basis of the optical properties represented by the indicatrix; it follows that we cannot use ellipsoidal optical properties to distinguish one crystal class from another within the same system.

4.4 The biaxial indicatrix

If we try to understand the transmission of light waves in biaxial crystals by employing a Huyghenian construction, we should first have to define the shape of the biaxial ray velocity surface. It is difficult to conceive on simple reasoning what shape such a surface should have; clearly it would be double-surfaced but since there is now no ordinary disturbance, neither of the sheets would be spherical. The form of this surface is derived in Appendix A, but for biaxial crystals it is simpler to start from the concept of the indicatrix, and to attempt to visualise what shape this must have to show the variation of refractive index with vibration direction for such crystals. The experiments with anhydrite, typical of biaxial optical properties, demonstrate that the refractive indices vary between a maximum and a minimum value associated with two mutually

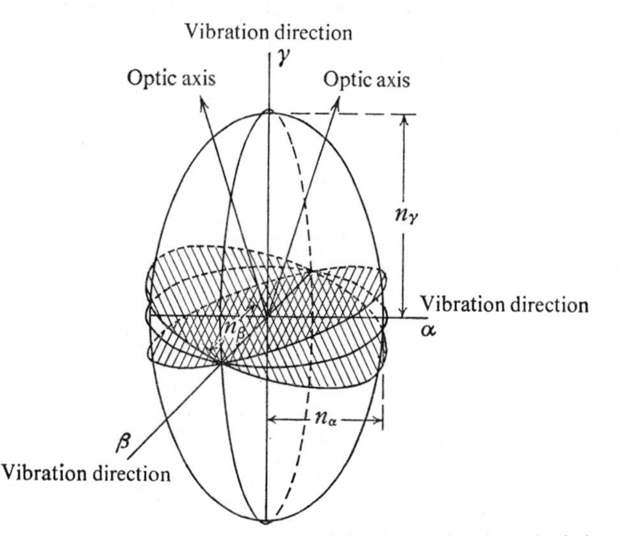

Fig. 4.7 The biaxial indicatrix. The circular sections are shaded and are normal to the optic axes symmetrically inclined in the γ–α vibration plane.

perpendicular vibration directions. Lying within the plane defined by these vibration directions are two symmetrically disposed optic axis directions; light vibrating perpendicular to the optic axis directions has an intermediate value of the refractive index, which must therefore be that observed when the light vector is perpendicular to the vibration plane of the maximum and minimum refractive indices.

From our previous knowledge of the indicatrix for uniaxial crystals, an ellipsoid of revolution with two principal refractive indices, n_o and n_e, it is a simple step to see that the indicatrix for biaxial crystals will be a triaxial ellipsoid with three principal refractive indices, n_γ, n_β and n_α.

The three principal axes of Fig. 4.7 represent the magnitudes and vibration directions for light having the greatest refractive index (n_γ), the smallest refractive index (n_α) and an intermediate refractive index (n_β).

This value of n_β is that appropriate to light vibrating in a direction perpendicular to the vibration plane of the other two principal values; it is intermediate to n_γ and n_α but bears no special relationship to them. If we consider this ellipsoid further, we see that it has two circular sections whose normals represent the two optic axes and that these normals must lie symmetrically in the γ–α vibration plane; the radius of the circular sections must be n_β. The triaxial ellipsoid is therefore the geometrical shape that satisfies the requirements of the observations on anhydrite, and may be generally taken as the form of the optical indicatrix for biaxial crystals. The properties of the biaxial indicatrix are generally the same as those described for the uniaxial indicatrix. Each general wave normal direction can be used to define an elliptical section perpendicular to it cut through the centre of the figure by the wave front. The axes of this section are the permitted vibration directions for such a common wave normal direction of propagation in the crystal; the lengths of the semi-axes therefore represent the magnitudes of the two refractive indices. For uniaxial crystals the ray directions associated with the transmitted wave fronts were simply constructed because of the similarity in shape between the extraordinary ray velocity surface and the indicatrix. For biaxial crystals there is not this simple relationship between the ray velocity surface and the indicatrix. The construction is correspondingly more complex, and will be postponed until Appendix A.

We can now examine the geometry of the triaxial ellipsoid in a little more detail. Its relationship to the uniaxial indicatrix can be seen by starting from the prolate ellipsoid of revolution which is the form for positive uniaxial crystals. If we now imagine that the single optic axis direction is divided into two symmetrically inclined optic axes, the original circular section of the ellipsoid of revolution becomes an ellipse symmetrically placed between the two new circular sections normal to the optic axes (Fig. 4.8*a*). The semi-axes of this new ellipse are different from each other but are both smaller than the third principal axis of the triaxial ellipsoid normal to them; the two smaller semi-axes are n_α and n_β, while the third (originally the optic axis of the uniaxial indicatrix) is n_γ. The separation of the optic axes always takes place in the γ–α vibration plane, often known as the *optic axial plane.* We observe, too, that the relation of n_β to n_α and n_γ is a measure of the angle between the optic axes; the smaller the difference between n_β and n_α, the smaller becomes the angular separation of the optic axes, the *optic axial angle.* The optic axial angle is commonly denoted $2V$, but to avoid ambiguities it is best to specify the principal vibration direction

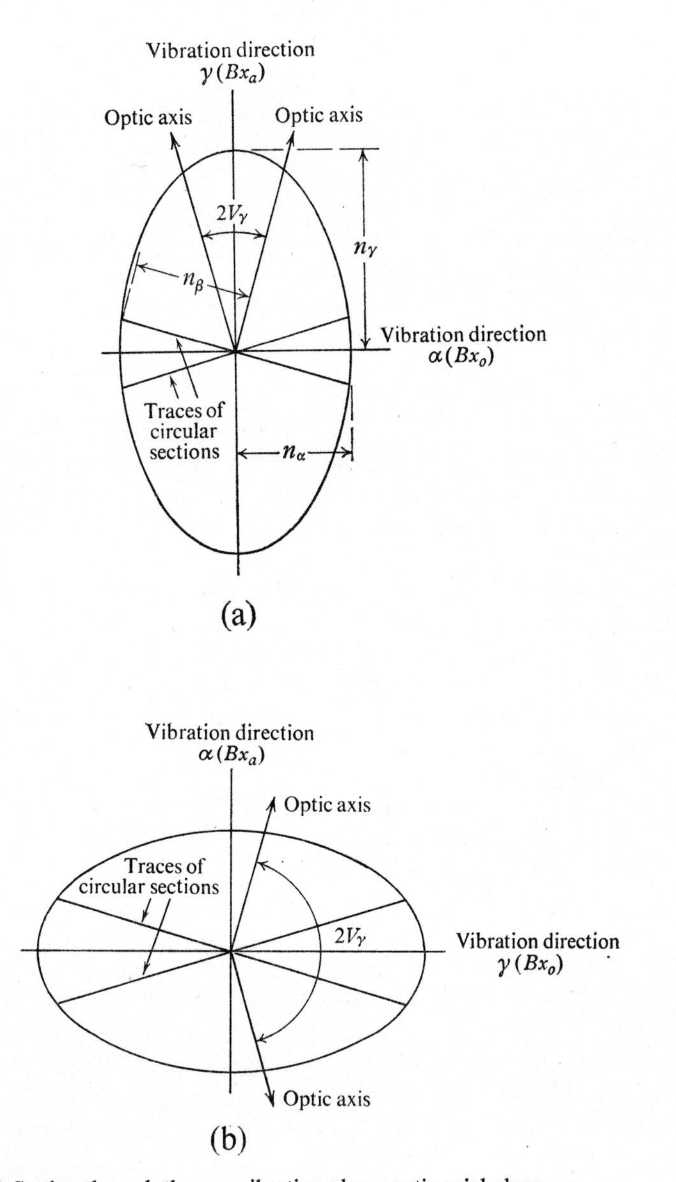

Fig. 4.8 Section through the γ–α vibration plane, optic axial plane of a biaxial indicatrix.
a. Positive optic sign.
b. Negative optic sign.

over which it is measured; thus in the figure it is marked as $2V_\gamma$. At present the value of the optic axial angle $2V_\gamma$ is small, so that the bisector of the acute angle between the optic axes, called the *acute bisectrix* (Bx_a), is the vibration direction of light with the greatest refractive index n_γ; thus we could say for our present crystal that $Bx_a=\gamma$. If we now imagine changing optical properties which allow $2V_\gamma$ to approach 90°, midway between the vibration directions γ and α, the geometry of the ellipse will have to change with n_β growing until it is more nearly midway between n_α and n_γ. (We should note that an optic axial angle of exactly 90° does not require that n_β is the exact mean of n_α and n_γ (see Appendix A), although this can be used as an approximation in crystals for which difference between n_γ and n_α is not large.) For all biaxial materials with $2V_\gamma<90°$, the optic sign is said to be positive, with the uniaxial case ($2V_\gamma=0°$) as a limiting one; alternatively, the definition of positive sign can be stated as $Bx_a=\gamma$. When the optic axial angle is 90°, the crystal is signless (or neutral). If the properties are changed so that $2V_\gamma>90°$, the acute bisectrix is now in the direction of the shortest axis of the ellipsoid, n_α. Such biaxial crystals are said to be optically negative, so that the definition of negative sign can be expressed either as $2V_\gamma>90°$ or as $Bx_a=\alpha$ (Fig. 4.8*b*). As $2V_\gamma$ approaches 180°, the two optic axes are more nearly coincident, so that in the limit ($2V_\gamma=180°$) we obtain the negative uniaxial indicatrix.

We can now profitably summarise this investigation of the geometry of the triaxial ellipsoid in so far as it defines the *optic sign* of biaxial crystals as:

Optically positive: Vibration direction γ parallel to the acute bisectrix, Bx_a (sometimes called first mean line)
Vibration direction α parallel to the obtuse bisectrix, Bx_o (sometimes called second mean line)
Vibration direction β parallel to third mean line (T.M.L.)
Consequently $2V_\gamma<90°$ (hence $2V_\alpha>90°$, since obviously $2V_\gamma+2V_\alpha=180°$).

Optically negative: Vibration direction α parallel to Bx_a
Vibration direction γ parallel to Bx_o
Vibration direction β parallel to third mean line
Consequently $2V_\gamma>90°$ (hence $2V_\alpha<90°$).

The geometry of the triaxial ellipsoid makes it clear that the inclination of the optic axes in the γ–α section of the indicatrix depends on the relative magnitudes of n_γ, n_β and n_α. It is shown in Appendix A that

$$\tan^2 V_\gamma = (1/n_\alpha{}^2 - 1/n_\beta{}^2)/(1/n_\beta{}^2 - 1/n_\gamma{}^2)$$

so that the definitions of optic signs that have been given can be expressed in terms of the principal refractive indices. For positive crystals $V_\gamma < 45°$, i.e. $\tan^2 V_\gamma < 1$, so that $(1/n_\alpha{}^2 - 1/n_\beta{}^2) < (1/n_\beta{}^2 - 1/n_\gamma{}^2)$; for negative crystals the inequality sign is reversed. These rather cumbersome refractive index expressions can be replaced for most practical purposes by the approximations

$$(n_\gamma - n_\beta) > (n_\beta - n_\alpha) \text{ for a positive crystal,}$$

and $$(n_\gamma - n_\beta) < (n_\beta - n_\alpha) \text{ for a negative crystal.}$$

It should be stressed that these simpler inequalities are only approximations. In particular they can lead to incorrect signs when the optic axial angle is near 90°, and must then be replaced by the exact reciprocal squares relationship.

Again it is necessary to define the orientation of the optical indicatrix with respect to crystallographic directions before it can be properly used. There is more latitude in orientation than for uniaxial crystals, and we shall have to examine separately each of the three crystallographic systems, orthorhombic, monoclinic and triclinic which have biaxial optical properties. For all three systems, the indicatrix has the same fundamental shape of a triaxial ellipsoid with the three geometrical axes of the ellipsoid defining the three principal vibration directions associated with the principal refractive indices n_γ, n_β and n_α. The orientation of the indicatrix is described in terms of the location of the principal vibration directions γ, β and α with respect to the crystallographic axes x, y and z whose directions are defined by the sides of the unit cell. Because light waves are symmetrical about their direction of propagation, optical properties are consistent with the maximum symmetry that can be displayed by a particular shape of cell, i.e. the symmetry of the holosymmetric class of a particular system. It is for this reason that we cannot distinguish different symmetry classes within a system by the optical properties expressed by the indicatrix. Nevertheless two of the optically biaxial systems, monoclinic and triclinic, will demand careful consideration, for their holosymmetric classes show less symmetry than the indicatrix itself.

Let us start with the more obvious case of biaxial crystals belonging to the orthorhombic symmetry system. For these, the optical indicatrix must be fitted to the holosymmetric arrangement of the three perpendicular diads with three planes of symmetry perpendicular to them; the three symmetry axes are conventionally chosen as the *x*, *y* and *z* crystallographic axes. Now the biaxial indicatrix is a shape which in itself has just this symmetry, for its three principal axes are special directions about which the figure has twofold symmetry, and it has three perpendicular central planes of symmetry. We should therefore expect the indicatrix to be orientated so that the principal vibration directions are parallel to the three crystallographic axes. There is, however, no criterion which fixes which of the optical vibration directions is parallel to which crystallographic axis (indeed it can only be convention which fixes which of the diad axes shall be called the *x*-crystallographic axis, etc.). We can therefore expect the orientation of the indicatrix to be different from one orthorhombic material to the next. The complete optical description of an orthorhombic crystal in terms of the indicatrix must record not only the magnitude of n_α, n_β and n_γ, probably together with $2V_\gamma$ (or $2V_\alpha$), but also the orientation of the indicatrix. For a particular material, this may be presented as $x=\gamma$ (or sometimes Z), $y=\beta$ (or Y) and $z=\alpha$ (or X) implying that in this case the optic axial plane (the γ–α plane of the indicatrix) is parallel to the (010) face of the crystal (Fig. 4.9*a*). With such a control over the orientation of the indicatrix, it is clear that for orthorhombic crystals, the optic axial plane must be parallel to faces {100}, or {010} or {001}, and the optic axes are situated in such planes symmetrically disposed about either the *x*- or *y*- or *z*-crystallographic axes.

Moving on to the less symmetrical monoclinic system the holosymmetric class has a single diad axis with a plane of symmetry perpendicular to it. Conventionally the unique diad axis is always chosen as the *y*-crystallographic axis, so that the mirror plane is the (010) plane of the crystal. The directions of the *x*- and *z*-crystallographic axes lie in this plane, but although they are necessarily perpendicular to the *y*-axis, they need bear no special relationship to each other; they are chosen for each material and are inclined to each other conventionally at an obtuse angle. If the orientation of the indicatrix with respect to these non-orthogonal crystallographic axes is considered, it is clear that the unique *y*-axis must conform to one or other of the principal vibration directions, with the (010) mirror plane parallel to one of the central symmetry planes of the indicatrix. It would be impossible for both the remaining two principal vibration directions to conform to the chosen *x*- or *z*-crystallographic axes, and indeed neither of them need do so,

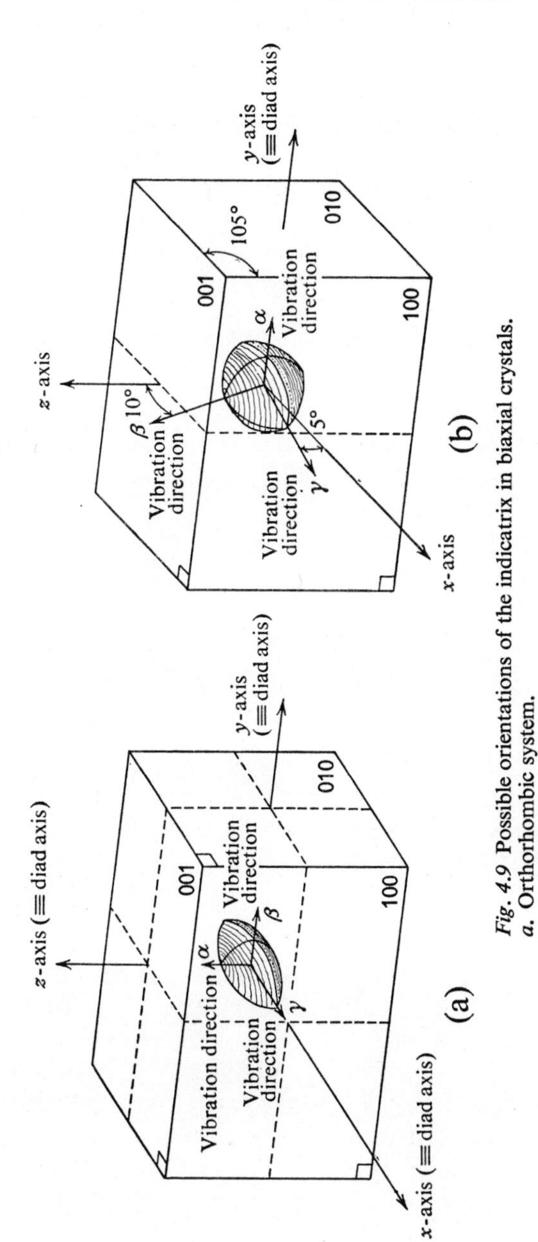

Fig. 4.9 Possible orientations of the indicatrix in biaxial crystals.
a. Orthorhombic system.
b. Monoclinic system.

for these chosen axial directions are of no crystallographic symmetry significance. For a monoclinic substance, the biaxial indicatrix has a degree of freedom in that it can twist into any orientation about the fixed optical direction parallel to the *y*-crystallographic axis; this orientation will be fixed for one particular material but will differ from one monoclinic substance to the next. An optical description of a

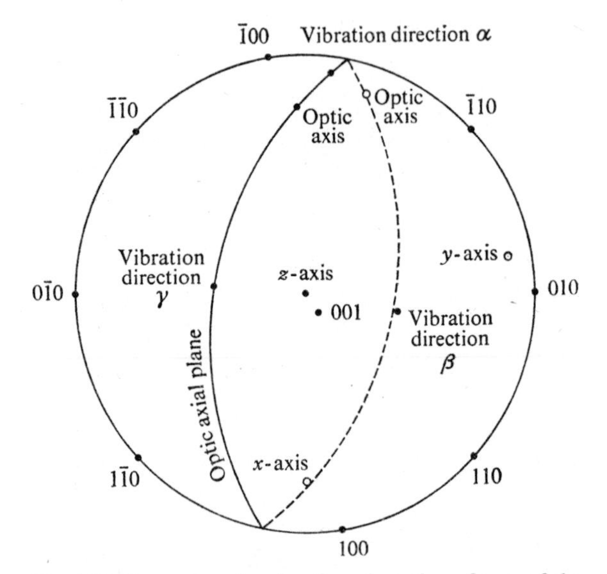

Fig. 4.10 Stereogram showing the orientation of axes of the indicatrix plotted with respect to crystallographic directions for a triclinic crystal (bustamite).

monoclinic material must not only state the magnitudes of the principal refractive indices and the size of the optic axial angle but also the orientation of the indicatrix with respect to the particular crystallographic axes which have been used; for example this might be specified $y=\alpha$, $x:\gamma=5°$ (in the obtuse angle between the crystallographic axes of 105°, i.e. $z:\beta=10°$) (Fig. 4.9*b*).

The third group of optically biaxial crystals belong to the triclinic system for which no symmetry axes are present; the holosymmetric class has only a centre of symmetry. There are no significant reference directions which can uniquely define the crystallographic axes, which are quite arbitrarily chosen for each material and are conventionally inclined with general angles between them. Since these axes define no symmetry directions, the orientation of the principal axes of the optical indicatrix will, in general, have no special relationship to the crystallographic axes; usually, none of the principal optical directions coincides with the axes. In our description of the optical properties of a triclinic crystal, we must specify the complete orientation of the indicatrix as well as its size and shape; this best represented stereographically (Fig. 4.10).

We notice that, in contrast with uniaxial systems, the orientation of the optical indicatrix differs in each of the three biaxial systems. This leads to characteristically different optical properties and allows the differentiation of the three systems by optical methods.

4.5 Summary

The optical indicatrix is a representation surface showing the variation of refractive index with vibration direction of linearly polarised light waves travelling in transparent media. Its properties allow the prediction of the vibration directions (and therefore the refractive indices) permitted for given wave normal directions; it can also be used to find the associated ray directions. The general characteristics of the optical indicatrix for each of the optical subdivisions of crystalline matter are summarised in Table 4.1. on p. 58.

4.6 Exercises

1. Use of Huyghens's construction for uniaxial crystals:

By employing Huyghens's construction using the appropriate sections of the ray velocity surface for calcite ($v_o \sim 1{\cdot}8 \times 10^{10}$, $v_e \sim 2 \times 10^{10}$ cm/sec):

(i) Account for the observations of the experiments in Exercise 2(i) of 3.5 [(0001) : $(10\bar{1}1) \sim 44\frac{1}{2}°$].

(ii) Account for the observations of the experiments in Exercise 2(ii) of 3.5.

2. Use of the uniaxial indicatrix:

Scapolites are members of a complex silicate mineral group with tetragonal symmetry. For one variety, the principal refractive indices were determined as $n_o = 1{\cdot}590$, $n_e = 1{\cdot}556$:

Use the properties of the indicatrix to determine the refractive indices displayed by sections cut parallel to (110), (101) and (111), given that $a = 12{\cdot}13 \times 10^{-8}$ and $c = 7{\cdot}69 \times 10^{-8}$ cm are the dimensions of the unit cell of this variety.

(Note: even with the moderate birefringence shown by this mineral, a graphical construction cannot give significant accuracy, and it is essential to use the equation of the uniaxial indicatrix given in Appendix A.1.)

Table 4.1

Summary of the characteristics of the optical indicatrix

Isotropic	*Anisotropic*	
	Uniaxial	*Biaxial*
Cubic crystals	Tetragonal, hexagonal and trigonal crystals	Orthorhombic, monoclinic and triclinic crystals
The indicatrix is a sphere whose radius is the principal refractive index, n	The indicatrix is an ellipsoid of revolution, whose axes are the principal refractive indices, n_o and n_e; the radius of the circular section is n_o, while n_e is the length of the radius normal to the circular section, the optic axis direction	The indicatrix is a triaxial ellipsoid whose three mutually perpendicular axes are the principal refractive indices, n_γ, n_β and n_α. There are two circular sections of radius n_β, whose normals, the two optic axis directions, are symmetrically inclined in the γ–α vibration plane. The angle between the optic axes ($2V$) is determined by the relative magnitudes of n_γ, n_β and n_α, and is a characteristic of a particular material
The orientation of the indicatrix does not arise	The orientation of the indicatrix is such that the axis of revolution, the optic axis, is always parallel to the z-crystallographic axis taken parallel to the tetrad, hexad or triad symmetry axis	The orientation of the indicatrix depends on the system. In orthorhombic crystals, the axes of the indicatrix are coincident with the crystallographic axes. In monoclinic crystals, one axis is parallel to the y-crystallographic axis, but the other two axes of the indicatrix are generally disposed in the plane of the x- and z-crystallographic axes. In triclinic crystals there is no necessary relationship between the crystallographic and indicatrix axes
There is no optic sign	The optic sign is positive if $n_e > n_o$; the optic sign is negative if $n_e < n_o$	The optic sign is positive if $2V_\gamma < 90°$, i.e. γ is the acute bisectrix; the optic sign is negative if $2V_\gamma > 90°$, i.e. α is the acute bisectrix

3. Use of the biaxial indicatrix:

Gypsum ($CaSO_4 . 2H_2O$) has holosymmetric monoclinic symmetry (class 2/m); many of the larger crystals which are found can be described as showing the forms {010}, {110} and {111} with the axial constants as $a/b : 1 : c/b = 0{\cdot}690 : 1 : 0{\cdot}412$, $\beta = 99\frac{1}{3}°$.

(i) Draw the appearance of the (010) face. Insert on your diagram the fast and slow vibration directions for parallel light travelling normal to the face, if the optical properties of gypsum are described as $n_\alpha = 1{\cdot}520$, $n_\beta = 1{\cdot}522$, $n_\gamma = 1{\cdot}529$; $y = \beta$, $z : \alpha = 37\frac{1}{2}°$ (in the acute z–$\bar{x}$ angle). What are the refractive indices for light travelling in this direction?

(ii) Insert on your diagram the directions of the optic axes.

(iii) A section is cut from the crystal so as to symmetrically bevel the edge in which the faces (110) and $(1\bar{1}0)$ meet. Determine the directions relative to the z-axis of the slow and fast vibration directions for parallel light normally incident on this section. What are the associated refractive indices?

(Note: again it is essential to use the equation of the biaxial indicatrix given in Appendix A.2.)

CHAPTER 5

ABSORPTION

5.1 General considerations

So far we have been regarding our media of transmission as ideally transparent, but of course some light is always absorbed in passing through solid matter. One effect of absorption is seen in the increasing reduction of the intensity of the light as it travels through the medium; the diminution in intensity for a particular wavelength depends exponentially both on the length (t) of the optic path in the absorber, and on the absorption coefficient (k), a constant for a particular substance. Since there is a direct relationship between the intensity and the square of the amplitude of the wave motion, as the waves travel through an absorbing medium the amplitude of the light vector must be decreasing in the form

$$a_t = a_0 e^{-kt/2}$$

where a_0 is the amplitude on entering and a_t is the amplitude after a path length t in the absorber. For materials usually classified as transparent, the product kt is so small as to make any reduction in amplitude negligible; this can be due either to a low absorption coefficient or short optical path, or both. Of course we can study with increasing difficulty the transmission of light through more highly absorbing crystals by using thinner and thinner sections, until a point is reached when the light transmitted by the thinnest possible section is so feeble that it cannot be detected. Such highly absorbing materials have to be studied by reflected light methods; their properties, and those of any substance for which there is moderate absorption, are significantly different from transparent media and are beyond the scope of this book.

However, there is one aspect of the phenomenon of absorption which is often apparent even for the slightly absorbing materials with which we are concerned. Many substances show dispersion of the absorption coefficient, i.e. a variation of k with the wavelength of the light, and this can lead to the materials appearing coloured when white light is passed through them. In Fig. 5.1, the ratio of transmitted to incident intensities after a fixed optical path, is plotted against wavelength in three hypothetical cases. In (*a*), the ratio is constant at 99 per cent throughout the visible spectrum, in (*b*) it is again constant, but at 33 per cent, while in (*c*) it is variable from 99 per cent at one end of the spectrum to 33 per cent at the other. In the first two cases, the material will appear white in incident white light; for (*a*) the reduction in intensity will barely be noticeable while in (*b*) only one-third of the intensity will be transmitted. In the third case there is dispersion of the absorption coefficient, with much more light absorbed at the long wavelength end of the spectrum; the

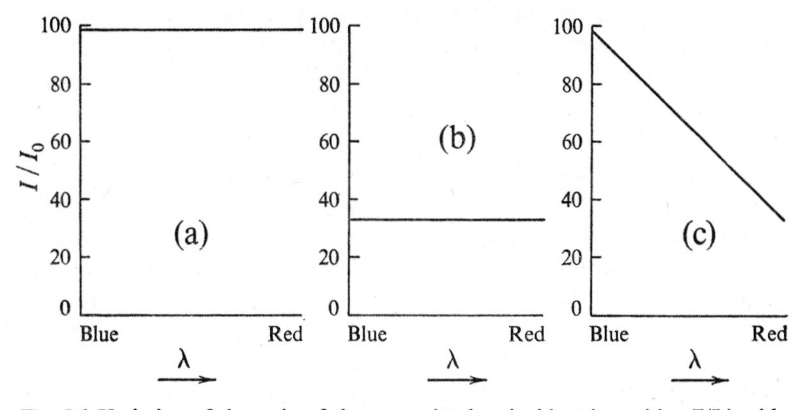

Fig. 5.1 Variation of the ratio of the transmitted to incident intensities (I/I_0) with wavelength (λ) in three hypothetical cases.

material appears to be coloured blue in transmitted light. Of course, the quality of the colour depends on the amount of the absorption. If the optical path in (*c*) was gradually shortened, the blue coloration would become paler until the reduction in intensity at both ends of the visible spectrum was so slight that it was not detectable by the eye; thus large crystals can be coloured while thin sections of the same materials appear to be colourless. In reality, the absorption is selective and occurs in bands within the visible spectrum. Such bands occur at wavelengths which depend both on the structure of the atoms and the crystal structure of the absorber; their widths depend, among other factors, on the dimensions of the crystal. The physical process which causes absorption is concerned with the movement of extranuclear electrons of atoms of the absorber to higher energy levels when activated by energy from the light waves. It can be profoundly affected by the presence of impurities and other defects in the atomic arrangement, so that the colours displayed by one substance can vary over a considerable range.

We are not concerned here with the detailed nature of these processes, but since the way in which they occur depends on the crystal structure, it is not surprising that absorption in crystalline matter can be anisotropic. The general description of absorption that we have given applies to isotropic materials; in anisotropic crystals there can be a dependence of absorption properties on the vibration direction of light, so that the visible effects can be a little more complex.

5.2 Absorption effects in uniaxial crystals

If the material under examination is optically isotropic, any absorption colour observed in transmitted light will be the same for similar path lengths in any direction, no matter whether incident white light is unpolarised or linearly polarised. But if we have an anisotropic crystal, the colour that is seen can depend on whether the incident light is unpolarised or not; if the incident light is linearly polarised, the colour transmitted can depend on its vibration direction.

We can illustrate the nature of these absorption effects for uniaxial crystals using the example of the trigonal mineral, tourmaline (a complex alumino-silicate). The precise form of the absorption effects for this substance varies with the small compositional changes from specimen to specimen, but what is now described may be regarded as fairly typical. Tourmaline crystals of a reasonable size are relatively common, and so we can obtain two sections of equal thickness cut from a uniform homogeneous crystal. One, a basal section, is perpendicular to the triad (or optic axis) direction and the other, a prismatic section, contains the triad axis. We can examine the colours transmitted by the two sections in both unpolarised and polarised white light. In unpolarised light the basal section appears deep brown, whilst the prismatic section is a deep yellow. The incident white light can now be linearly polarised by the use of a polar before it strikes the sections. Starting first with the prismatic section, the colour varies between two extremes, deep brown and yellow, depending on the orientation of the polar. When the light transmitted by the polar is vibrating perpendicular to the optic axis, the crystal appears deep brown. As the polar is rotated the absorption decreases and more light is transmitted; at the same time the colour gradually changes, until with the light vector parallel to the optic axis the other limiting colour, yellow, is seen (Fig. 5.2). This experiment suggests that the absorbing crystal shows two distinctive colours, one (deep brown) associated with the ordinary vibration direction, and the other (yellow) with the other principal vibration direction, the extraordinary. With the polar in intermediate positions, light incident on the section is resolved into components parallel to these principal vibration directions, to give colours which are mixtures of the deep brown and yellow in the appropriate proportions. This is confirmed by examination of the basal section; whatever the position of the polar, the section shows the deep brown coloration of the ordinary vibration. We can realise, too, that the deep yellow of the prismatic section in unpolarised light is due to the admixture of the two distinctive colours which occurs

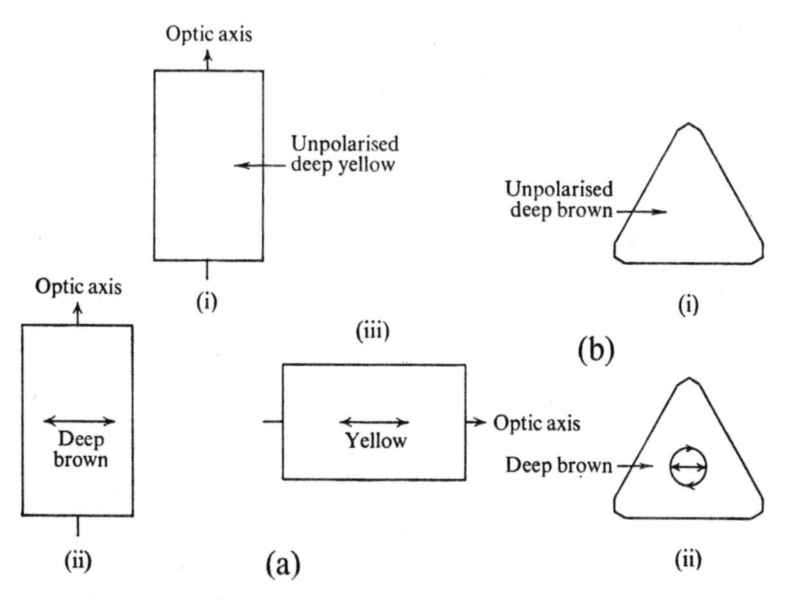

Fig. 5.2 Absorption effects for tourmaline.
a. Prismatic section: (i) unpolarised light; (ii) light vector perpendicular to optic axis; (iii) light vector parallel to optic axis.
b. Basal section: (i) unpolarised light; (ii) light vector in all orientations in plane.

with the resolution into the permitted principal vibration directions; naturally, the basal section perpendicular to the optic axis will show the deep brown colour for unpolarised light.

The nature of the absorption effects described for tourmaline are characteristic of many coloured uniaxial crystals, though there are not always such marked colour changes. The variation of the transmitted colour with vibration direction of light is called *pleochroism.* Strictly, this term applies only where there is a distinct colour change and not merely a variation in intensity, but in practice it is used wherever the eye can distinguish any change of absorption on rotation of an aniso-tropic section over a polar. As for tourmaline, in pleochroic uniaxial crystals there are two distinctive colours, those associated with the two principal vibration directions, and so such crystals are sometimes said to be dichroic. In describing them the absorption formula and the dichroic scheme are recorded, e.g. for tourmaline, since the absorption of the ordinary waves is greater than that of the extraordinary waves in a standard thickness, the absorption formula is written $O>E$; the dichroic scheme is then *O*, dark brown; *E*, yellow. The colours for all other vibration directions are mixtures of those given by the dichroic scheme, as also are those seen in unpolarised light. The colours of the dichroic scheme are sometimes called axial colours since they are seen when light vibrates parallel to principal axes of the indicatrix. The colours of the basal and prismatic sections in unpolarised light are described as face colours; they are also often quoted for they aid recognition when a polar is not available. However, in describing colours it is important to remember that the shade depends on the thickness of the crystal section; axial and face colours are usually given for a standard thickness of 0·003 cm. Moreover the axial and face colours for a particular crystalline material are very sensitive to slight variations in constitution and defects in the crystal structure; for example, the dichroic schemes of other tourmaline varieties can show *O*, pink, pale green and *E*, colourless, pale yellow.

5.3 Absorption effects in biaxial crystals

Similar effects can be observed for some coloured biaxial crystals, though, as we would expect, there are three colours in the pleochroic scheme. For example, coloured varieties of andalusite (a form of Al_2SiO_5 with orthorhombic symmetry) show pleochroism. Sections parallel to pinacoidal faces show the colour range to extend from rose red through to a light green and an even paler green (Fig. 5.3). As before, the colours for general vibration directions are mixtures of these three distinctive colours, as will be the face colours seen in unpolarised light. By analogy with uniaxial crystals the pleochroic effects are described by means of the absorption formula and the scheme; in this example, the absorption formula is $X>Y>Z$ with the pleochroic (or trichroic) scheme as *X*, rose red; *Y*, light green; *Z*, very pale green.

In this example, the absorption axes, which give the colours of the pleochroic scheme, coincide with those of the indicatrix; white light vibrating parallel to one of the principal vibration directions is transmitted by the crystal as the appropriate colour of the scheme. While this is always valid for orthorhombic crystals, it does not necessarily remain true for the less symmetrical monoclinic and triclinic crystals. For monoclinic crystals, one absorption axis is parallel to the y-crystallographic axis (which is always a principal axis of the indicatrix);

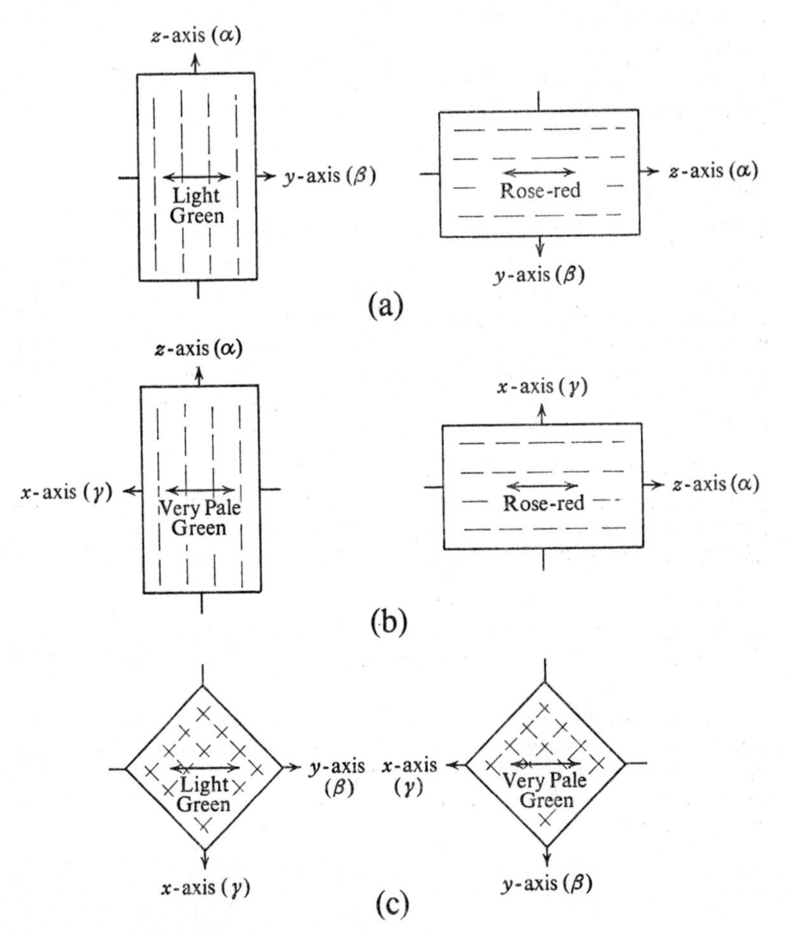

Fig. 5.3 Absorption effects for andalusite.
a. (100) section; *b.* (010) section; *c.* (001) section. The traces of the {110} cleavages are shown on each section.

the other two lie in the (010) plane but are not necessarily coincident with the other two axes of the indicatrix. These other two absorption axes can be determined by rotating a polar with the white light incident on an (010) section, and locating the positions at the limits of the colour range; fortunately such experiments show that for most materials the absorption and indicatrix axes are coincident for all practical purposes. Similarly in triclinic crystals, where there is no necessary correspondence between the absorption axes and those of the indicatrix, the difference is often so slight that white light vibrating parallel to one of the principal vibration directions is transmitted with a colour which can be taken as part of the pleochroic scheme.

5.4 Exercises

1. The effect of thickness upon transmitted colour:

A number of sections of different thicknesses are cut from the same crystal of a garnet (a complex alumino-silicate mineral group with cubic symmetry). Examine the appearance of these sections when placed in front of a source of white light; note particularly the relationship between the transmitted colour and the thickness of the absorbing path. By inserting filters in the incident light path, confirm the region of the spectrum in which the absorption takes place.

2. Pleochroic effects in uniaxial crystals:

(i) Use a prismatic crystal of schorlite (an iron-rich tourmaline) and a polar to confirm the general nature of the observations described in 5.2.
(ii) Repeat (i) with crystals of a coloured variety of corundum (Al_2O_3).

3. Pleochroic effects in biaxial crystals:

(i) Use sections of staurolite (a hydrous iron-aluminium silicate with orthorhombic symmetry) cut parallel to (100), (010) and (001) to study pleochroic effects in this material.

(ii) A cube of piedmontite (a member of the epidote mineral group with monoclinic symmetry) is cut so that its faces are parallel to (100) and (010); the other faces are perpendicular to the *z*-axis. If the absorption axes are almost perpendicular to the faces of this cube, examine the absorption effects shown by this material.

CHAPTER 6

POLARS AND LINEARLY POLARISED LIGHT

6.1 General requirements

We have already seen that one of the characteristics of optically anisotropic crystals is that their properties can vary with the vibration direction of linearly polarised light passing through them. In the observation of these properties, we have also demonstrated that it is necessary both to have linearly polarised incident light and to be able to analyse the light transmitted by the crystal. In earlier chapters there has been reference to a *polar*, a device which only transmits light vibrating parallel to a particular direction; we shall now look at the nature of such devices in detail.

The earliest experiments on the production of linearly polarised light utilised Brewster's observation that complete polarisation of the reflected beam occurs when unpolarised light is incident on the surface of a transparent material at a certain angle (see 3.1). Though this affords a simple, convenient polar, it is not very efficient owing to the high percentage of the incident light transmitted by refraction through a transparent plate. This disadvantage can be overcome by using a number of glass plates placed one on top of the other. For each plate of the pile, reflection occurs at both surfaces, and for the correct angle of incidence a relatively strong beam of linearly polarised light is reflected. The pile of plates is separated by spacers (sheets of black paper with central apertures will suffice), otherwise the plates make good contact with each other and act as a single slab. There are, however, some practical snags in using this pile of glass plates as a polar. The pile is rather cumbersome and quite sensitive in adjustment; moreover since most glasses are dispersive, the Brewster angle varies with wavelength, so that complete polarisation of all wavelengths does not occur at one setting. The method has long been discarded in favour of more efficient devices.

Before describing modern forms of polars, we can set down the desirable characteristics that they should possess. First, the device should be as efficient as possible in producing a linearly polarised beam from unpolarised light. Then, polarisation must be complete for the widest possible cone of incident wave normals, for in practice there will always be some spread of wave normal directions within the incident beam; the device should have a reasonably large incident aperture so as to produce polarised plane wave fronts of appreciable area. It is also essential that the vibration direction of the polarised light transmitted by the device shall be the same for all wavelengths so that the polar may be used both for monochromatic and for white light. The material of which the polar is made must have a low absorption coefficient both to ensure the efficient transmission of light energy and to avoid any coloration being given to white light passing through it. Finally, it is desirable that the polar should be as compact as possible with simple setting and adjustment of its permitted vibration direction, for these devices form an essential part of polarising microscopes used in optical examination, and should interfere as little as possible with the light path through the lens system of the microscope. Modern polars which attempt to fulfil these conditions fall into two main categories, those which produce polarisation by double refraction and those where the polarisation is by absorption.

6.2 Polarisation by double refraction

The double refraction shown by most crystalline materials produces two linearly polarised waves. If one of these disturbances can be eliminated, a polarising device, with at best 50 per cent efficiency, can be produced. All such polarising devices are prisms constructed so that one of the doubly refracted waves suffers total internal reflection within the prism; it is removed by absorption whilst the other is transmitted. To construct the prisms, a material must be used in which the double refraction is quite marked to ensure sufficient separation of the two disturbances and, of course, we must be able to obtain relatively large perfect crystals. The most suitable material is calcite of which the mineralogical variety, Iceland spar, provides crystals of the quality and size necessary for prism type polars.

One of the earliest and simplest polarising prisms was devised by Nicol. We shall describe the original *Nicol prism* in detail as an illustration of the way in which prism type polars function. An optically perfect cleavage rhombohedron $\{10\bar{1}1\}$ of calcite, about three times as long as it is wide, is cut diagonally across in a plane parallel to the long diagonal of the end faces; the cross-section should be of the order of a square centimetre to allow a reasonable aperture for the incident light. A principal section (ABCD) of the split rhombohedron is shown in Fig. 6.1*a*. The two halves are then ground so that the cut AC is perpendicular to the end faces AD and BC; this condition is almost satisfied in the original rhombohedron so that very little grinding of the end faces is required. After the two pieces have been polished upon the cut faces they are cemented together with balsam.

When unpolarised light travelling parallel to the length of the polar enters the composite prism through the lower surface (BC), it splits into

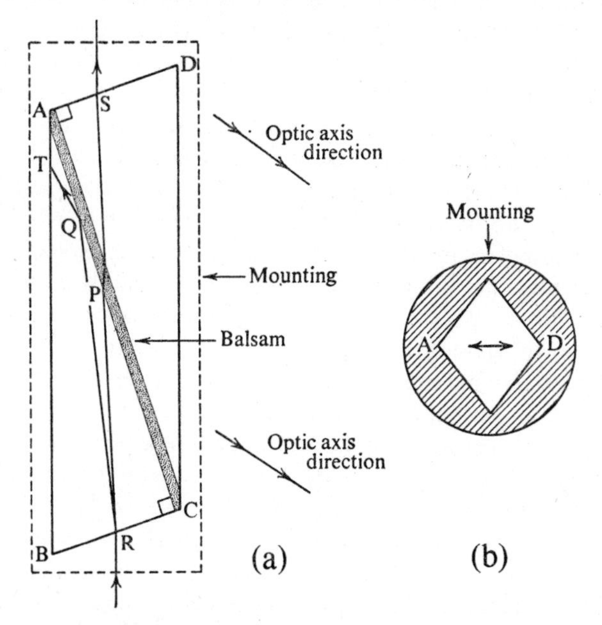

Fig. 6.1 The Nicol prism.
a. Ray paths through a principal section parallel to the length.
b. End view, showing vibration direction of transmitted light.

two polarised disturbances which follow the ray paths RP and RQ. One of these, represented in the diagram by RQ, is the ordinary disturbance which for calcite has a refractive index ~1·66. The other, represented by RP, is the extraordinary disturbance, which for the negative calcite crystal can have refractive index values from about 1·66 to 1·48 depending on the direction of vibration. The geometry of the Nicol prism is arranged so that the vibration direction associated with the extraordinary ray direction RP has a refractive index which is much the same as that of the balsam cement (about 1·54). The extraordinary waves pass through the balsam and emerge from the second half of the prism following the ray path PS. The ordinary waves, however, have a much greater refractive index than the balsam cement, and the geometry of the prism ensures that they strike the balsam interface between the two halves of the prism at an angle greater than the critical angle for the boundary; they are then totally reflected along the path QT to be absorbed in the blackened sides of the prism mounting. In this way the Nicol prism transmits only light vibrating in a principal plane, i.e. parallel to the shorter diagonal of the end face of the prism (Fig. 6.1*b*).

This simple prism, although it produces a linearly polarised beam of about 40 per cent of the intensity of the incident beam, is not without disadvantages. It is of necessity of quite large dimensions so that large optically clear calcite crystals are needed. The inclination of the end faces results in some loss of light by reflection, and, more important, a marked lateral displacement of the light path through it. Furthermore, to achieve complete removal of the ordinary waves, the incident light must be restricted to a limited cone, which is defined by an aperture in the base of the mount (see Exercise 1 of 6.4); otherwise some ordinary waves strike the balsam interface at angles less than the critical angle for the boundary, and are transmitted into the upper half of the prism. Even with this restriction on the maximum cone of incident light, the extraordinary waves emerging from the upper face of the prism are not all vibrating in precisely the same direction. In the latter half of the nineteenth century many ingenious developments of this simple prism were described. By using different geometrical arrangements their designers sought to improve the Nicol prism by using smaller pieces of calcite, by having the end faces perpendicular to the length, by increasing the cone for which complete polarisation is produced and by achieving a more precise definition of the permitted vibration direction. An interesting account of the variations is given in Johannsen's *Manual of Petrographic Methods*, but in all of them the essential function of removing one of the doubly refracted wave trains by total internal reflection is the same. The prism type polars still fitted to some modern microscopes are likely to be adaptations of one of these later designs. Indeed such was the universality of the prism-type of polarising device that the term 'nicol' is synonymous with polar. In more modern usage the term 'polar' is to be preferred for it has not got the connotations of polarisation by double refraction using calcite prisms; this change of terminology has been brought about by the development and increasing use of polarising devices employing an entirely different mechanism, polarisation by absorption.

6.3 Polarisation by absorption

In Chapter 5 we described how optical anisotropy leads to absorption effects which can depend markedly on the vibration direction of the light. For some crystals, this can mean that one set of the linearly polarised waves produced by the double refraction of unpolarised incident light is more heavily absorbed than the other; if a sufficiently thick section is used only one of the doubly refracted waves emerges, and the light is linearly polarised. In tourmaline $O \gg E$, so that with a sufficiently long absorbing path, unpolarised light passing through a prism section will emerge as a linearly polarised disturbance vibrating in a principal plane. The existence of absorption effects of this kind suggests a simple and convenient way of making a polar provided a suitable material can be found; tourmaline, and similar crystals, are not suitable, for the polarised light which they produce is considerably reduced in intensity and is coloured.

The earliest attempts to obtain transparent absorbing crystals with the right absorbing properties were made with synthetic substances in the last century by Herapath, but the technical difficulties of adaptation to give a practical polar were insurmountable at that time. The first of the modern absorption filter type polars used a strictly oriented aggregate of very fine needles of quinine sulphate periodide (herapathite) embedded in a plastic base; such filters were not entirely successful due partly to the technical difficulties of preparation and partly to coloration of the transmitted light. Later developments made use of the discovery that certain organic films (among them cellulose hydrate and polyvinyl alcohol) showed the right kind of selective absorption if they were stretched almost to breaking-point and then impregnated with an organic dye. Absorption filters of this kind can produce high quality polars comparable and sometimes better in performance than calcite prisms. The name polaroid (a trade name used by the Polaroid Corporation of America) is generally applied to absorption type filters; in the polar, the actual film of dyed plastic is mounted between optically worked glass flats for protection. Polars made from polaroid are being fitted increasingly to polarising microscopes, for as well as their compactness, their use is compatible with a large aperture for the incident light; this allows the redesign of certain parts of the optical system of the microscope with advantage. The absorption type polars used on microscopes transmit about 30–40 per cent of the intensity of the unpolarised incident light.

6.4 Exercises

1. The limiting angular aperture of a Nicol prism:

The effectiveness of the original Nicol prism is limited by two factors, (*a*) when the inclination of the incident light to the length of the prism is so large that the ordinary disturbance is no longer totally reflected by the balsam, and (*b*) when the inclination of the incident light to the length of the prism is such as to give total reflection of both the ordinary and extraordinary disturbances by the balsam. The geometry of the original Nicol prism is such that in the principal section of Fig. 6.1*a*, the angle of the parallelogram (at D) is 68°, and the optic axis direction is inclined at 41·3° to the direction of the balsam. Given that for calcite $n_o=1{\cdot}66$ and $n_e=1{\cdot}48_5$, and that the refractive index of balsam cement is 1·54:

(i) Determine the angle of inclination to the length for light entering the prism so that the ordinary disturbance reaches the balsam film at the critical angle.

(ii) Carry out a similar determination for the extraordinary disturbance. (Remember that the extraordinary refractive index varies with the direction of propagation inside the calcite, and must be calculated from a principal section of the indicatrix.)

(iii) From these values, deduce the limiting angular aperture of a Nicol prism.

2. The properties of polaroid:

(i) Use the absorption properties of tourmaline (5.2) to establish the permitted vibration direction for the polaroid.

(ii) Examine the intensity of light of different wavelengths transmitted by the polaroid.

(iii) With a second piece of polaroid, confirm that no light of any wavelength is transmitted when its permitted vibration direction is in the same plane, but perpendicular (or crossed) with respect to that of the first piece. Examine the change in intensity as the first piece is rotated in its own plane.

(iv) With the pieces of polaroid initially in the crossed position, investigate the effect of oblique incidence by rotating one piece about its permitted vibration direction.

CHAPTER 7

THE POLARISING MICROSCOPE

7.1 General introduction

THE bulk of crystalline material does not normally occur in such a way as to provide the large single crystals or crystal sections which can be examined by simple experiments such as we have described for calcite; nor do the optical properties always lend themselves so readily to this type of investigation. Generally we must be content with specimens either in the form of small crystals and tiny crystal fragments or with sections of such crystals, often embedded in a matrix of other crystalline matter. Usually it is only possible to identify and characterise optical properties by microscopic examination. A microscope suitable for this work must satisfy some additional experimental requirements as well as acting as an ordinary compound microscope.

The essential function of the compound microscope is to provide a magnified image of an object so that it may be seen in focus by an observer. In the polarising microscope, it is also important to be able to polarise linearly the incident light and to analyse the polarisation of light transmitted by the specimen. The most important additional features of the polarising microscope are the two polars capable of insertion into the light path before and after it passes through the specimen. Since it is necessary to change the orientation of the permitted vibration directions of these polars with respect to the specimen, either they should be able to rotate or the stage carrying the specimen should rotate. It is also advantageous that the mutual vibration directions of the polars be variable, so that their rotations should be independent. Further, it should be possible to insert an auxiliary testing instrument into the path of the light through the instrument. In addition to having a lens system capable of giving a clearly resolved magnified image, it should be possible to use the polarising microscope as a conoscope, or wide angle telescope; under certain circumstances an image formed in the principal focus of the objective by a strongly convergent light beam can give valuable data on anisotropic character. The use of the polarising microscope in different ways emphasises the importance of versatility in the adjustment of the illumination of the specimen, so that it also needs a number of subsidiary lenses, diaphragms, etc. to facilitate this.

There are a large number of different models of polarising microscopes manufactured. The manner in which the features of a compound microscope are supplemented to satisfy the requirements of the study of crystal optics depends on the maker and also on the cost of the instrument. It is impossible to set down here all the variations which have been adopted and so we shall describe only how the components are arranged for a typical, moderately priced instrument of a kind usually available for laboratory classes, together with a few brief comments on the differences between older and more modern expensive designs.

7.2 The use of the polarising microscope to produce a magnified object image

In what is often known as orthoscopic use, the main lens system of the microscope is arranged to produce a magnified image of the object; we may use some of the auxiliary components of a polarising microscope to examine the appearance of this image under different conditions, but essentially the main optical system is that of the compound microscope.

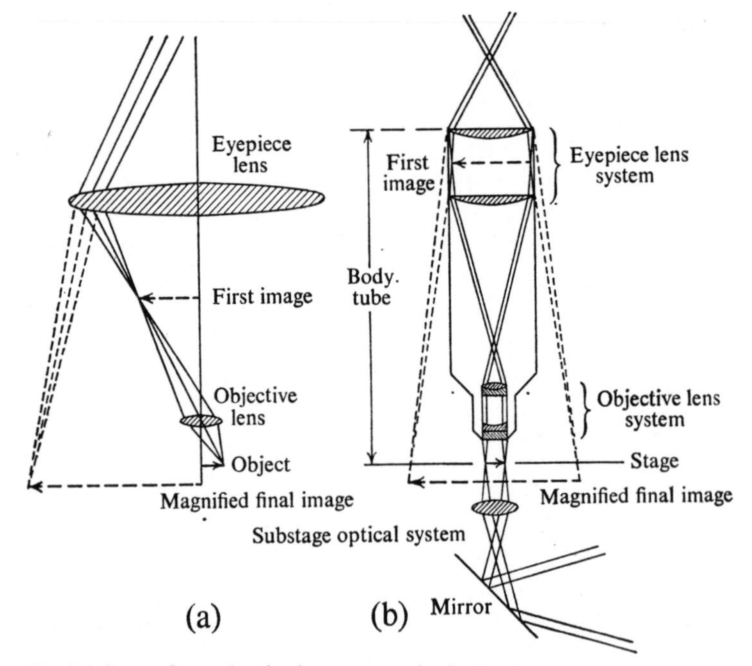

Fig. 7.1 Image formation in the compound microscope.
a. Magnification by simple lens system.
b. Schematic representation of image formation in orthoscopic use of compound microscope.

Basically the optical arrangement is very simple (Fig. 7.1*a*). The primitive compound microscope has an objective, a lens of very short focal length, which forms a real image of an object placed just past the principal focus. This first image is viewed through an ocular (or eyepiece) of greater focal length, which forms a magnified virtual image of the object; this should be viewed with the eye placed at the point where an image of the optical centre of the objective is formed by the ocular. The magnification is determined primarily by the magnifying powers of the two lenses, which depend inversely on their focal lengths.

Fig. 7.1*b* shows the adaptation of this system which is used in the modern microscope, and traces the ray paths forming the magnified final image. Fig. 7.2*a* shows the essential mechanical construction of the typical polarising microscope. The objective and ocular are mounted in the body (or draw) tube; they may be readily changed so that the magnification can be varied. The body tube is attached through a rack

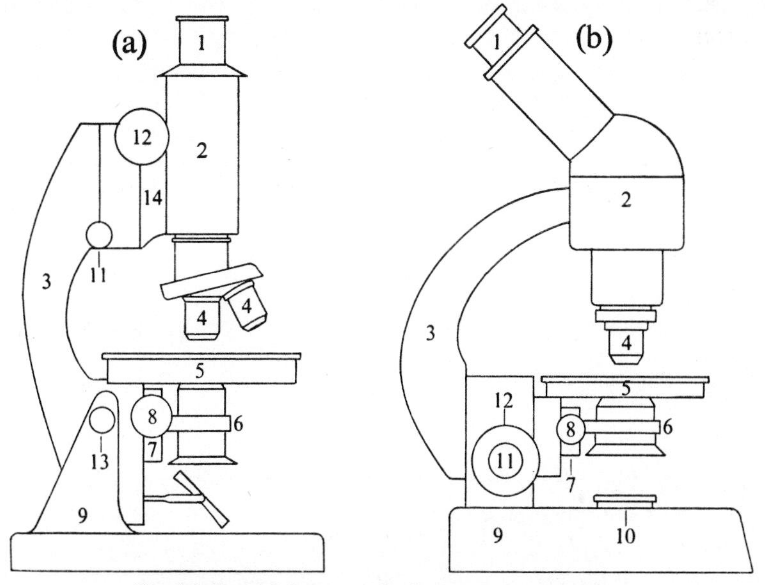

Fig. 7.2 General features of microscope construction.
a. Hinged stand.
b. Fixed stand.

1. Ocular
2. Body-tube
3. Arm
4. Objective
5. Stage
6. Sub-stage system
7. Rack and pinion movement for sub-stage system
8. Adjustment for this movement
9. Foot
10. Lamp
11. Fine adjustment
12. Coarse adjustment
13. Hinge connecting arm and foot
14. Rack and pinion movement for body-tube

and pinion movement to the arm of the instrument. Coarse and fine adjustments of this movement allow the focusing of the microscope on an object placed on the stage, which is also mounted on the arm so that its surface is always perpendicular to the length of the body tube; often the controls of the focusing adjustment of the body tube are calibrated to allow depth measurements in the specimen. The substage system controlling the illumination of the object is also carried on the arm of the microscope. The other part of the microscope stand consists of the foot to which the arm is connected through a hinge. The foot is massive and usually shaped like a horseshoe; its function is to stabilise the instrument, even when the arm, carrying the whole optical arrangement, is tilted into a comfortable working position. In modern and more expensive instruments, the hinged stand is sometimes replaced by a fixed stand (Fig. 7.2*b*). In this the lower half of the body tube is attached to a unified arm and foot so that it is always vertical; by means of a prism, light is refracted to enter an adjustable inclined ocular. This kind of stand has the advantage that the plane of the specimen stage always remains horizontal; focusing is achieved by movement of the stage through coarse and fine adjustment of the rack and pinion movement by which it is attached to the stand. Often a lamp source is built into the foot, so that once adjusted it is always ready for use. More expensive models have additional refinements such as binocular eyepieces, built-in cameras with automatic exposure timers, etc.

So far we have only briefly described in outline the general features of the polarising microscope in so far as it fulfils the function of producing a magnified image. We must now look at its various components more closely and also see how the extra subsidiary lenses, polars, etc. are arranged.

7.3 Substage system and stage

In hinged stand microscopes light is reflected by a mirror attached to the arm under the stage (Fig. 7.3), so that it travels up the tube of the microscope; one face of the mirror is flat while the other is concave. Above the mirror, or built-in lamp, is the first polar, known as the *polariser*. The polariser is usually mounted on a pivoting bracket arm which allows it to be inserted into or pulled out of the light path as required. When inserted it is usually capable of rotation about the axis of the microscope, i.e. a line through the centre of the optical system; the mount of the polar often carries an engraved angular scale to allow measurement of this rotation. Although this movement allows the orientation of the linearly polarised light transmitted by the polariser to be changed, the polariser is more often used in a fixed position in which it is located by some sort of spring locking device. In this position it transmits light vibrating parallel to one of the crosswires set in the eyepiece which act as reference directions for the microscope.

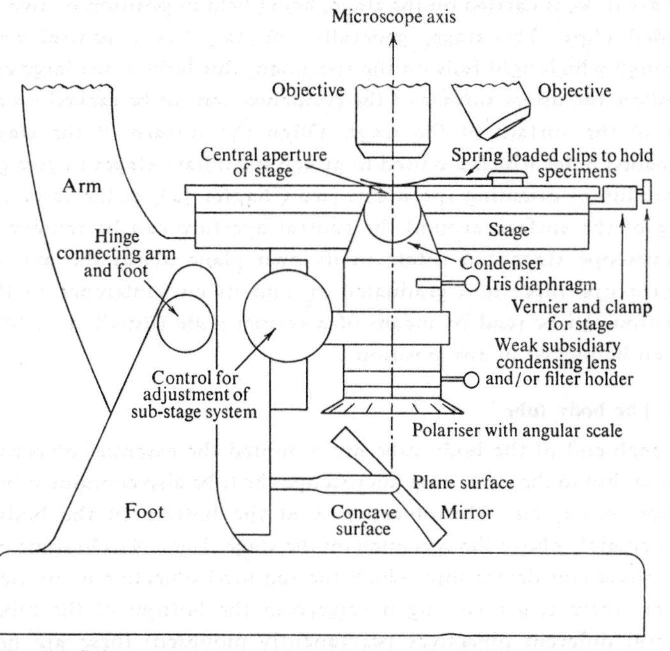

Fig. 7.3 Substage system and stage of a typical polarising microscope.

Usually, a weakly-condensing lens or lens system comes next, which affects a slight concentration of light on the object. In some microscopes this is permanently inserted, but in others it may be easily removed, sometimes independently of the polariser; there are often removable filter holders carried by the arm in this position, and most manufacturers also provide a substage iris diaphragm. Immediately above this, just below the object on the stage, there is on all polarising microscopes a short focal length plano-convex lens. On most models this can be easily put in or out of the light path. This strongly converging lens (known as the *condenser*) has a special function in the conoscopic examination of specimens as we shall see in 7.7. In many models the whole of this substage system (excluding the mirror) is mounted so that it can be raised or lowered relative to the stage by a rack and pinion movement attaching it to the arm. The independent movement of the various components of the substage system out of the light path, to which we have referred, varies from model to model; sometimes all the components are in the same mount and move together.

The object under examination, usually a section or grains mounted on a glass slide, is carried on the stage, being held in position by two spring loaded clips. The stage, generally circular, has a central aperture through which light falls on the specimen; this hole is just large enough to allow the upper surface of the condenser lens to be racked up almost flat to the surface of the stage. Often the surface of the stage has threaded holes which are used to attach subsidiary stages to give greater flexibility in orienting specimens (see Chapter 12); at the same time, a ring of the surface around the central aperture can be removed. The microscope stage can rotate in its own plane about the axis of the microscope tube; it is graduated around its circumference so that its position can be read by means of a vernier scale (usually to 1/10°), and it can be locked in any position.

7.4 The body tube

At each end of the body tube are mounted the essential objective and ocular, but in the polarising microscope the tube also contains subsidiary lenses, polar, etc. The objective is at the bottom of the body tube immediately above the specimen on the stage (Fig. 7.4). On some models there is a clip device into which the required objective is inserted. On others there is a revolving nosepiece at the bottom of the tube with several different objectives permanently mounted; these are brought into operation by rotating the mounting until the selected lens is locked into position by a spring device. The objectives are centred using two perpendicular adjusting screws (see 7.8). Above the objective is a slot to permit the insertion of various testing instruments into the light path; the direction of this slot bisects the angle between the vibration directions for the normal orientations of the polars, i.e. it is at 45° to the crosswires of the microscope. Next as we go up the body tube is the second polar, known as the *analyser*, mounted so that it can be easily pushed in or out of the light path. It is usually set so that its vibration plane is perpendicular to that of the polariser in the locked position, i.e. parallel to the second microscope crosswire; when both polariser and analyser are in the light path in their normal orientations with perpendicular vibration directions, it is said that the microscope is being used with crossed polars (or crossed nicols). In some older models, the second polar is located external to the body tube above the eyepiece; this 'cap analyser' is usually coupled to the polariser, so that they can be simultaneously rotated about a fixed stage. In most microscopes, the *Bertrand lens* is situated above the analyser; this subsidiary lens is

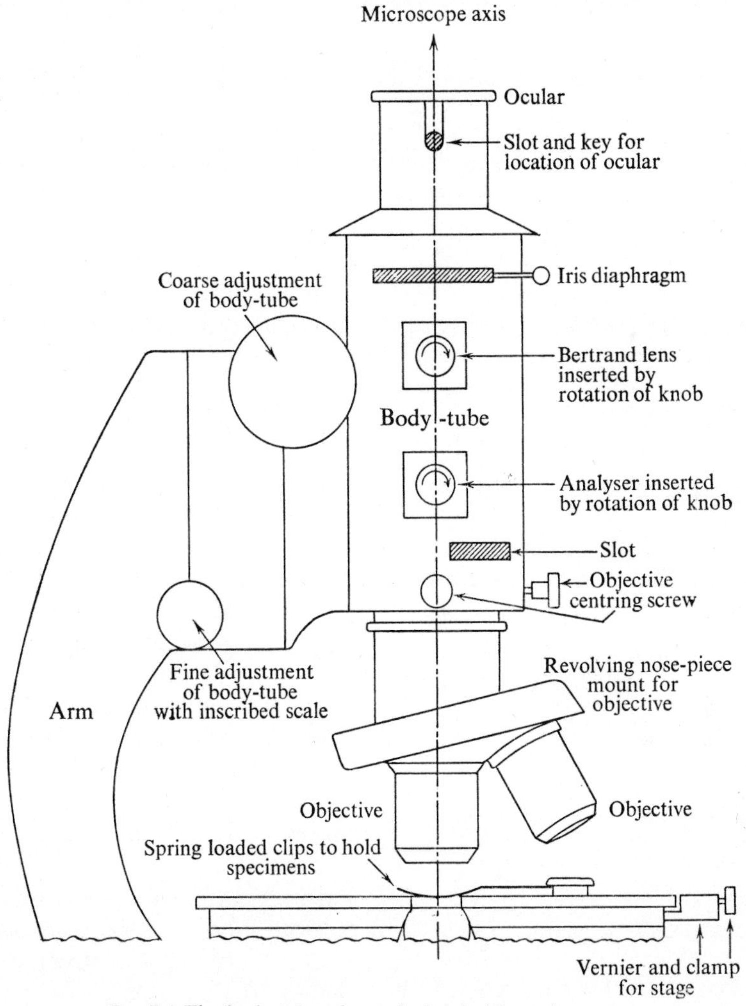

Fig. 7.4 The body tube of a typical polarising microscope.

inserted when the microscope is used conoscopically and its function is discussed in 7.7. Immediately above the Bertrand lens, many models have an adjustable iris diaphragm. Finally at the top of the body tube is the ocular, with two perpendicular crosswires arranged so that they can be seen simultaneously with the object. These crosswires, usually parallel to the vibration directions of the crossed polars, act as reference directions for the microscope, and so the orientation of the ocular, which is removable from the body tube, is located by a key which fits into a slot in the tube.

The performance of a microscope depends on the quality of its components, not least on the objective and eyepiece, which must be carefully designed and made. These are both lens systems rather than single lenses, for defects and distortions of the quality of the image are best corrected in this way. The objective system attempts to correct for chromatic and spherical aberration; the correction is never perfect and is best for ray directions almost parallel to the axis of the microscope. Chromatic aberration is usually overcome by using lenses which are achromatic doublets, a concave lens of glass of high dispersion in combination with a convex lens made from glass with less dispersion; it is particularly important that all the lenses in a polarising microscope be free from strain. The correction for spherical aberration is more complex; the use of certain kinds of lenses (e.g. hemispherical lens) can be made, and the effect can be minimised by using several weaker lenses instead of one stronger one. The complexity of the lens system increases with the power of the objective; low power objectives (up to magnifications of 5×) often consist of one achromatic doublet, while medium power (up to 20×) and high power (up to 100×) objectives have systems of increasing complexity employing several doublets with a hemispherical entrance lens (Fig. 7.5). Low power objectives allow simultaneous observation of objects in different planes of the specimen and the object-objective distance is quite large (of the order of a few centimetres); for high power objectives the depth of focus is small, and the working distance is short (one or two millimetres, see Table 7.1).

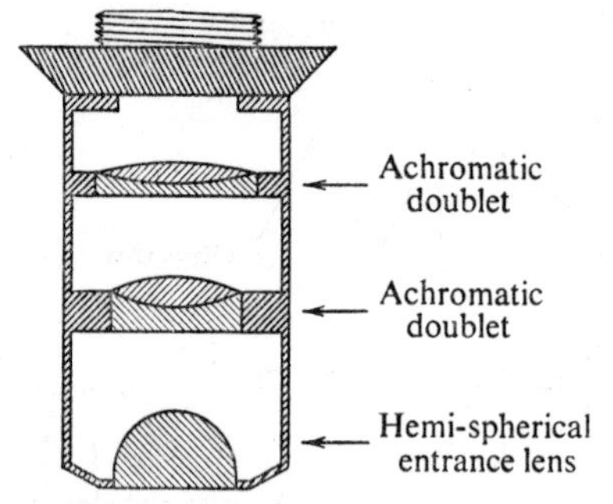

Fig. 7.5 Lens structure of a typical high power objective.

The ocular is also a lens system, though of less complex construction for it has only to deal with ray directions close to the axis of the microscope; it usually consists of two lenses, the field lens (nearer the object) and the eye lens. In many oculars, of the Huyghens type (Fig. 7.6*a*), both are plano-convex lenses mounted with their convex faces towards the object; light from the objective forms a real enlarged image of the object in the focal plane of the eye lens, so that in some ways we can regard the field lens as part of the lens system of the objective. The real image is then observed as a magnified virtual image through the eye lens. In a correctly balanced ocular the field lens has a focal length two or

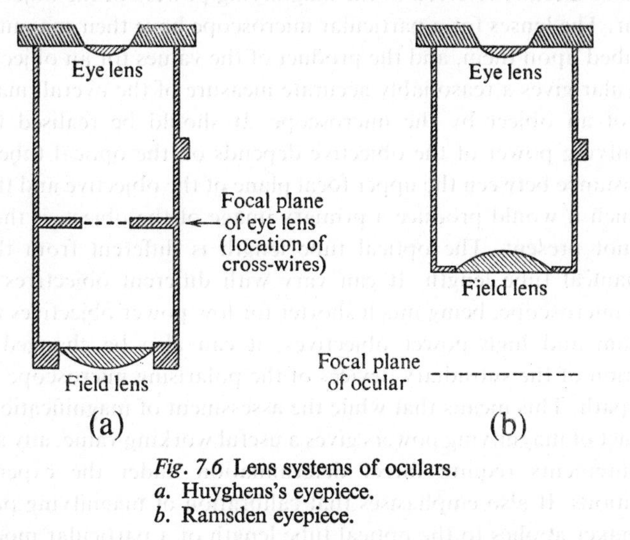

Fig. 7.6 Lens systems of oculars.
a. Huyghens's eyepiece.
b. Ramsden eyepiece.

three times that of the eye lens, and they are separated by a distance equal to about twice the focal length of the eye lens; the diameter of the eye lens is usually smaller than that of the field lens. In the Huyghens ocular, the crosswires are mounted between the lenses in the focal plane of the eye lens, when they can be viewed simultaneously with the image. This type of ocular cannot focus on objects outside the lenses, and this can be a disadvantage. For example, if such a system is used to construct a graduated micrometer eyepiece, the scale would have to replace the crosswires; in this position, the aberrations introduced by the lenses would be different for the object image and the scale image, and inaccuracies would be introduced into measurement. To overcome this and other difficulties, the Ramsden type ocular can be used (Fig. 7.6*b*). Essentially this consists of two plano-convex lenses of equal focal length mounted at a distance apart of two thirds of this common focal length; now the field lens has its planar side facing the object. The focal plane is outside the lens system, and the object image must be formed by the objective in this plane; both the object image and that of a scale placed in this plane would now suffer the same distortions. The magnification achieved by most oculars depends on the lenses used in their construction; it is quite small, usually in the range of five to twenty times.

7.5 Magnification and resolution

We have already referred to the magnifying powers of the objective and ocular. The lenses for a particular microscope have their magnifications inscribed upon them, and the product of the values for an objective and an ocular gives a reasonably accurate measure of the overall magnification of an object by the microscope. It should be realised that the magnifying power of the objective depends on the optical tube length, the distance between the upper focal plane of the objective and the plane in which it would produce a primary image of the object, if the ocular was not present. The optical tube length is different from the fixed mechanical tube length. It can vary with different objectives for the same microscope, being much shorter for low power objectives than for medium and high power objectives; it can also be changed by the insertion of the subsidiary devices of the polarising microscope into the light path. This means that while the assessment of magnification as the product of magnifying powers gives a useful working value, any accurate measurements require direct determination under the experimental conditions. It also emphasises that calibration of magnifying power by the maker applies to the optical tube length of a particular model, and misleading results can be obtained if objectives and eyepieces are interchanged between different instruments.

The total magnification of a microscope is changed by using different objectives and oculars, and it seems at first sight that there is no limit to the magnification that can be obtained with suitable combinations of lens systems. But, in addition to its magnifying power, a most important property of any lens system is its *resolving power*, or its ability to allow the finer details of an object to be distinguished. Nothing is to be gained by increasing the magnifying power without increasing the resolving power, for one would only obtain a more enlarged but no more distinct image of the object. The resolving power is usually expressed inversely as the *limit of resolution*, by which we mean the smallest distance between two objects which can still be separately distinguished in the image. A limit to the resolution of any instrument is imposed by the diffraction of light by an object or aperture; diffraction arises naturally from the wave theory, and implies that while light waves generally travel in straight lines, they can bend round corners to a limited extent. For a microscope, this limit of resolution set by diffraction depends on the objective, for the ocular only magnifies the first image formed by the objective. There are various theories of microscopic resolution based on different assumptions about experimental conditions, but they all show with some approximation that the limit of resolution is $\lambda/2n\sin\varrho$, where λ is the wavelength of the light, n is the refractive index of the medium between object and objective, and ϱ is the semi-angle of the largest cone of light which can be subtended at the aperture of the objective by a point on the object. The quantity $n\sin\varrho$ is known as the *numerical aperture* (*N.A.*), and furnishes a criterion of the quality of the objective lens system; it is substantially independent of the magnifying power. Table 7.1 shows data for various objectives together with the theoretical magnifications obtained when they are used with oculars of magnifying power 5×, 10× and 15× such as are normally available with a polarising microscope.

Table 7.1

Some data on objectives

Objective					*Total magnification with oculars*		
Focal length (cm)	*N.A.*	*ϱ (deg.)*	*Working distance (mm)*	*Magnifying power*	5×	10×	15×
40·0	0·11	6·0	34·5	3·2	16	32	48
15·0	0·20	11·6	9·0	14·0	70	140	210
4·0	0·82	55·0	0·42	48·0	240	480	720
1·8 (oil immersion)	1·30	59·0	0·12	95·0	475	950	1425

From this it will be understood that the manufacture of objectives is an expensive process, and that they should be treated and used with great care. In optical microscopy medium and low power objectives may be used for much of the work. They allow a much greater area of the specimen to be surveyed than does a high power objective. Nevertheless, whenever it is necessary to examine the fine structure of an object, the greater limit of resolution of the high power objective must be used for nothing will be gained by changing oculars; the large numerical aperture of such objectives, which allow them to accept a wider cone of rays from the object, is also essential in conoscopic work (see 7.7 and 10.1). As a rough guide, the useful magnification of a microscope is limited to 500–1000 times the numerical aperture of the objective, and it is not worth while using combinations of oculars and objectives for which the total magnification lies outside this range. The limit to the numerical aperture is set by the difficulties of making a lens system of a suitable quality, but the numerical aperture can obviously be increased by increasing n. Normally objectives are used dry, with air

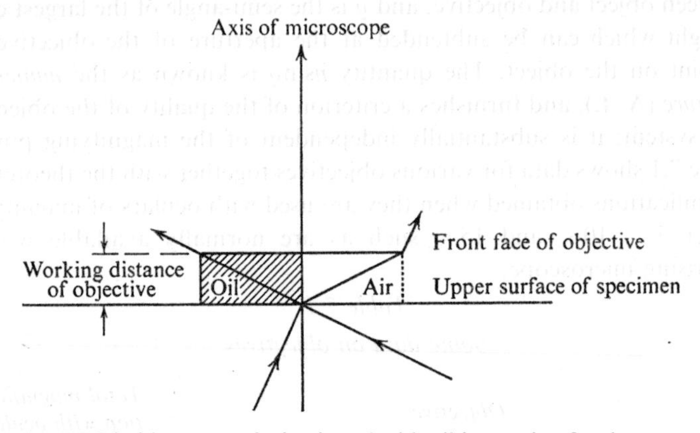

Fig. 7.7 Limiting ray paths in air and with oil immersion for the same objective.

separating them from the object so that $n=1$. Some objectives have been developed for very high magnification and resolution in which the object is immersed in an oil into which the plane front surface of the objective is placed. Clearly the limit of resolution is decreased in proportion to n, the refractive index of the oil, when compared to an objective of the same angular aperture used dry. Fig. 7.7 shows the limiting ray paths for the same objective both with and without oil immersion. Although it would appear that it is advantageous to have n as large as possible, it is best to use an oil with a refractive index which matches as closely as possible that of the glass of the front surface of the objective; this leads to reduced distortion by aberration. The performance is also improved by using the same oil between the upper surface of the condenser and the lower surface of the glass slide carrying the specimen. In addition to increased resolving power, oil immersion leads to increased brightness of the object by reducing light losses by reflection at the various boundaries. Naturally these objectives are very expensive to manufacture, and they should be handled with great care, according to the makers' instructions.

7.6 Illumination

The problem of illumination can be treated in two parts, the nature of the light and its source before it enters the optical system of the microscope and secondly the most efficient use of the light by the optical system.

For most purposes, white light is perfectly adequate. Nowadays this is usually provided by artificial sources, though if these are not available, a clear north light is most suitable, with an east facing position as a second choice; direct sunlight should not be used without a diffusing screen of ground glass or thin white paper. An artificial source is most simply constructed using a frosted electric light bulb mounted, with sufficient ventilation, in a box with an aperture placed about six inches from the microscope mirror; the light should pass through a faint blue glass screen to eliminate its predominant yellow tint, and if possible, it is useful to have an iris diaphragm across the aperture of the light box. More recently low voltage high intensity lamps have been employed instead of ordinary electric light bulbs; when used with a subsidiary condensing lens they can be more efficient than the simple light source, for more of the light can be directed on to the microscope mirror. A variety of this type of bulb is used in the built-in lamps of fixed stand microscopes, often with a rheostat to control intensity. Occasionally very high intensity sources are needed and are provided by an incandescent bead of tungsten (in the Pointolite lamp) or by some form of arc discharge (carbon or xenon). With these sources there is always considerable radiant heat emitted with the light, so that the optical components of the microscope should be protected by heat-absorbing glass, or liquid screens.

For some specific purposes, it is important that the optical determinations are carried out in monochromatic rather than white light. The method chosen depends on how closely it is desired to approach the ideal single wavelength. One of the most obvious methods is to use a small part of the white light spectrum dispersed by a prism device, known as a monochromator. The band width of frequencies allowed to enter the microscope can be controlled, and the position of the band can be continuously varied throughout the spectrum. In practice to achieve sufficiently narrow band widths while still retaining sufficient intensity, it is essential that the original white light source shall be very strong, e.g. an arc discharge; this and other practical difficulties mean that monochromators are little used. A more convenient source of high quality monochromatic light is provided by the vapour discharge lamp, in which there is discharge between electrodes in a volatile metal; frequencies characteristic of the particular metal vapour are excited together with very weak lines of an inert gas used to trigger the discharge. A sodium vapour lamp is the most commonly used, though there are others to provide a series of strong sharp lines throughout the visible spectrum; if necessary the inert gas lines can be eliminated by filters. The convenience of these lamps greatly outweighs the disadvantage, compared to a monochromator, that the wavelength cannot be continuously variable. If the required wavelength spread is less exacting, approximately monochromatic light can be obtained by passing white light through coloured filters, made of dyed gelatine mounted between glass; particular care should be taken not to overheat these filters for the gelatine damages easily. Finally recent developments have led to the introduction of interference filters, in which interference between light reflected from the front and back of metallised glass surfaces enclosing a dielectric layer controls the wavelength transmitted when white light is passed through the filter. By using a wedge-shaped layer of the dielectric, the transmitted wavelengths can be made to vary continuously over the visible spectrum; this feature gives these newer filters some advantage over the older coloured filters.

We can now discuss the second part of the problem of illumination, for having decided on the light source, we must utilise the light incident on the microscope in the most efficient manner. The difficulty is that the most efficient use of light depends on the purpose for which we want to use the microscope. If we wish to have maximum resolution in the magnified image, it is essential that the angular aperture of the objective is filled by the cone of incident light. For polarising microscopes this condition is met most conveniently by what is known as *critical illumination*, in which an image of the source is formed in the object plane. Critical illumination is a method which can be employed when the light source is relatively large and uniform, and can be produced in such a way that both the variation of the angle of the incident cone (necessary when different objectives are used) and the illuminated specimen area are easily controlled. Light from the source is reflected by the plane side of the mirror; the iris diaphragms of the source and the substage are half closed. The condenser is inserted and a fine-grained rock section is placed upon the stage (any object showing fine structure to be resolved will do). The microscope, using a medium power ocular and a low power objective, is focused on the object. Then, an image of the iris diaphragm of the lamp is focused in the object plane, using the vertical movement on the substage system containing the condenser. When the sharpest image has been found, the lamp iris is opened until its image just fills the field of view of the microscope. Next with the substage iris diaphragm nearly closed, we view its image in the focal plane of the objective; this can either be done by removing the ocular or inserting the Bertrand lens (see 7.7). The image should be central about the microscope axis through the centre of the objective lens system, if the microscope is in correct alignment. The substage iris is then opened until light just fills the back lens of the objective, satisfying the condition that the angular aperture of the objective is completely filled with light. After replacing the ocular or removing the Bertrand lens the magnified image can be viewed through the microscope. It may then be that the field is too bright. If this is so, it can sometimes be corrected by placing a neutral filter in front of the source; otherwise the glare can only be reduced by slightly closing the substage iris, though this will mean some loss in resolution. Contrast and resolution in the object image are not necessarily compatible, and often one must be sacrificed for the other. When changing to higher power objectives, the iris diaphragms of the lamp and substage will require adjustment. The procedure is the same as before, first achieving full illumination of the new field of view with the lamp iris and then just filling the aperture of the objective with light by adjustment of the substage diaphragm. There may be some difficulty in this latter step with objectives of the highest numerical aperture in that they are not filled with light even when the substage diaphragm is completely open; this can be overcome by opening the lamp iris slightly, though it will then probably be necessary to close the substage iris again to reduce glare in the object image.

Just as the adjustment of the illumination to produce a magnified image with best contrast and resolution is something of a compromise, so are the other adjustments necessary to obtain the best operating conditions in the other uses of the polarising microscope. In some cases we wish to use the microscope conoscopically; to obtain the best image in this case, the microscope should be arranged to focus, in the focal plane of the objective, the rays making the greatest possible angle with the axis of the microscope (see 7.7). This requires the use of high power objectives of large numerical aperture, and the conditions of illumination will be those specified at the end of the last paragraph, with the iris diaphragm of the substage opened to its fullest extent, and any further light necessary obtained by widening the lamp iris; the conoscopic image produced by these conditions does not suffer from glare. On the other hand, the polarising microscope is sometimes used with light as accurately parallel to its axis as possible. Of course strictly parallel light cannot be obtained; there is always some slight divergence of wave normals passing through the crystal section. We can make the light as nearly parallel as possible by removing the condenser, and stopping down the substage diaphragm to the smallest size compatible with reasonable illumination of the object; if the condenser is not removed, the substage should be racked to its lowest position.

The adjustments which have been described for a typical polarising microscope emphasise that to a certain extent the optimum experimental arrangement is a matter of trial and error. Within the broad outlines above, the student should be continuously experimenting and adjusting to suit the particular experiment and the particular specimen. The best operating conditions for photo-micrography and other techniques involving high-intensity sources are more sensitive to adjustment, and details can be found in more advanced works.

7.7 Conoscopic use of the polarising microscope

We have made reference already to the conoscopic use of the polarising microscope as a method giving data on anisotropic properties more readily than other methods. In a conoscope the lens system is focused on infinity, not on an object; parallel rays of light passing through the specimen are brought into focus at a point on the image, which is made up so that each point corresponds to a different direction of travel in the specimen. We do not therefore observe a direct magnified image of the object (as in orthoscopic use) but rather a *directions image*.

Fig. 7.8 shows the conoscopic arrangement of the polarising microscope. Highly convergent light is passed through the specimen, and is then focused by the objective into the curved focal surface immediately behind it to form the directions image; each point of this small but real image is formed by wave trains passing through the specimen in one particular direction. This image cannot normally be seen through the ocular since it is too distant from its focal plane. We can observe it directly by removing the eyepiece; it then appears small and sharp, and inverted with respect to the object image obtained in orthoscopic use. More usually, however, we can insert the auxiliary Bertrand lens in the body tube of the microscope to bring the directions image into the focal plane of the ocular (see Fig. 7.8). The image can now be viewed through the eyepiece; it is much larger but rather less sharp than in direct observation with the ocular removed. Some disadvantage in clarity is offset by being able to view the crosswires simultaneously with the image, which is not now inverted with respect to the object image.

In practice it is necessary to use a medium to high power objective with a large numerical aperture. This ensures that rays with a reasonable inclination to the microscope axis can be focused by the objective,

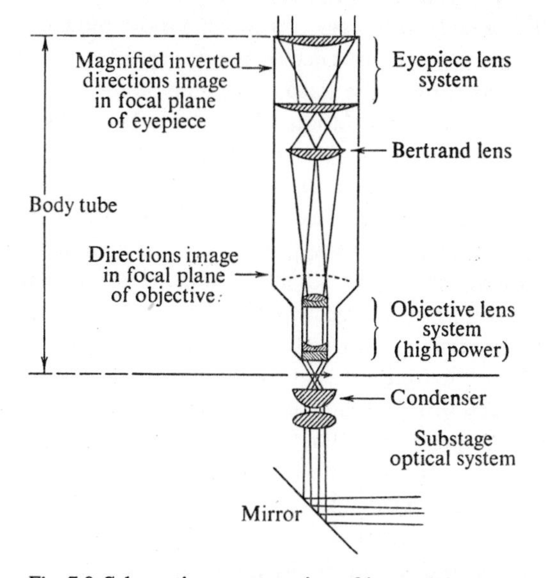

Fig. 7.8 Schematic representation of image formation in conoscopic use of polarising microscope (polars not shown).

giving the widest angular spread of wave normals in the crystal included within the image; if the numerical aperture of the objective is reduced, while the size of the directions image is substantially unchanged, the angle between those wave normals focusing at points on opposite ends of a diameter of the image is reduced. From this it follows that the illumination must be arranged so as to provide convergent light of sufficient angular spread to fill the objective; this can be done by inserting the condenser and adjusting the diaphragms of the lamp and substage as described in 7.6. The directions image which is produced conoscopically is of no determinative value unless it is viewed between crossed polars, but we will defer discussion of the interference effects that these produce until Chapter 10.

7.8 Adjustment and care of the polarising microscope

In 7.6, we have described the adjustment of the optical system for various uses of the microscope. These adjustments assumed that the components of the microscope were aligned and centred on the axis of the microscope. For all components except the objective, the correct positioning is set by the manufacturers, to whom the microscope should be returned if any defect occurs. However, most modern instruments allow adjustment into coincidence of the optical axis of the instrument and the axis of rotation of the stage, so that an object at the centre of the field remains unmoved by rotation of the stage. This is usually achieved by lateral movements of the objective, controlled by two perpendicular centring screws at the bottom of the body tube, located on the collar into which an objective fits (see Fig. 7.4). In correct adjustment, a general point in the field of view should describe a circle centred on the intersection of the crosswires when the stage is rotated. If it does not (Fig. 7.9), centring of the objective by means of the centring screws is simply carried out. A point on the object initially under the crosswire intersection is rotated until it is at its greatest distance from its original position; it is then brought back half-way towards the centre of the field by the screw motions. This adjustment is repeated until the objective is correctly centred. A check that the objective is centred should be carried out every time the microscope is used, and whenever an objective is changed; low power objectives are more tolerant of adjustment than high power ones, and will probably require less attention. On more expensive models, centring of the substage system is also provided.

Microscopic techniques often require the use of *crossed polars*. In correct adjustment, light will not reach the eye unless there is an anisotropic crystal on the stage. With the stage empty, the analyser is inserted in its fixed orientation, and the polariser rotated until the illuminated field becomes dark; usually there is a spring catch which locks the lower polar into the correct crossed position. Sometimes, as we shall see, it is important to observe the passage of linearly polarised light through the specimen. With the polars in the crossed position, the analyser is removed; for most microscopes the vibration direction of the polariser is now parallel to the east-west crosswire. Occasionally on an unfamiliar microscope it may be necessary to check the vibration plane of the polariser; this can easily be done using another polar of known vibration direction or a pleochroic crystal of known absorbing properties (e.g. tourmaline).

Long periods of microscopic work impose strain on the eyes, which should be used alternately, though many microscopes can now be fitted with binocular eyepieces. The eye which is not in use should be kept open and de-focused; this is facilitated by attaching a black cardboard screen high up on the body tube.

Modern polarising microscopes are precision made instruments, and as such are expensive; great care should be taken in their use and maintenance. Most of the precautions require only common sense; the

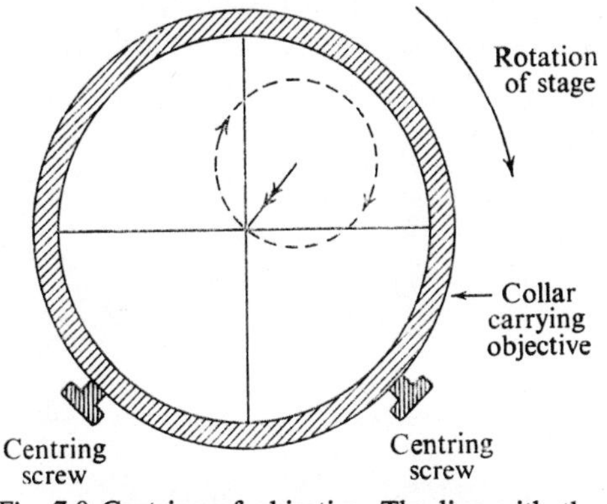

Fig. 7.9 Centring of objective. The line with the double arrow shows direction and amount of adjustment to be made with centring screws.

instrument should be carried by the arm, with the foot supported; it should be protected from dust and cleaned regularly; it should be lubricated regularly according to the makers' instructions; it should not be used in a corrosive atmosphere; it should not be overheated or subjected to large temperature variations, for this would damage the lens systems and polars. Perhaps the commonest damage is done to objectives. In particular with high power objectives, objects should be brought into focus by racking up the body tube; the depth of focus and working distance is so small that attempts to focus by racking down the tube will eventually result in hitting the stage (or object), which can cause serious damage. Final adjustments to focusing should only be made with the fine control. Great care should be taken not to get immersion liquids on to the front face of the objective; any trace of such liquids should be removed as soon as possible, using the special lens tissues available for cleaning all exposed surfaces of the optical system. Finally, if serious damage should occur, the repairs should only be undertaken by skilled technicians.

7.9 Exercises

1. Familiarisation with the mechanical and optical construction of the microscope:

(i) Arrangement of components: locate the positioning and operation of the following features of the substage and stage: mirror (if any), polariser, iris diaphragm (if any), condenser; investigate the movement and locking of the stage and substage (if any). Repeat for the following features of the body tube; objectives and the method of interchange, centring adjustment, slot for test plates, analyser, Bertrand lens, iris diaphragm (if any), removable ocular and orientation of crosswires; investigate the use of the coarse and fine focusing adjustments.

(ii) Coincidence of axes of microscope and stage: bring a thin section (a fine-grained rock slice will do) into focus with a low power objective. Practise making the adjustments of the centring screws to bring the axes into coincidence; investigate whether further adjustments are required with different objectives.

(iii) Illumination: using the same object, for each objective study the effect on the intensity of illumination, the size of the field, and the definition of the image for the following operations; changing from the flat to the concave surface of the mirror, adjusting the aperture of the substage iris diaphragm, inserting and adjusting the position of the condenser, and adjusting the aperture of the upper iris diaphragm. Arrange the illumination system to produce 'parallel light' and 'critical illumination' as described in 7.6.

(iv) Field of view: use the image of a calibrated graticule to measure the width of the field of view for all objectives.

(v) Magnifying power of objectives: with the calibrated graticule on the stage and the low power objective, raise the body tube as high as possible; remove the ocular and observe the real image of the graticule. Lower the body tube until this image coincides without parallax with a similar scale laid across the top of the tube; hence estimate the magnifying power of the objective. This should be repeated, where practical, with all other microscope objectives.

(vi) Overall magnifying power: replace the ocular, and using the low power objective adjust the focusing until the virtual image of the graticule is approximately in the plane of the microscope stage. Compare the image with a similar scale laid on the stage; hence estimate the overall magnification. This should be repeated with all other microscope objectives.

(vii) Depth of focus: using the thin section, adjust the fine focusing of the body tube to discover, for each objective, how much displacement can occur before the focus is visibly disturbed; this gives a measure of the depth of focus for each objective. At the same time note the approximate working distance of each objective.

(viii) Flatness of field: again with the thin section, adjust the fine focusing to give the sharpest image of a point near the centre of the field. Investigate, for each objective, what small change (if any) in adjustment is necessary to bring points near the periphery of the field into sharpest focus.

(2) Use as a compound microscope:

Carry out the following exercises on crystal growth, paying attention to the adjustment of illumination and magnification at all stages:

(i) Morphology: place a drop of a cold saturated solution of sodium nitrate on a microscope slide; after a few minutes, observe the crystals which have grown. Note their general shape, and make tentative deductions about the symmetry and forms present, using measurements of any characteristic plane angles. Try to confirm your deductions by using a needle to change the orientations of individual crystals.

Repeat the exercise using potassium chlorate.

(ii) Dimorphism: grow crystals from a hot solution of potassium nitrate, watching the stages of crystallisation carefully. Confirm that the substance is dimorphous by characterising the differences between the crystals which grow initially near the edge of a drop and those which appear later.

CHAPTER 8

THE MEASUREMENT OF REFRACTIVE INDICES MICROSCOPICALLY

8.1 The principles and practice of immersion methods

IT has been shown in the previous chapters that many of the most important properties of a material can be expressed in terms of the optical indicatrix. The shape of the indicatrix is determined by the variation of refractive index with vibration direction, and it will differ from one substance to the next; but as we saw in Chapter 4 the specification of the size of the indicatrix requires only the measurement of one refractive index for isotropic crystals, and the values of the two and three principal refractive indices for uniaxial and biaxial crystals respectively. In this chapter we are concerned with the methods for determining a refractive index value; we shall not be concerned with the problems of selecting specimens of anisotropic materials to give principal values, nor with the problems of determining the orientation of the indicatrix with respect to the crystallographic axes that can arise in the lower symmetry systems. In other words, we shall regard all crystalline matter as if it were optically isotropic. Even with this proviso, it must still be realised that, like other optical properties, the refractive index is dependent both on the temperature of observation and the wavelength of light. A rise in temperature lowers refractive index values for both solids and liquids, though the change is much greater in liquids than in solids; for the usual temperature variations the effect can be neglected for solids. Both solids and liquids usually have higher refractive indices at shorter wavelengths. Again the change is generally greater for liquids than for solids, though for some solids significant variations can occur over the range of wavelengths in the visible spectrum. Detailed consideration of wavelength dispersion of the indicatrix is given in Chapter 11, and our initial discussion will neglect dispersion of any kind.

The physical condition of the specimen is clearly of importance in deciding how its refractive index is to be determined. There are two general lines of approach depending on whether the crystals of the specimen are of a size which demands microscopic examination or whether they are large enough for other non-microscopic methods. On the whole, non-microscopic methods can be simpler to use, more accurate and informative about anisotropy, but their use is very restricted. With synthetic materials, particularly organic compounds, it is often possible to grow large crystals, but with most naturally occurring and some synthetic specimens there are usually only small crystals or crystalline fragments so that microscopic work is essential. We are concerned only with the more widely applicable microscopic methods in this chapter, but a selection of methods for larger crystals is given in Appendix C. Even for microscopic work, the specimen may be available in two essentially different states, either as a powder or in a thin section. A sieved powder of grains of roughly the same size may come from the separation, or purification, of a material, perhaps prior to chemical analysis. A thin section is prepared by grinding a slab of material to a uniform thickness (usually 0·003 cm) which will transmit light without appreciable absorption; it could be made from a large single crystal, but more usually is from a polycrystalline aggregate (as in a rock section), in which there will often be crystals of more than one substance. In all cases while the determination of refractive indices must form an important part of any optical examination, the highest accuracy is not always necessary and simple comparison methods to give rapid order of magnitude values are most useful.

All the simple methods for small microscopic crystal fragments depend on the fact that when a colourless solid is mounted in a colourless medium of identical refractive index it is not visible; a match is obtained because there are no reflection or refraction effects at the mount-crystal interface. If the refractive indices are different, a border denoting the outline of the crystal can be recognised. The clarity with which this border is seen is called the *relief*; if there is an appreciable difference in the refractive indices of medium and crystal, the crystal stands out boldly, and it is said that its relief is high (Fig. 8.1). The relief of a grain in a thin section depends to some extent on the refractive indices of the surrounding crystals but more importantly on that of the mounting cement (usually $n=1{\cdot}54$) by which the section is attached to its glass slide and cover-slip; the grains of a powder are usually mounted in an immersion liquid, and the refractive index of this liquid determines the relief. In whatever form the specimen occurs, there will usually be some relief when it is examined on the microscope stage. This relief allows an estimate of the disparity of refractive indices to be made by an experienced observer, but in itself it does not show whether the refractive index of the crystal is greater or less than that of the mount. There are two common tests which allow this to be decided.

In the first of these two tests, the *central illumination* (or *Becke*) *test*, the mount-crystal boundary is observed with a medium-high power objective in parallel or weakly convergent light. As the body tube is racked slowly upwards out of focus, the bright line (the Becke line) around the periphery of each grain appears to move into the medium of greater refractive index, becoming broader and fainter as the tube is

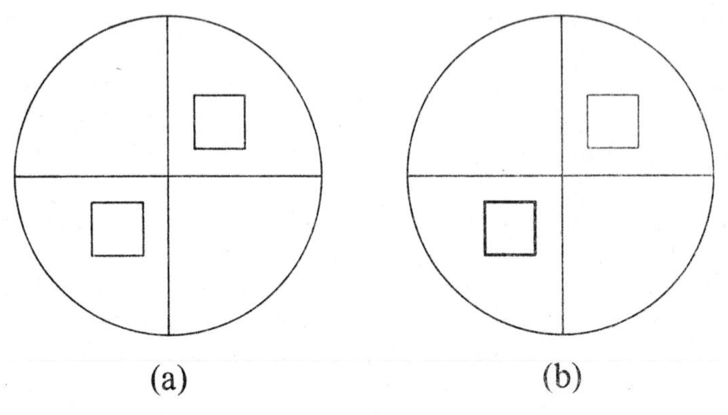

Fig. 8.1 The relief of crystals in immersion media.
The two crystals are of NaCl (top right, n=1·544) and CaF_2 (bottom left, n=1·434).
a. Immersion medium n=1·49; the relief of both crystals is the same.
b. Immersion medium n=1·54; the CaF_2 crystal stands out boldly while the NaCl crystal is barely visible.

racked higher (Fig. 8.2*a*). Conversely if we reverse the procedure and lower the body tube from the position of sharp focus, the Becke line moves into the medium of lower refractive index (this is not to be recommended as normal working procedure as careless movement can push the objective into the specimen). Several explanations of this phenomenon can be offered. In the simplest of these, it is assumed that since the edges of crystal fragments are usually thinner than the centres, the crystals have an approximately lenticular form; if this is so, a fragment will act as a convex (or converging) lens when its refractive index is greater than that of the mounting medium and as a concave (or diverging) lens when it has the smaller refractive index. Other simple explanations depend on plane-sided fragments, while a more sophisticated treatment is based on the fact that the appearance of the Becke line corresponds, in geometrical optics, to a displacement of the object from the focus of the objective. Without discussing the validity of the various assumptions, we can accept without prejudice that the movement of the Becke line provides a simple test to discover whether the refractive index of the crystal is greater or less than that of the mounting medium. In practice it sometimes happens that two bright lines are seen which appear to move in opposite directions when the body tube is raised; this usually occurs with larger crystals of rather irregular shape. Attempts

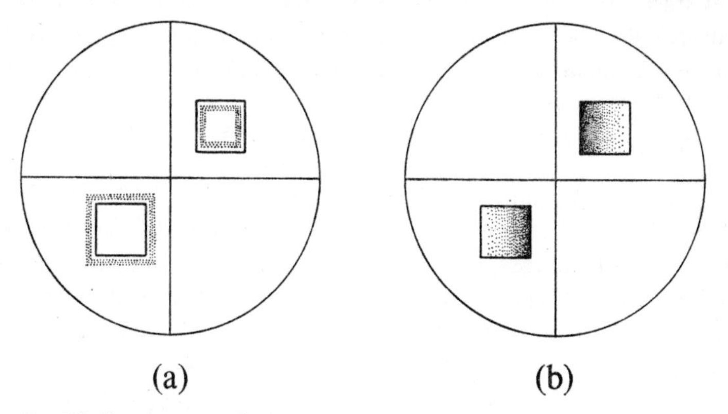

Fig. 8.2 Simple comparison tests.
The two crystals NaCl (top right, $n=1{\cdot}544$) and CaF_2 (bottom left, $n=1{\cdot}434$) are immersed in a medium for which $n=1{\cdot}49$.
a. The Becke test; the figure shows the appearance of the Becke lines after the microscope tube has been racked upwards.
b. The van der Kolk test; the figure shows the shadow appearing on the crystals; the light is inclined so as to be incident on the mount from the left-hand side (there is assumed to be no image reversal).

to remove the second Becke line can be made by stopping down the substage iris diaphragm; alternatively we may apply the second simple comparison test.

In this, the *oblique illumination* (or *van der Kolk*) *test*, the crystals are viewed through a low power objective with inclined illumination. When the refractive index of the crystal is greater than that of the mount, the side of the grain opposite to that from which the oblique illumination is coming appears bright, while the other side is in shadow (Fig. 8.2*b*). Conversely if the refractive index of the crystal is less than that of the mount, the side opposite to that of the light source is in shadow. Again we shall not discuss the detailed reasons for the effect, but content ourselves with its practical use. The inclined illumination can be obtained by tilting the microscope mirror to one side (with the condenser removed, if possible) or by inserting a stop (a card or pencil) into the light path in the substage so that the light aperture is about half covered. In applying the van der Kolk test it is important to take care in interpreting the observations, for the description given above depends on there being no image inversion by the optical system of the microscope. For example, if a stop is inserted, we must find out which side of the incident beam is being cut out; because of the different designs of microscope, insertion of the stop at different positions on the same microscope, or at the same position in the optical path on different microscopes, may effectively lead to opposite inclinations of oblique illumination and apparently conflicting observations. It is probably best when applying the van der Kolk test for the first time to observe the light and shadow effects on a specimen for which the refractive index is known.

Both these tests should be familiar to the student, the choice being dictated by experimental conditions. For example, the van der Kolk method has advantages if it is necessary to make a survey of the comparative refractive index values of a large number of crystals in the field of view. These simple comparison tests and the relief can, with experience, be used to give order of magnitude values for refractive indices. While this information is valuable, it is often necessary to perform rather more accurate determinations. Essentially this must be done by changing the refractive index of the mount until a match with the crystal is obtained, i.e. there is no relief and the specimen cannot be seen; the refractive index of the matching mount is either previously known or can be readily determined. Obviously this cannot be done for a grain in a permanently mounted thin section; the only possibility is to lift the glass cover-slip protecting the section (by warming or a suitable solvent) and to cut out the grain using a drill or diamond cutter. The grain from the section can then be treated in the same way as the grains of a powdered specimen, and immersed in different refractive index liquids to obtain a match. To prepare a simple mount, a small quantity of the specimen is spread on to a clean microscope slide, and a thin glass cover-slip placed over it. The liquid is introduced on the end of a dropper which is touched against the edge of the slightly raised cover-slip. When the slip is lowered, the liquid spreads itself uniformly to immerse the specimen; more liquid can be added in the same way if necessary. In addition to spreading and confining the liquid, this cover-slip also protects the objective from accidental contact with the liquid during adjustment. It can, however, be a nuisance if it is necessary to manipulate the specimen with a mounted needle during the examination; ease of manipulation to change the orientation of anisotropic crystals is particularly important. It may also be necessary to transfer a single fragment (e.g. one cut from a section) from one mount to another; the grain should be washed with a suitable solvent and thoroughly dried between immersions. Great care should be taken of the objective when making observations on an uncovered mount.

The final refractive index value for the specimen is approached through a series of mounts, each successive preparation giving a better approximation to the refractive index of the crystal. It is often sufficient to bracket the refractive index value between two liquids differing by 0·01 in refractive indices; an estimate of the third decimal place can then be made from the relative reliefs in the two mounts. Occasionally it is necessary to try to obtain the highest accuracy (about ±0·002 under favourable conditions) by using intermediate mounting liquids, but in this case it is usually better to use the more advanced methods described in 8.4.

8.2 Immersion liquids

With these comparison methods, liquids of standard refractive index are required. It is convenient for most purposes to have available a permanent set of liquids whose standardised refractive indices increase in steps of about 0·01. Many different liquids have been suggested to satisfy certain essential requirements in forming a standard set. The liquid must be relatively colourless so that it does not obscure the test material; it must be chemically stable so as to retain its optical properties over long periods; it must be chemically inert to the extent that it will not dissolve or attack the test material; it should be readily miscible with other liquids of the same set and have much the same boiling point as them; and unless it is required for special techniques (see 8.4) the dispersion or variations of refractive index with temperature and wavelength should be relatively small. Very many liquids have been proposed (see Johannsen's *Manual of Petrographic Methods* and other texts in the Bibliography).

To a certain extent, the choice of liquids depends on the nature of the specimen and the range of refractive indices that it is proposed to cover. Table 8.1 shows combinations that have been found by experience to be most useful for inorganic and many organic materials from 1·450 to 1·740, a range which contains refractive indices of many crystalline solids; these liquids can be used to provide a standard laboratory set at intervals of 0·01 which is reasonably stable. The intermediate members are made by mixing together the appropriate volumes of the pure liquids, though the refractive index of the resulting mixture should always be standardised using a refractometer (see 8.3). The set of liquids should be kept in air-tight bottles each with its own dropper, and when not in use should be stored in the dark to avoid the deleterious effect of light upon some liquids. Contamination must be carefully guarded against and the set should be standardised at regular intervals.

Table 8.1

Suitable liquids for combination to form a standard laboratory set

Mixtures of:	*Range of n (Sodium D light, $\lambda=5800\times10^{-8}$ cm)*
Petroleum and turpentine	1·450–1·475
Turpentine and 1 : 2 ethylene dibromide or clove oil	1·480–1·535
Clove oil and α-monobromonaphthalene	1·540–1·635
α-monobromonaphthalene and α-monochloronaphthalene	1·640–1·655
α-monochloronaphthalene and methylene iodide	1·660–1·740

There will be some substances for which this standard set is unsuitable either because the material is attacked by certain of the liquids or because its refractive indices fall outside the range of the set. In the former case there is little to be done except to consult lists of liquids that have been used to find a suitable inert combination. The range of values covered by the liquids can be extended though it is not worth while to include the extra liquids in the standard set. For the few solids with refractive indices less than 1·45, suitable immersion liquids can be readily obtained from mixtures of glycerol, glycol and water, but higher refractive index liquids are notoriously difficult to prepare and are usually very unstable. Up to values around 1·79, solutions of sulphur in methylene iodide can be used, though the dissolved sulphur has a tendency to precipitate on standing; above 1·79, very noxious preparations of methylene iodide, antimony iodide, arsenic sulphide, antimony sulphide and sulphur can be used up to about 1·96. Above 1·9, the preparation of suitable media becomes very difficult. Sometimes an amorphous glass is formed by heating together two or more components (say sulphur and arsenic sulphide) near their boiling point and allowing the mixture to solidify around the specimen crystals; the method cannot be used with crystals which are sensitive to heat, and in any case is both tedious and rather unsatisfactory. For all immersion media above about 1·74 it is best that they should be made up as required, and their refractive index values checked both before and after use.

8.3 Refractometers

From time to time, refractive index sets must be standardised, and the values of new liquids established; these determinations are carried out using instruments known as refractometers. Essentially these instruments are of two kinds, those which depend on the refraction of light through a liquid prism, and those which depend on the critical-angle measurement at a liquid-solid interface.

A simple form of prism experiment would be an adaptation of that described in Appendix C for crystalline solids, in which the angle of minimum deviation is determined for light refracted through a hollow prism filled with the test liquid. This is only possible when rather a large volume of liquid is available, though the amount required can be drastically reduced by using a solid metal prism with one corner truncated; a small volume of liquid is then placed between cover-slips attached to the sides of the prism to complete the missing volume. The minimum deviation of light refracted through this liquid allows the determination of its refractive index. The size and angle of the prism are fixed by the range of refractive indices that is to be measured; for example, for higher values ($n \sim 1{\cdot}75$ and above) prisms of a small angle avoid too large a deviation angle and the absorption of too much light in the coloured liquid. Although such instruments can give the highest accuracy they suffer from disadvantages in that they are not direct-reading and the measurements are time consuming unless the highest accuracy is required; moreover there are many occasions such as when an exact liquid-crystal match has been obtained by mixing liquids in the mount, when the volume of the test liquid is too small even for the truncated prism. Some refractometers which are marketed overcome these difficulties; typical of these instruments is the Leitz-Jelley refractometer which gives direct readings of reasonable accuracy over a wide range of values. The instrument (Fig. 8.3) employs refraction through a prism, though not at conditions of minimum deviation. A slit source, cut into a graduated scale is viewed through an aperture over which the prism containing the liquid is placed. The prism is often simply a glass slide with a cover-glass cemented to it to give a prism of small angle and size. When the slit source is viewed through the aperture, light passing through the prism is refracted upwards or downwards depending on the refractive index of the liquid. A displaced image of the slit is seen superimposed upon the scale, which has been previously calibrated using liquids of standard index values, and the index of the liquid is read off. The method is very rapid and requires the smallest amount of the liquid; it can cover a range from about 1·35 to 1·90. While not giving the highest accuracy, the values are sufficiently reliable for most

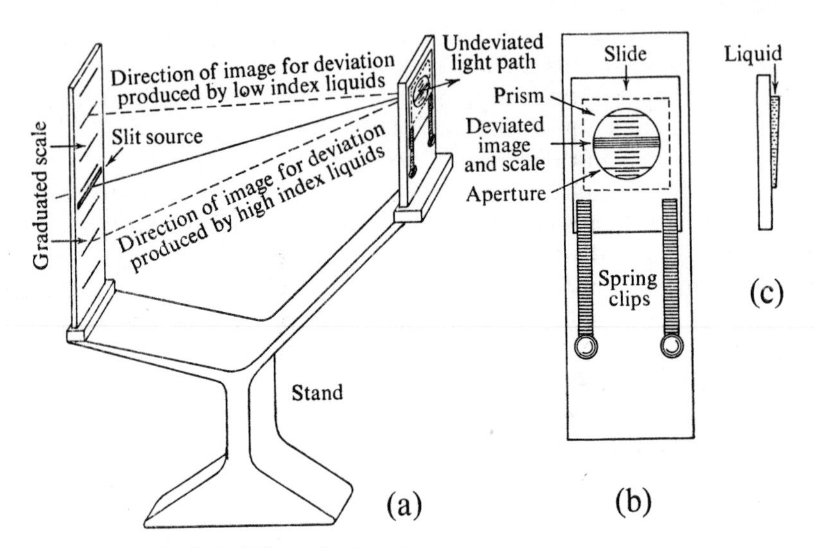

Fig. 8.3 The Leitz-Jelley refractometer.
a. The general appearance of the instrument.
b. The view through the aperture showing the deviated image and scale.
c. Cross-section through the slide and prism.

practical purposes provided that the adjustment of the calibrated scale is checked from time to time.

The other group of refractometers uses measurements of the critical angle of reflection of light. Essentially the light passes through the liquid and is reflected from a boundary with a solid of lower refractive index; if the refractive index of the solid is known, that of the liquid can be obtained from the critical angle (see 3.1). If sufficient volume of the liquid is available, the Kohlrausch refractometer for solids described in Appendix C could be adapted for use; but usually it is necessary to use some other experimental modification. In one of the simplest Abbé refractometers, a polished plate is made to adhere to the plane surface of a polished glass hemisphere by a thin film of the test liquid. Light is incident on one side of the hemispherical surface, and the field of the other half is observed through a telescope which can pivot about the centre of the hemisphere. Only that light which is incident on the boundary at angles greater than the critical angle will be reflected, and so adjustment of the telescope position will enable a light-shadow division of the field to be located (Fig. 8.4). The position of the boundary is

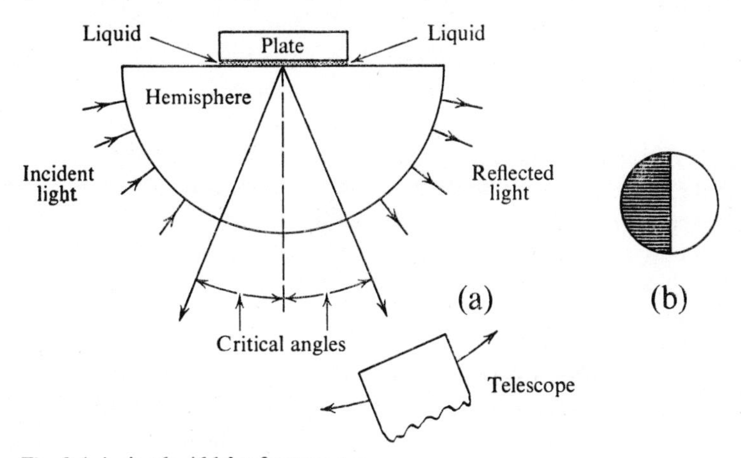

Fig. 8.4 A simple Abbé refractometer.
a. The general arrangement of the apparatus.
b. The appearance through the telescope of the light shadow boundary at the critical angle.

fixed by the critical angle; this will change as different liquids are used, and a direct graduated scale of index values can be related to the position of the telescope when looking at the light-shadow boundary. Alternatively this same optical system can be employed with the light source arranged to permit grazing incidence parallel to the flat face of the hemisphere. Even at the maximum angle of incidence, no ray can pass through the hemisphere at an angle less than the critical angle; this can again be measured from the position of a light-shadow boundary in the telescope. Modern commercial instruments of this kind usually have a little more sophisticated design in which the hemisphere is replaced by a prism or series of prisms; to achieve the highest range of refractive index values is very expensive, for it is difficult to obtain suitable glasses and diamond prisms are sometimes used.

Both types of instrument are used with a monochromatic light source, such as a sodium vapour lamp. Although refractive index liquids are chosen with minimum dispersion, they usually show some spread of refractive indices with wavelength; this would make the scale readings rather difficult in white light. Some manufacturers also supply direct reading instruments for use on the microscope stage, though these are generally less convenient and flexible than the external instruments which have been described. We have noted the limitation of the upper range of the direct-reading instruments. In such circumstances either the hollow prism minimum deviation method must be used or, if more approximate values are permitted, the liquids may be calibrated by matching them with immersed isotropic substances of known refractive index. Such substances can either be artificial glasses or cubic crystals; suitable substances of the latter can be found in the data given in Winchells' *Microscopic Characters of Artificial Inorganic Solid Substances or Artificial Minerals*. Even so, this method requires rather more test liquid than direct reading refractometers and is only ever used outside the range of these instruments.

8.4 Variation methods

In order to improve the accuracy of ordinary immersion methods, some refinements in technique have been devised. These utilise the fact that the dispersion of liquids is greater than that for solids. We may often see the effect of wavelength dispersion when trying to match a fragment to a liquid in white light. If we assume for the present that the crystal is not dispersive but that the liquid is, when the crystal is matched to the liquid for yellow light at the middle of the spectrum it will not be matched at the ends of the spectrum; the refractive index for the shorter blue wavelengths is larger than for the longer red wavelengths. If we were to apply the simple Becke test and rack the microscope tube upwards, we should see two coloured Becke lines, a blue one moving into the liquid and a second, red, moving into the crystal. Similarly with the van der Kolk test opposite sides of the crystal would have red and blue colorations. In the improved immersion technique, we use immersion liquids for which the variation is relatively large and already known; the dispersion can be due to wavelength changes and to temperature changes. By varying the temperature and wavelength either separately or simultaneously we can artificially change the refractive index of the liquid to get the best match with the crystal. Suitable liquids can have a variation of refractive index of up to 0·04 if both the wavelength and temperature (about a 50°C change) are used.

In a *single variation* method, only one of the two variables of wavelength and temperature is changed, the other being kept constant. It is more usual to employ the temperature variation, as it is easier to devise methods of changing the temperature of a bath of liquid than to obtain a continuously variable monochromator which will give a reasonable intensity of illumination. Preliminary work establishes the range within which the refractive indices of the test fragments must lie. The crystals are then immersed in a thermostatically controlled bath of suitable liquid. A match is obtained by varying the temperature of the bath, when the refractive index is obtained either by simultaneous examination of the immersion liquid with a refractometer or from its known temperature variation. In principle, the method is simple, but to realise the greatest possible experimental accuracy, the conditions of measurement must be carefully controlled. Various models of the cell in which liquid and crystal are contained on the microscope stage have been proposed; the thermal balance of the system is sensitive and may be upset by draughts or radiation from the illuminating system. Accuracies of measurement of at least 0·001 are claimed, with higher accuracies under favourable circumstances. More detailed description of the experimental arrangements and the design of the cell will be found in the references in the bibliography.

A *double variation* method uses both temperature and wavelength dispersion, so that it can conveniently undertake investigation of the dispersive properties of the crystal itself. The intensity difficulties of monochromatic radiation mentioned earlier are sometimes avoided by using suitable filters or by isolating the lines from a mercury vapour lamp to obtain a discontinuous change of wavelength through the spectrum. Double variation methods, apart from the particular advantages for special measurements, are claimed to have even higher accuracy (probably $\pm 0{\cdot}0005$) than the single variation technique, although they must necessarily be more complex to set up and use.

The advantages of variation methods are that, after a preliminary investigation, they need fewer mounts than simple comparison tests; further, they have potentially a greater accuracy, and can conveniently deal with dispersion measurements. Their disadvantages lie in the complex and costly apparatus, which is nevertheless relatively easy to use once it is set up. For most problems, extreme accuracy is not required, so that variation apparatus is found only in laboratories where a specialised problem has demanded its use.

8.5 Exercises

1. Refractive indices of permanent mounts:

You are provided with crystallites of a number of isotropic materials permanently mounted in a cement of refractive index 1·54:

(i) Examine the crystals of fluorite (CaF_2). Confirm that the refractive index is less than that of the cement by using the parallel and oblique illumination tests. Observe the relief shown by these crystals of refractive index 1·43.

(ii) Repeat with sodalite (a complex silicate), refractive index about $1{\cdot}48_5$.

(iii) Repeat with halite (NaCl), refractive index, $1{\cdot}54_4$.

(iv) Repeat with spinel (a complex mixed oxide), refractive index about 1·75.

(v) Repeat with almandine (a variety of the complex alumino-silicate garnet group), refractive index about 1·80.

2. Refractive indices of crystal fragments:

Three unlabelled bottles contain a separated fraction of a hexagonal material. It is known that the three materials are:

(*a*) Beryl (a complex alumino-silicate) with optical constants quoted as n_o=1·568–1·598; n_e=1·564–1·590.

(*b*) Apatite (a calcium fluor-phosphate) with optical constants quoted as n_o=1·630–1·651; n_e=1·633–1·651.

(*c*) Corundum (Al_2O_3) with optical constants quoted as n_o=1·767–1·772; n_e=1·759–1·763,
but it is not known which bottle contains which material.

(i) By examining simple mounts made with refractive index liquids, determine which bottle should be labelled (*a*), (*b*) or (*c*).

(ii) A fourth bottle contains a mixture of two of these materials. Again using simple mounts determine which two are present in the mixture.

3. Use of refractometer:

Use the powdered crystals of KCl (cubic symmetry) to determine the refractive index of this substance:

(i) Examine a mount made with a liquid of refractive index 1·54. Use the relief and comparison tests to estimate the lower refractive index liquid to be used in the preparation of the next mount.

(ii) Continue to approach the refractive index by varying the liquid until an approximate match is obtained.

(iii) Using an uncovered mount, obtain the best possible match by mixing the liquids of the standard set, if necessary.

(iv) Determine the refractive index of the final liquid with a refractometer.

CHAPTER 9

INTERFERENCE EFFECTS IN PARALLEL LIGHT

9.1 Interference conditions and the polarising microscope

In 2.2 it was shown that two simple waves of the same frequency travelling in the same direction with the same vibration plane can be combined to give a new wave form; a phase-amplitude diagram is used to predict the amplitude and phase of the resultant wave. We can expect finite wave trains emitted by a light source to produce interference effects which can be treated in this way, provided that the interfering wave trains are coherent (as discussed in 2.3.) and come from the same pulse emitted by the same atom. When light travels along a general wave normal direction of an anisotropic crystal, we know that only two mutually perpendicular vibration directions are permitted for which the light waves travel with different speeds. On emerging from the crystal after equal path lengths, the two waves have a phase difference between them, but they are still vibrating in perpendicular planes. To study any interference between them, we must arrange that a component of each is made to vibrate in the same plane, i.e. we must resolve light transmitted by the crystal with a polar. Thus, so far it would appear that to see interference effects, we must set up the polarising microscope, with its analyser inserted, to allow parallel light to pass normally through an anisotropic section.

Let us suppose that this has been done in such a way as to have the experimental conditions for complete destructive interference. A section just thick enough to produce the necessary phase lag is in position on the stage illuminated by parallel monochromatic light; its orientation is arranged so that the permitted vibration directions of the crystal are equally inclined to that of the analyser so that resolution by the polar yields components of equal amplitude. When there is complete destructive interference between these components we expect that no light at all will pass to the microscope ocular. However, in practice, the introduction of the analyser makes no difference to what the eye sees; there is no darkening of the field due to destructive interference. (It is true that the polar ensures that the light now reaching the eye is linearly polarised, but the eye is insensitive to the state of polarisation and responds only to wavelength and colour.) We must consider the implications of this observation, which is perhaps a little unexpected, both to understand why it occurs and to make the essential adjustment to the interference conditions. So far, the light incident on the section is unpolarised, i.e. it consists of finite wave trains at random intervals in random vibration planes. Let us follow two of these pulses through the system. First, we will take a wave train polarised so that its vibration direction is symmetrically inclined to those of the anisotropic section. On entering the crystal this pulse is resolved into two vibrations of equal amplitude; these emerge from the crystal with the phase lag imposed by different speeds in the crystal. They are then resolved by the analyser into components of equal amplitude vibrating in the same plane; with this phase lag total destructive interference occurs and no light energy from this pulse is transmitted. The second pulse we will consider differs in that it has a vibration direction generally inclined to those of the crystal. On entering the section it is resolved into two mutually perpendicular components of unequal amplitude. These emerge from the crystal with the same imposed phase lag to be resolved by the analyser into the same vibration plane, but now the interfering components are of unequal amplitude. Destructive interference takes place, but it can never be complete (see Appendix B); some light energy is always transmitted. Since complete annihilation can only occur for pulses of the first kind, which must be greatly outnumbered by those of the second kind, we can understand why the introduction of the analyser alone does not allow us to see interference effects.

To eliminate this swamping effect due to the random vibration planes of the pulses in unpolarised light, it is evidently another essential condition that light incident on the crystal shall be linearly polarised. We must therefore insert the polariser in the substage system of the microscope. This ensures that the resolution of every incident light pulse by the crystal will be the same, though the relative amplitudes of the two waves within the crystal will depend on the orientation of the vibration direction of the polariser relative to those of the crystal. When it is symmetrically situated the amplitudes of the resolved components will be equal, and the conditions for complete destructive interference can be satisfied; in other positions, the amplitudes within the crystal will be unequal, and any interference can only be partial.

In order to obtain interference effects in parallel light, then, it is essential that the anisotropic crystal section should be viewed through the microscope with both polariser and analyser inserted. Usually these are arranged with their vibration planes mutually perpendicular (crossed polars), occasionally with them parallel (parallel polars); after this general discussion we must now consider the interference conditions for these positions more thoroughly.

9.2 Interference effects between crossed and parallel polars

The most usual microscopic arrangement has crossed polars and the stage set so that the crystal section has its permitted vibration directions symmetrically bisecting those of the polars; the section is said to be set in *the 45° position*. The experimental arrangement is shown schematically in Fig. 9.1*a*, though we can examine the stages in the propagation of parallel light through the microscope more conveniently in the light vector diagram of Fig. 9.1*b*. Polarised light from the polariser of amplitude $OP(=a)$ enters the section, and is resolved into two mutually perpendicular vibrations of equal amplitude OS_1 and $OS_2(=a \cos 45°)$. These travel through the section of thickness t with differing velocities to emerge with a phase angle difference δ still vibrating in different planes. After resolution into the vibration plane of the analyser, interference can take place between two waves of equal amplitude OA_1 and $OA_2(=a \cos^2 45°)$ with a phase lag between them.

Now we must consider this phase lag rather carefully. In 2.2 we saw that if the phase angle difference is 180° or odd multiples thereof ($=(2n+1)\pi$ radians, n integral), the waves are completely out of phase and there is complete destructive interference; similarly if the phase difference is 360° or multiples thereof ($=2n\pi$ radians, n integral), there is complete reinforcement. Now we must realise that in using the polarising microscope with crossed polars, we cannot immediately identify the phase lag (δ) introduced by the anisotropic crystal section with the phase lag (Δ) after resolution into the same plane by the analyser; it is the value of Δ which will determine the nature of the final interference effect. We can, however, understand their relationships by a simple argument. Suppose that the crystal section introduced no phase lag ($\delta=0$). In Fig. 9.1*b* the vibrations are exactly in step; both will reach their crests of maximum displacement at S_1 and S_2 simultaneously, and when resolved by the analyser their displacements are equal and opposite, OA_1 and OA_2. They therefore cancel one another out, no light is transmitted, and $\Delta=\pi$. If, on the other hand, they are exactly out of step on leaving the crystal ($\delta=\pi$), while one wave reaches its crest at S_1, the other displacement is simultaneously at its trough at S_2'.

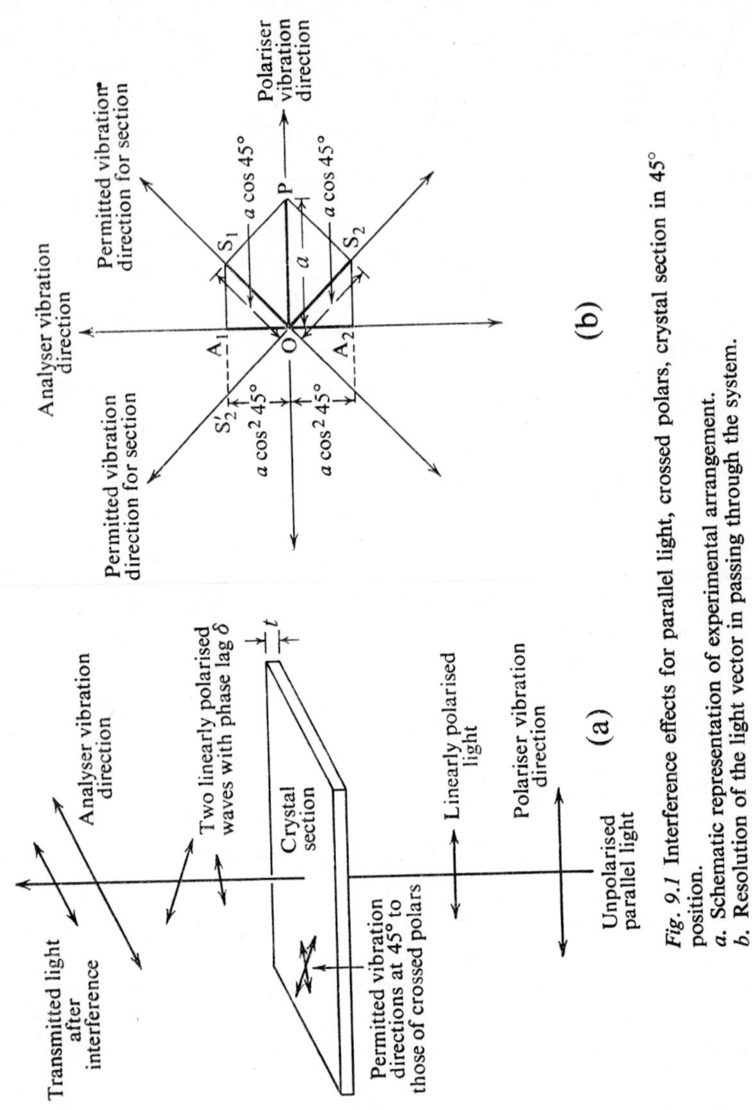

Fig. 9.1 Interference effects for parallel light, crossed polars, crystal section in 45° position.
a. Schematic representation of experimental arrangement.
b. Resolution of the light vector in passing through the system.

Resolution by the analyser produces components which are in the same sense so that there is complete reinforcement and $\Delta = 2\pi$. This argument shows that resolution of the components by the analyser has the effect of introducing an extra phase lag of π over and above that introduced by the crystal plate, i.e. $\Delta = \delta + \pi$. We can now express the conditions for complete destructive interference and reinforcement for path differences measured in terms of the wavelength λ, of the light. For complete destructive interference $\Delta=(2n+1)\pi=\delta+\pi$, so that $\delta=2n\pi$; therefore

$$d=\delta(\lambda/2\pi)=n\lambda,$$

i.e. whenever the path difference (d) introduced by travel in the crystal is a whole number of wavelengths, there is complete interference and no light is transmitted. Similarly complete reinforcement occurs when $\Delta=2n\pi=\delta+\pi$, so that $\delta=(2n-1)\pi$; therefore

$$d=\delta(\lambda/2\pi)=(2n-1)\lambda/2,$$

i.e. whenever the path difference introduced by travel in the crystal is an odd multiple of a half wavelength, there is complete reinforcement, and light is transmitted with maximum intensity. Intermediate values of d lead to partial interference and the transmission of light of intermediate intensities.

We must now relate the path difference introduced by the crystal to its thickness and the refractive indices n_1 and n_2 associated with the permitted vibrations for this wave normal direction. In Chapter 3, it was shown that the refractive index was inversely proportional to the speed of travel, and that the wavelength of the motion was similarly changed. Thus

$$n_1=\lambda/\lambda_1=c/v_1;\ n_2=\lambda/\lambda_2=c/v_2$$

where c and λ are the velocity and wavelength in air, and v_1, λ_1 and v_2, λ_2 are the values for the two disturbances within the crystal. For convenience we will designate our vibration directions *slow* and *fast*, referring to their velocities; if $n_1>n_2$, then $v_2>v_1$, so that λ_1 is the wavelength associated with the slow vibration direction and λ_2 that associated with the fast vibration direction. The path difference can be simply expressed in terms of wavelengths in air; it is the difference between the number of wavelengths in the thickness t of the crystal for the slow and fast vibrations, i.e.

$$t/\lambda_1-t/\lambda_2=t(n_1-n_2)/\lambda$$

so that

$$d=t(n_1-n_2)$$

(n_1-n_2) is called the *birefringence of the section*; in anisotropic materials its value will depend on the direction of the wave normal for the light within the crystal. When multiplied by the thickness the quantity

$t(n_1-n_2)$ is called the *relative retardation of the section* or the *optical path difference*. The unit of thickness is usually taken as the micron ($\mu=10^{-4}$ cm) and the optical path difference is measured in micro-millimetres or milli-microns ($m\mu=10^{-7}$ cm). Whenever this optical path difference is a whole number of wavelengths there is complete destructive interference, whenever it is an odd number of half wavelengths there is complete reinforcement.

So far the crystal section has remained in the 45° position, and we must consider what will happen when its orientation is varied by rotating the stage of the microscope. The optical path difference is unchanged by this movement, and so the interference conditions giving total or partial interference or complete reinforcement remain the same. But the amplitudes of the components travelling within the crystal will now differ, and so two waves of unequal amplitudes with the same phase lag as before emerge from the crystal. Nevertheless, as Fig. 9.2 shows, resolution by the crossed analyser produces interfering components in the same vibration plane which have equal amplitudes, but of smaller size than the maximum resolved amplitudes for the 45° position. It is apparent that as the stage is rotated from the 45° position, the amplitudes of the interfering wave trains fall, until, when the crystal vibration directions are parallel to those of the crossed polars, they are zero. Thus as we rotate from the 45° position, the intensity of any light transmitted after interference gradually decreases until there is complete darkness after a rotation of 45°. Further rotation will bring the return of transmitted light which reaches its maximum intensity after another rotation of 45°. Obviously a section showing total destructive interference in the 45° position remains dark at all positions of the stage. For all other sections there are four positions of maximum brightness (45° positions) in every complete revolution of the stage which are bisected by four positions of darkness. Whenever the stage is set to produce complete darkness, the crystal is said to be put into *extinction*. Extinction positions are important because they can locate the permitted vibrations for any general anisotropic section; we will discuss their use more fully in 9.5.

In terms of this description for crossed polars, we can readily understand the analogous interference effects with parallel polars. The interference conditions can be derived by an extension of the argument used earlier. The optical path difference and phase lag (δ) produced by the crystal is unchanged, but we must consider again the phase lag (Δ) after resolution by the analyser. In Fig. 9.1*b* with the crystal in the 45°

position, if $\delta=0$, both waves reach their crests of displacement at S_1 and S_2 simultaneously, and resolution by the parallel analyser produces components in the same sense and complete reinforcement; similarly if $\delta=\pi$, resolution by the parallel analyser produces equal and opposite components, and there is complete destructive interference. Now, resolution by the analyser introduces no additional phase lag, i.e. $\Delta=\delta$.

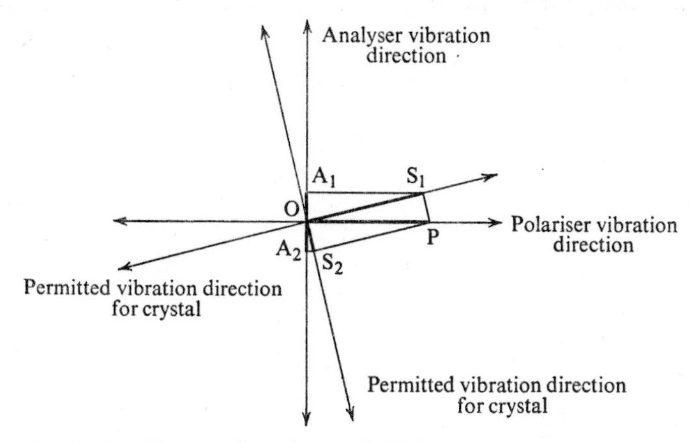

Fig. 9.2 Interference effects for parallel light, crossed polars, crystal in general orientation.
Resolution of the light vector through the system shows that interfering wave trains have the same amplitude ($OA_1=OA_2$) which is smaller than in 45° position in Fig. 9.1*b*.

In other words, complete destructive interference occurs when the path difference is an odd multiple of half wavelengths, and complete reinforcement occurs when the path difference is a whole number of wavelengths. The interference conditions are interchanged when the polars are parallel rather than crossed; a section which shows the maximum intensity between crossed polars will be completely dark with parallel polars and vice versa. When the crystal is rotated into a more general position (Fig. 9.3), resolution by the parallel analyser produces unequal interfering amplitudes, until after a rotation of 45° one resolved component is zero and the other is unchanged. Thus, the extinction positions of crossed polars are replaced by positions of maximum brightness with parallel polars, while the 45° positions again show the maximum effect of any interference due to the conditions imposed by a given thickness of section.

Earlier we showed that for a particular wavelength, the optical path difference depends on the birefringence of the section and its thickness. The birefringence for a particular material is related to the wave normal direction within the crystal. With a given wave normal direction, a convenient method of displaying the dependence of the interference effects on thickness uses a wedge of an anisotropic material. Later we shall see that such wedges are convenient testing instruments, and a quartz wedge, commonly used for this purpose, provides a convenient

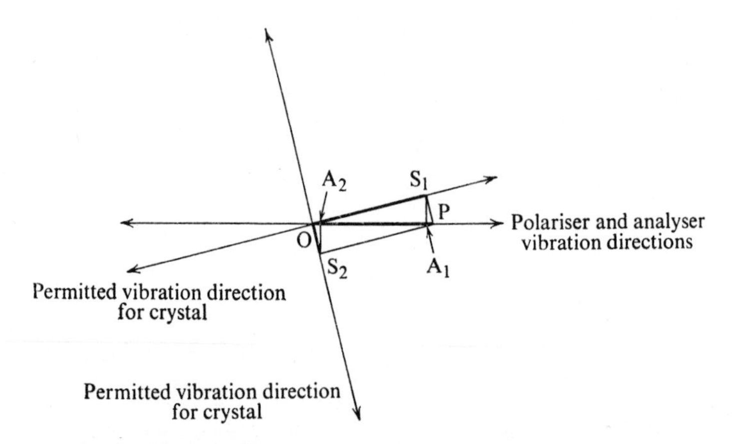

Fig. 9.3 Interference effects for parallel light, parallel polars, crystal in general orientation.
Resolution of the light vector through the system shows that interfering wave trains have unequal amplitudes ($OA_1 \neq OA_2$).

specimen. This is a shallow wedge of a half a degree or less in angle, cut with a flat base parallel to the optic axis direction, and enclosed in protective glass covers; it is cut so that its principal vibration directions are parallel and perpendicular to its length. When placed with its flat base on the microscope stage, normally incident parallel light travels with a wave normal direction perpendicular to the optic axis, so that the birefringence is $n_e - n_o$ (=0·009); the variation of path difference is provided by the change in thickness of the wedge along its length from zero (at the tip, never realised in practice) to 250–500μ (0·25–0·50 mm) at the thickest end. When this wedge is set in the 45° position between crossed polars and illuminated in monochromatic light, we see a series of equally spaced dark bands across it; these dark bands are separated by light bands of the monochromatic colour, with continuous intensity changes along the length (Fig. 9.4). The dark bands correspond to complete destructive interference where the optical path difference is

λ, 2λ, 3λ, . . . and the interleaving maximum intensities are due to complete reinforcement with path differences $\lambda/2$, $3\lambda/2$, $5\lambda/2$. . . . Rotation of the stage causes the bright bands to lose intensity, until the whole wedge is in extinction when its length is parallel to the vibration direction of analyser or polariser. If the wedge is turned back into the 45° position, and the polars set parallel, the light and dark bands are

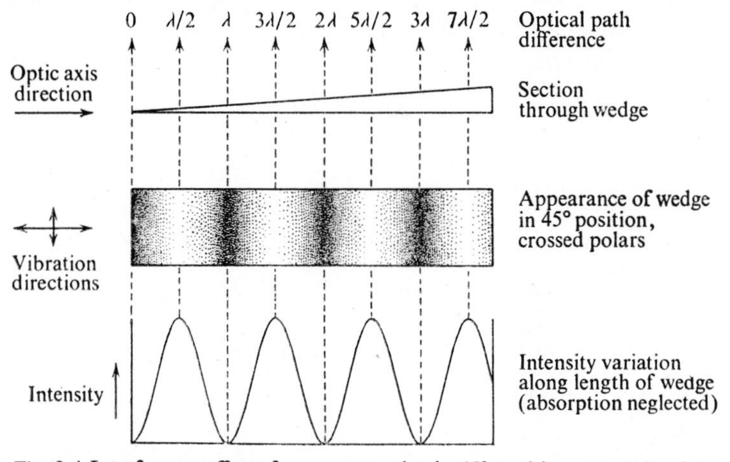

Fig. 9.4 Interference effects for quartz wedge in 45° position, crossed polars, monochromatic light.

again present but their positions are interchanged compared to crossed polars; rotation of the stage causes the dark bands to become brighter until the whole wedge is of uniform intensity when its length is parallel or perpendicular to the vibration direction of the polars.

So far we have confined our description and explanation of interference effects to those seen in monochromatic light; a fuller analysis is given in Appendix B. However many of our optical observations are carried out in white light, and we must expect the presence of a spread of wavelengths to have some effect on what we see.

9.3 The scale of interference colours in white light

The experiments with the quartz wedge in the 45° position between crossed polars provide a convenient starting point for the discussion of interference effects in white light, for it is clear that the positions of the dark (and light) bands in the wedge depends on the wavelength of the the light (Fig. 9.5). In white light there is a continuous spread of wavelengths from the red end of the spectrum (about 7500×10^{-8} cm =

750 mμ) to the blue or violet limit (about 4000×10^{-8} cm $\equiv$ 400 mμ), and we must add together the effects for all wavelengths in this band. At a particular point on the wedge there will be complete subtraction of that wavelength (λ') for which an integral multiple is equal to the path

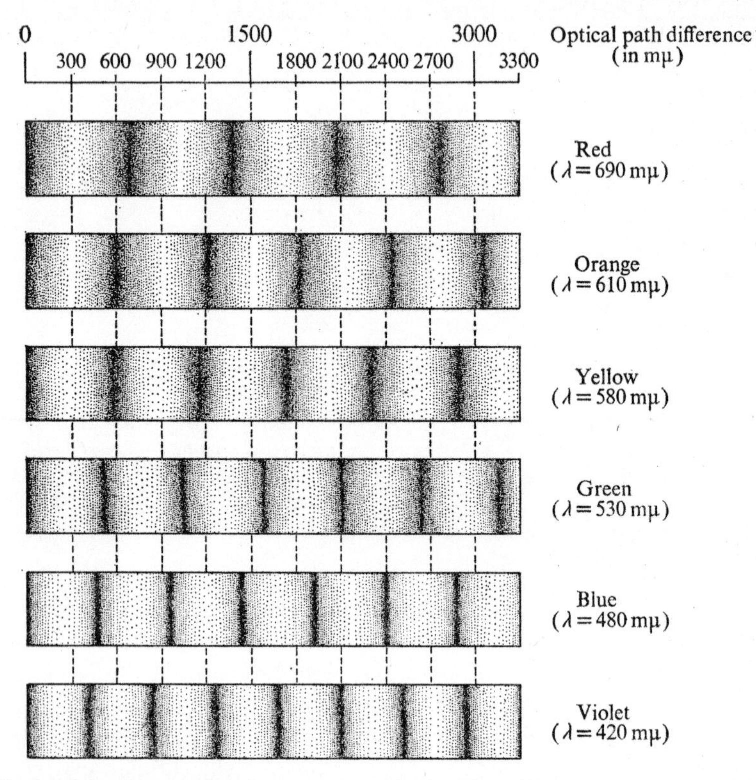

Fig. 9.5 Interference effects for a quartz wedge in 45° position, crossed polars, with primary spectrum colours.

difference, together with partial subtraction of all other wavelengths decreasing to zero for the wavelengths $\lambda'/2$ and $3\lambda'/2$ (though these wavelengths may not lie within the visible range). The result is that, due to the complex subtraction of the various wavelengths in varying amounts from the white light, the interference produces a colour at a particular point on the wedge. The sequence of colours produced in white light by increasing retardation along the wedge is known as a scale of interference colours.

The *normal scale of interference colours*, or *Newton's scale*, is that seen with the quartz wedge and crossed polars. This scale begins from the tip of the wedge with a colour sequence which terminates in a characteristic violet shade. There is then a different sequence ending in another violet band across the wedge; this sequence is subsequently repeated, the essential difference being that the tints become paler with each successive repetition. The repetition within the colour scale allows its division into orders. The violet bands are equally spaced and are taken to establish divisions between the *orders of colours* in the scale; a colour occurring between the tip of the wedge and the first violet band is said to be a first order colour, one between the first and second violet bands is a second order colour and so on. The violet bands dividing the orders in the colour scale are often known as sensitive tints. The wavelength whose complete subtraction coincides with the first order sensitive violet lies in the yellowish-green part of the spectrum ($\lambda' \sim 550$ mμ, though the value depends to some extent on the observer); the eye is particularly responsive to this colour, and its elimination is responsible for the ready recognition of the sensitive violet dividing the orders on the colour scale. Moreover a small change in retardation at these positions on the wedge produces a more marked colour change than elsewhere on the colour scale, a fact which is employed in the sensitive tint test plate (see 9.4). The periodicity and shade of colours within the different orders is not exact, so that a third order green, for example, is not quite the same shade as the greens of other orders. The repetition has its origin in a kind of beat phenomenon which occurs whenever two or more wave motions of different frequencies are superposed; the phenomenon is perhaps best known for sound waves of different pitch, but we have already had some manifestation of it in the discussion of the analysis of light pulses into simple wave forms. In the quartz wedge, the scale of interference colours is due to the superposition of the interference patterns for all visible wavelengths; each wavelength shows a sequence of light and dark bands, but with different wavelengths the separation of the bands changes, so that the result is to give a colour sequence which has some recognisable periodicity.

When the interference effects in white light are to be used in optical determinations, the exact colour sequence of Newton's scale is important. Some makers of polarising microscopes sell a coloured chart which represents the variation along the length of the wedge quite well; a schematic description is shown in Fig. 9.6 and the colours may be seen on the Michel-Levy chart in the folder at the back of the book. We notice, as mentioned above, that the first order colours are somewhat

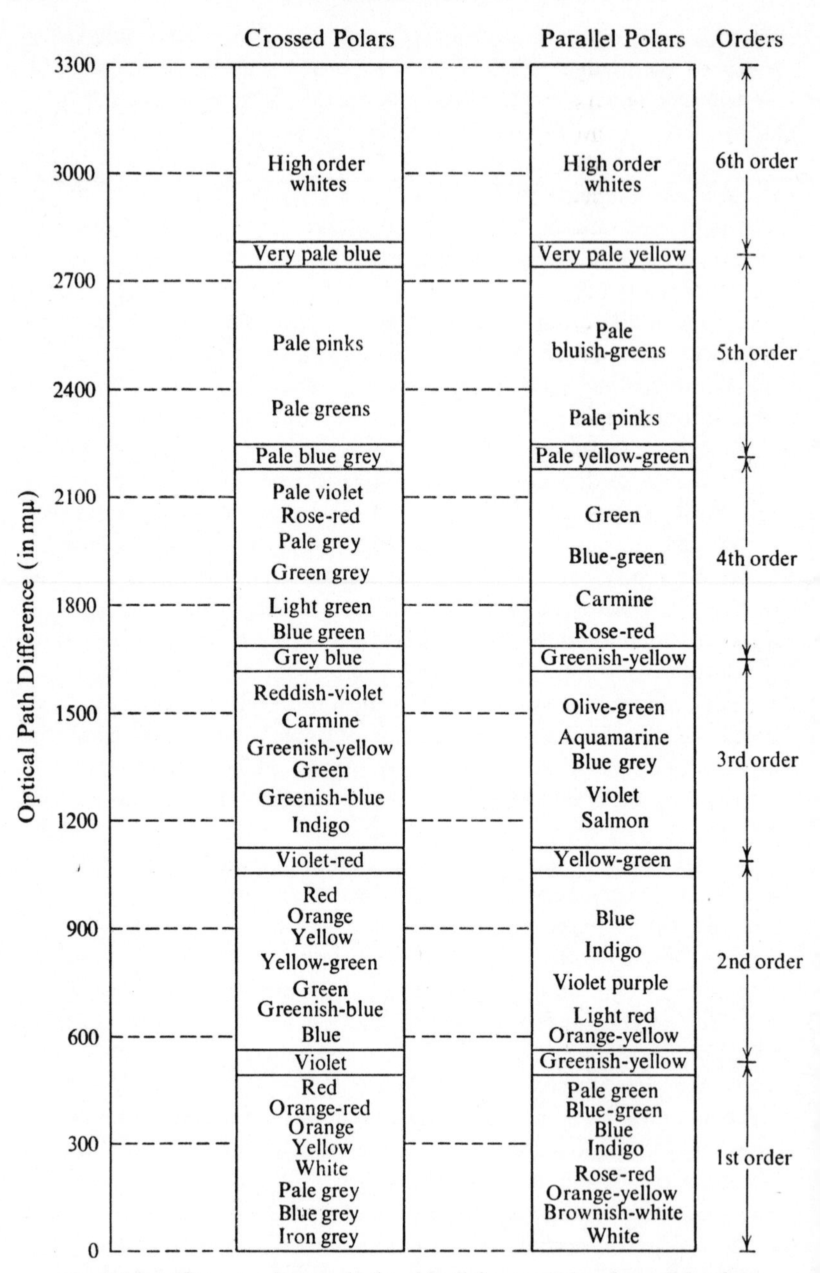

Fig. 9.6 Interference colour scales in white light, crossed and parallel polars.

different from those of higher orders. From the tip of the wedge a series of blue-greys gradually merges into white; although there is some partial interference at this point, its effect is insufficient to cause the eye to recognise any coloration. Following the first order white, the colours become more clearly defined and pass through a yellow-orange-red sequence to the violet which marks the end of the first order. In the second and higher orders the colours roughly follow the sequence blue-green-orange-red, though the precise shades vary from order to order. The colours are well defined for the second and third orders, though they become paler and more diffuse in subsequent orders. Most people can still make distinctions up to the fifth and sixth orders, but finally the colours appear to merge to give white light. In this high order white light, the retardation has become large enough at a given point on the wedge to allow subtraction of a selection of wavelengths in the visible range; the eye still interprets the combination of remaining wavelengths as white light.

The normal scale of interference colours depends on the realisation of certain conditions in the optical properties of the material of the wedge. For example, it has been assumed that the birefringence is independent of wavelength, a condition which may not be met in some dispersive substances; a strong body colour can also affect interference colours. Any scale of interference colours which does not match Newton's scale, whatever the cause, is referred to as anomalous or abnormal. Even with a suitable material, like quartz, the normal scale is only observed with crossed polars. With parallel polars, there is the interchange of the interference conditions for complete reinforcement and interference, and the sequence of colours along a wedge is rather different; the colour at each point is complementary to that observed between crossed polars (Fig. 9.6). The colours follow much the same sequence, between crossed and parallel polars, but particular colours are displaced. For example, pinks and greens change places, so that the greenish colours about the divisions between orders in parallel polars are found in the middle of similar orders for crossed polars. Although interference colours are usually observed with crossed polars, the parallel position can be used to help confirm the order of a particular colour. In particular, it can be used to distinguish between low and high order whites. The retardation which gives a first order white between crossed polars will produce a dark colour with parallel polars, whereas a high order white will be unchanged irrespective of the orientation of the polars (see Fig. 9.6).

9.4 Compensation

If a section of an anisotropic crystal is observed in the 45° position between crossed polars in parallel white light, the interference colour depends on its relative retardation. We can add or subtract a known extra retardation to that produced by the crystal, and from the changes in interference colour determine the slow and fast vibration directions of the crystal and the value of its relative retardation.

To change the retardation, we use auxiliary testing instruments known as compensators. One of the simplest compensating devices is the quartz wedge that we have already described. This has a wide range of compensating power, and can deal with retardations up to those which give high order whites; for some purposes, it has the disadvantage that its insertion into the optical path produces a non-uniform field. If the interference colour due to the specimen lies in the first two or three orders, as is usual for sections of standard thickness of most materials, we can use other simple devices employing compensating plates of comparable retardations. One of the most widely used is a plate showing a first order sensitive violet colour between crossed polars; this is commonly made of an (010) cleavage flake of gypsum ($CaSO_4$; $2H_2O$) of the appropriate thickness. It is particularly valuable for the investigation of small retardations, which produce an easily observable colour change; the sensitive tint, being a plate and not a wedge, shows a uniform field. Other plates of weaker retardation are useful if the interference colour for the specimen is due to moderate path differences in the first order. Often such plates have a retardation of about a quarter of a wavelength for sodium light; such quarter wave plates are often made of (001) cleavage flakes of white mica (a complex silicate), though sometimes anisotropic plastic sheets are used. All these simple compensators are elongated like the quartz wedge; they are mounted between glass plates for protection and bound around the edges to minimise the risk of breakage. They are all cut so that their permitted vibration directions are parallel and perpendicular to the length of the mount. The slow and fast vibration directions are marked upon the compensator, though it is immaterial whether the slower or the faster lies along the length. In describing their use, we shall always take the slower vibration direction to lie along the length, i.e. a length-slow plate.

The same technique is used for all these testing instruments. The stage of the microscope, carrying the specimen viewed in parallel white light and crossed polars, is turned until the crystal is in extinction. The stage is then rotated through 45° to show the interference colour at maximum intensity. We now know that the vibration directions of the crystal section bisect those of the polars (and the directions of the crosswires), but we do not know which is fast and which is slow. We can insert the compensator into the slot in the body tube just above the objective (see 7.4); its vibration directions also bisect the crosswires and so are parallel to those of the crystal section. The total retardation of the system (specimen and compensator) is either increased or decreased by this act. If the slow and fast vibration directions of specimen and compensator are parallel, there will be an addition of relative retardations; the interference colour will move up the interference scale by an amount equal to the retarding power of the compensator (Fig. 9.7*a*). On the other hand, if the slow vibration direction of the compensator is parallel to the fast vibration direction of the crystal (and vice versa), there is a subtraction of relative retardations; we are then said to have partial compensation, and the interference colour moves down the scale by the appropriate amount (Fig. 9.7*b*). In practice we can observe the change in colour as the compensator is inserted, and decide whether there has been addition or subtraction of retardations; since the slow and fast directions for the compensator are known, those of the crystal can be deduced.

If we know the relative retardation of the compensator, it should be possible to deduce that of the specimen from the total retardation producing the combined interference colour. In practice this observation is carried out most reliably using the quartz wedge. The wedge is inserted so that subtraction of relative retardation occurs; the position of the wedge is then adjusted within the slot until complete compensation is obtained, when the effects of the crystal and wedge are exactly balanced. At this position there is zero total retardation, and a black band is seen across the wedge (Fig. 9.8). The specimen is then removed so that an interference colour reappears; the wedge is slowly withdrawn from the slot to allow recognition of the colour and its order. Once the position of the colour has been found (e.g. yellow of the second order) the retardation can be determined. The most convenient way of doing this employs a coloured chart (often known as a *Michel-Lévy chart*) showing the interference scale, together with retardations, and lines representing the loci of constant thickness and birefringence; this allows measurement of the birefringence of the section if its thickness is known (see Fig. 9.9 and the folder at the back of the book). Unfortunately it is not now

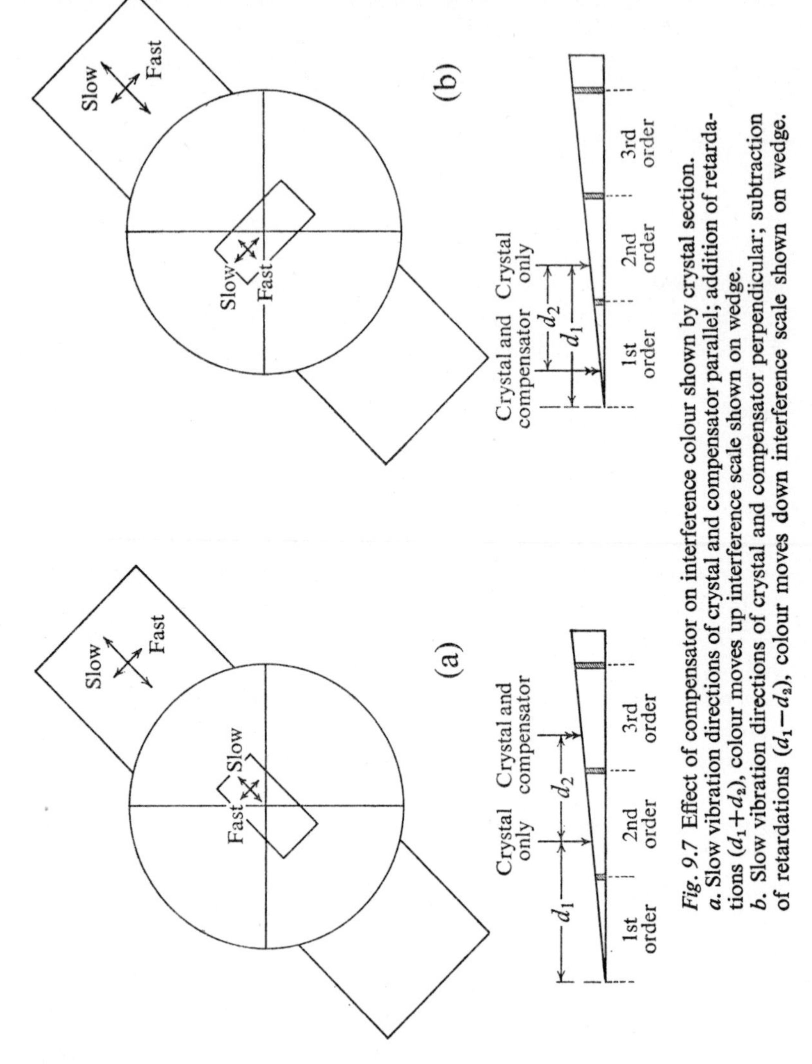

Fig. 9.7 Effect of compensator on interference colour shown by crystal section.
a. Slow vibration directions of crystal and compensator parallel; addition of retardations (d_1+d_2), colour moves up interference scale shown on wedge.
b. Slow vibration directions of crystal and compensator perpendicular; subtraction of retardations (d_1-d_2), colour moves down interference scale shown on wedge.

possible to purchase such charts, but old copies are available in most laboratories. Superior quartz wedges have values of retardation engraved upon them, but for most purposes matching the observed colour to that of the chart gives sufficient accuracy.

More refined forms of compensator have been designed to give higher accuracy and to cope with retardations beyond the range of the simple

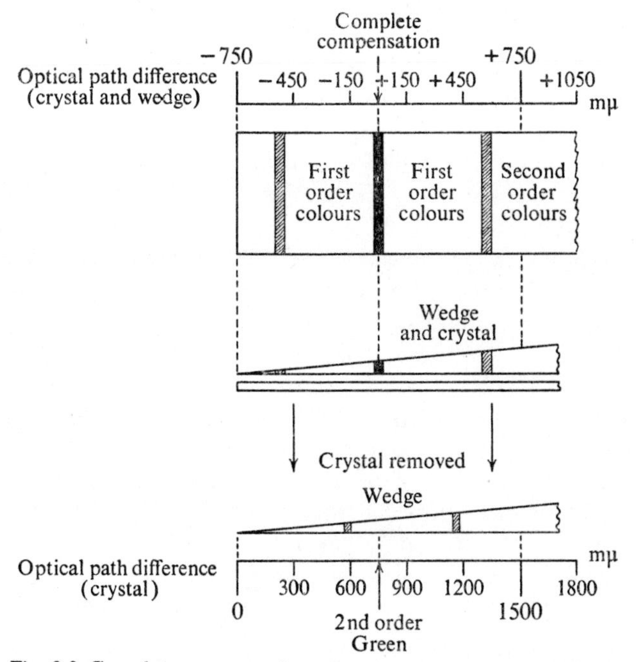

Fig. 9.8 Complete compensation of an interference colour using a quartz wedge.
The upper diagrams show the appearance of wedge and crystal at complete compensation; the lower diagrams show the appearance of the wedge with crystal removed.

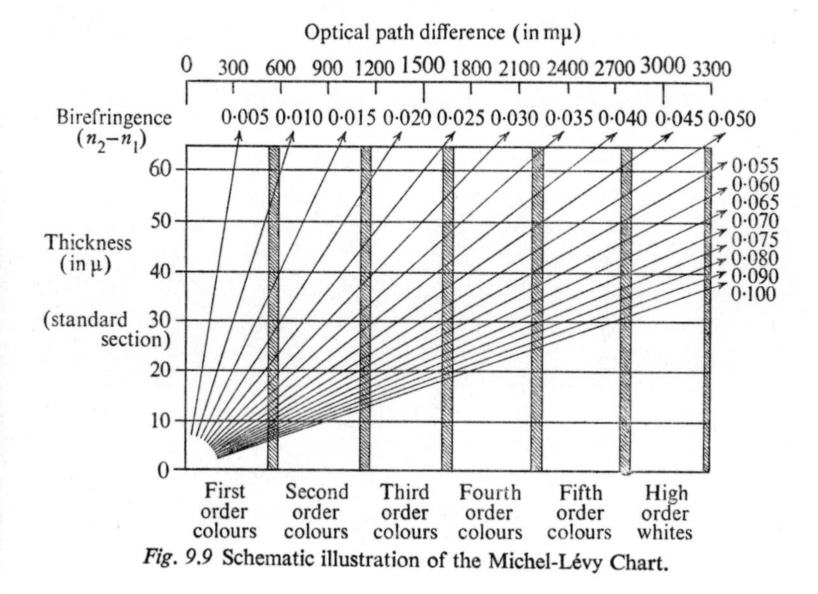

Fig. 9.9 Schematic illustration of the Michel-Lévy Chart.

quartz wedge. The most widely used of these is an adaptation by Berek of an early compensating device due to Babinet. It consists of a calcite plate (0·1 mm thick) cut perpendicular to the optic axis. It is mounted in a frame which is secured in the microscope slot by a spring mechanism; the frame permits rotation of the plate about a horizontal axis lying in its plane, and the rotation can be read off from a graduated drum attached to the rotation axis. The angle of rotation corresponding to complete compensation can then be converted to a measure of retardation using the calibration tables provided with each instrument.

9.5 Extinction angles

Our examination of a crystal section between crossed polars in parallel light allows us to deduce the permitted vibration directions for the section from the positions of extinction. The permitted vibration directions for the specimen are related to sections of the indicatrix as described in Chapter 4; for the normal incidence of a parallel beam on the crystal they are parallel to the major and minor axes of the central section parallel to the plane of the crystal section. So a study of extinction positions can tell us something about the orientation of the indicatrix, and the angle between an extinction position and a prominent crystallographic feature of the section can be an important characteristic of the material under examination. If the extinction direction is parallel to the crystallographic feature (it may be the trace of a cleavage or an edge), we are said to have *straight* or *parallel* extinction; if it bisects the angle between two such reference lines, it is said to be *symmetrical*; if it is neither symmetrical nor straight, it is said to be *oblique* or *inclined.* For anything other than straight extinction there is an extinction angle to be measured.

The measurement of an extinction angle may be carried out on the stage of the microscope by setting the crystallographic feature, which is to act as the reference direction, parallel to a crosswire and rotating the stage until the position of extinction is reached; the difference between the angular positions of the stage gives the extinction angle. Normally it is sufficient to use white light, though for some materials, there is significant dispersion of the orientation of the indicatrix with wavelength and monochromatic light has to be used. Often it is difficult to judge when the specimen is exactly in the position of extinction, but for most purposes an average of several measurements will be adequate. If the specimen does not occupy the whole of the field view, we can attempt to determine the extinction positions more accurately by inserting a sensitive tint plate. Away from the specimen we now see the characteristic sensitive violet. Further, when the specimen itself is exactly in extinction, we shall also see the sensitive violet colour; but if the crystal is slightly rotated from this position, it effectively adds a small retardation to that of the tint plate and the colour changes to the adjacent blue or yellow on the interference scale depending on the sense of the rotation and the sign of the extra retardation. The extinction position may therefore be found by rotating the microscope stage until the colour of the field and

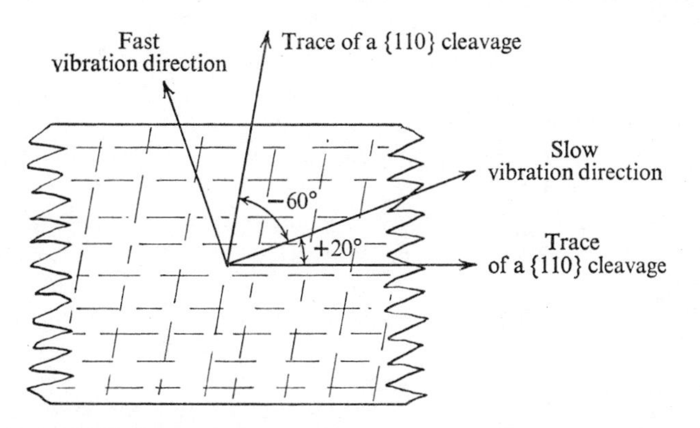

Fig. 9.10 Example of description of extinction angles. The signs attached to the angles denote opposite senses of rotation from the slow vibration direction.

the crystal are matched. This method works best for materials which are effectively colourless and of low birefringence.

These measurements can be used in some simple cases as a diagnostic property or they can help to build up information about the optical indicatrix, in particular its orientation with respect to crystallographic axes; examples of both applications are given in Chapter 12. One of their virtues lies in the simplicity of measurement, but equally it is important that the measurements must be carefully specified. This means that not only must we state the size of the extinction angle, but also the vibration direction (fast or slow) from which it was measured and the nature of the reference direction. Thus the description of the crystal section shown in Fig. 9.10 would be: 'extinction angles for this section of an orthorhombic crystal measured between the slow vibration direction and the traces of the {110} cleavage planes in the plane of the section are +20° and −60°'. If we have a complete knowledge of the indicatrix, it is possible to predict theoretically the values of any extinction angles.

A convenient method of doing this is given in Appendix A, which could be used to check the validity of the experimental measurements for the orthorhombic crystal given above.

9.6 Exercises

1. Interference effects with testing instruments:

Place the quartz wedge on the microscope stage illuminated by parallel red light. After setting it into extinction between crossed polars, rotate the stage through 45°:

(i) Examine the intensity distribution along the length of the wedge.

(ii) Check that interference effects are not visible if either the analyser or polariser is removed.

(iii) Observe the variations in intensity at particular points on the wedge as the stage is rotated between crossed polars.

(iv) Reset the wedge into the 45° position, and observe the variations in intensity at particular points as the polariser is rotated from the crossed position.

(v) Repeat (i)-(iv) using green light, noting particularly the spacing of the dark bands compared to red light.

(vi) Repeat (i)-(iv) using white light. Pay particular attention to the sequence of colours seen in the normal interference scale with crossed polars and the 45° position. Note the colours at points on the wedge corresponding to successive dark bands in red and green light.

(vii) Using the permanently mounted prismatic sections of calcite crystals on the stage, confirm from the extinction positions that the permitted vibration directions are parallel and perpendicular to the length of the crystal. After removing the analyser at each extinction setting, compare each of the corresponding refractive indices with that of the mounting medium; thus determine which is the slow and which the fast of the two permitted vibration directions. Reset the crystal into the 45° position between crossed polars, and with the quartz wedge inserted into the testing slot adjust the position of the wedge until complete compensation is obtained for the calcite crystal; hence determine whether the slow or fast vibration direction of the quartz wedge is parallel to its length.

(viii) Examine the interference colours produced by the sensitive tint and quarter waves plates between crossed polars in white light. Determine whether the slow or fast vibration direction of each of these testing instruments is along their length.

2. Birefringence of a thin section:

You are provided with a permanently mounted $\{10\bar{1}1\}$ cleavage flake of calcite of known thickness (20μ):

(i) Determine the order of the interference colour shown in white light, and hence the birefringence of the section from a suitable chart.

(ii) Confirm the value you obtain by calculating the birefringence of this section, given that for calcite $n_o=1{\cdot}66$ and $n_e=1{\cdot}48_5$, and $(0001):(10\bar{1}1)\sim44\frac{1}{2}°$. (See Appendix A.1.)

3. Measurements of extinction angles:

(i) Measure the value of the extinction angle for an (010) section of diopside (a complex alumino-silicate of monoclinic symmetry), using the traces of the {110} cleavages as reference directions. Indicate on a diagram the positions of the fast and slow vibration directions for this section relative to the cleavage traces.

(ii) A thin section shows many coloured hornblende (another complex alumino-silicate of monoclinic symmetry) crystals in random orientation. Most crystals show the traces of {110} cleavage cracks $[(110):(1\bar{1}0)\sim56°]$; use this information to select those selections which contain the *z*-axis. Measure the extinction angles for a number of these sections, and so obtain the characteristic maximum value for this material.

4. Calculations of extinction angles:

(i) Using the data given for calcite in 2(ii) above, determine the angles between the extinction positions and the edges of a face of the cleavage rhombohedron $\{10\bar{1}1\}$ when light is incident normally on the face.

(ii) A specimen of pigeonite (a monoclinic member of the complex silicate pyroxene minerals) has {110} cleavages; its optic orientation is given as $y=\beta$, $z:\gamma=20°$ in the obtuse x–z angle, with $2V_\gamma=40°$. Use the Biot-Fresnel construction of Appendix A.2 to plot the variation of the angle between the slow vibration direction and the trace of the cleavage for sections parallel to the *z*-axis at various inclinations to (010).

(iii) A variety of augite (another monoclinic member of the pyroxene group) has the same cleavage and orientation of the indicatrix except that $2V_\alpha=50°$. Repeat the exercise of (ii) for this specimen.

(iv) Compare the extinction curves of (ii) and (iii), and note the implied limitation on the location of an {010} section of a monoclinic substance from the measurements of extinction angles alone (see also 12.4, Example (*f*)).

CHAPTER 10

INTERFERENCE EFFECTS IN CONVERGENT LIGHT

10.1 The principles and practice of conoscopic methods

IN the previous chapter we were concerned with interference effects in parallel light, and we saw how these gave us some information about the optical character of the crystal for one particular direction of propagation. With anisotropic specimens, more than one orientation of section is often required to build up a full picture of optical properties by orthoscopic methods. For any section, however, we can try to extract more data by examination in convergent light so that not only do we observe the properties for light travelling normal to the section, but also we simultaneously see effects due to all wave normal directions within a limited cone about this section normal. In this way certain facets of anisotropy are revealed which can be valuable either in describing the properties of the specimen or in using optical studies as a means of identification.

The arrangement of the polarising microscope for this conoscopic work has been described in 7.7. Highly convergent light is obtained by adjustment of the illumination system with the condenser inserted; after passing through the specimen the light is focused by a medium high power objective to form a directions image which is usually brought into the focal plane of the ocular by the Bertrand lens. The ray paths through the microscope were shown in Fig. 7.8, and for our present purposes it is enough to remember that each point on the directions image is due to all light waves travelling parallel to one particular direction in the crystal. The polars are inserted in the microscope, usually in their crossed position, and with an anisotropic section on the stage, we observe interference effects in the directions image. The directions image formed under these conditions is usually known as the *interference figure* given by the section; clearly the nature of an interference figure depends both on the optical properties of the crystal and on the orientation of the section.

However, before discussing the appearance of interference figures in some detail, there are one or two further practical points to be considered. The specimen may be in the form of a section or powdered grains; grains should be immersed in a refractive index liquid to avoid reflection of the incident light from surface irregularities. In either case, it often happens that, even using the high power objective, the magnified image of the crystal from which the interference figure is to be obtained does not fill the whole field of view; in conoscopic use, this can affect the quality of the image, particularly if there are other grains within the illuminated field received by the objective. It is best to isolate the interference figure of a selected grain either by ensuring that it is the only crystal illuminated or by using diaphragms above the stage to remove all light but that which has passed through it. There are various simple ways of satisfying these requirements provided that the optical system (both lenses and diaphragms) is in strict alignment; the most convenient method depends on the design of the microscope. Where there is an iris diaphragm in the substage system, both diaphragm and condenser are lowered until a sharp image of the diaphragm aperture is seen simultaneously with a magnified image of the crystal through the microscope. The size of the aperture is then adjusted to include only the chosen crystal within the field, when the interference figure can be obtained in the usual way. This method usually implies some restriction on the angular spread of the limiting wave normals focused by the objective, and is restricted to microscopes with adequate movement in the substage system. On some microscopes there is an iris diaphragm in the plane of the object image above the Bertrand lens which can be used in a similar way. To focus the object image in order to adjust the aperture, another small auxiliary lens is required; this must be removed before the interference figure is seen through the Bertrand lens. Finally, when viewing an interference figure directly, with the ocular and Bertrand lens removed, the centre of the field can be isolated by fitting caps with small central holes of different sizes over the top of the body tube; again, if it is necessary, the object image can be observed within the aperture through a small positive lens above the cap.

10.2 Interference effects for uniaxial crystals

We must now give some thought to the complex problem of what kind of interference effects will be seen in the conoscopic examination of sections of anisotropic materials between crossed polars; there are no interference effects (and no interference figures) for isotropic substances. There will be a wide variety of interference figures for anisotropic crystals depending both on their properties and the orientations of the section. It is simplest to start with uniaxial crystals, and to take first a uniform section normal to the optic axis direction.

In parallel light this section is isotropic and is extinguished at all positions of the microscope stage. However, in the interference figure this wave normal direction is only one within the cone of directions which contribute to the image. It will give rise to the point at the centre of the directions image, and this point is dark for all positions of the stage between crossed polars. All other points on the interference figure are due to wave trains in the convergent light travelling in directions inclined to the optic axis; for such wave normals there will be double refraction and the possibility of interference. If we take one particular inclined wave normal direction within the crystal, the permitted vibration directions and associated refractive indices can be derived from the appropriate central section of the indicatrix (Fig. 10.1*a*). For waves in this direction a retardation will be introduced during the optical path in the crystal. This retardation will determine the interference effect observed when the two vibrations emerging from the crystal are resolved by the analyser; the effect will be just the same as that seen for the same retardation at a point on a wedge, and it will be observed at the position on the interference figure to which these wave trains are focused (Fig. 10.1*b*). But we remember that the uniaxial indicatrix is an ellipsoid of revolution about the optic axis; thus with a section normal to the optic axis, all wave normals of equal inclination to the optic axis suffer the same retardation on passing through the crystal section. In the directions image all waves whose normals lie on a given cone about the axis of the microscope are focused on a circle about the centre of the image, so that the interference figure shows the same interference effect around a circular fringe about the centre (Fig. 10.1*c*). Moreover, considering all such cones of wave normals present within the convergent beam, it is clear that the retardation will increase as the angle of the cone gets larger. Thus as we move along a radius from the centre of the figure, the optical path difference increases and the sequence of interference effects is the same as that seen in progressing from the tip along the length of a wedge in parallel light; in the figure, however, the scale is not linear, and the retardation increases more rapidly with distance from the centre. The convergent light interference figure from this section shows concentric circular interference fringes, alternately light and dark in monochromatic light and following the interference colour scale in white light.

These fringes of equal retardation are only one aspect of the interference

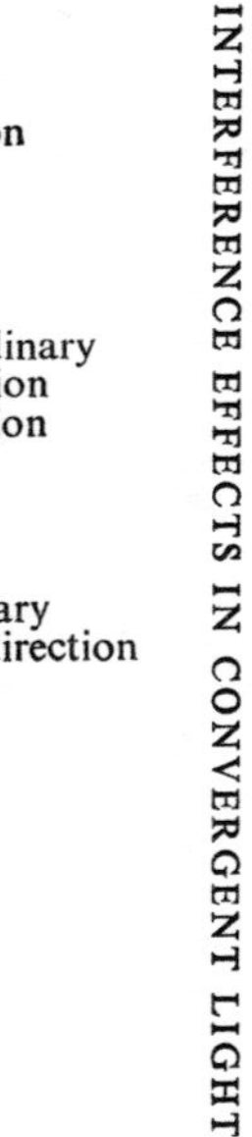

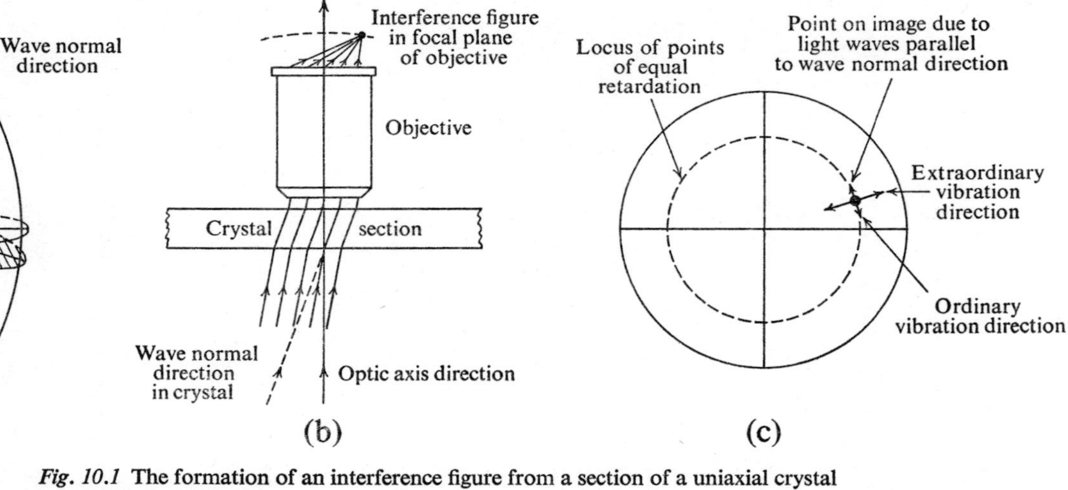

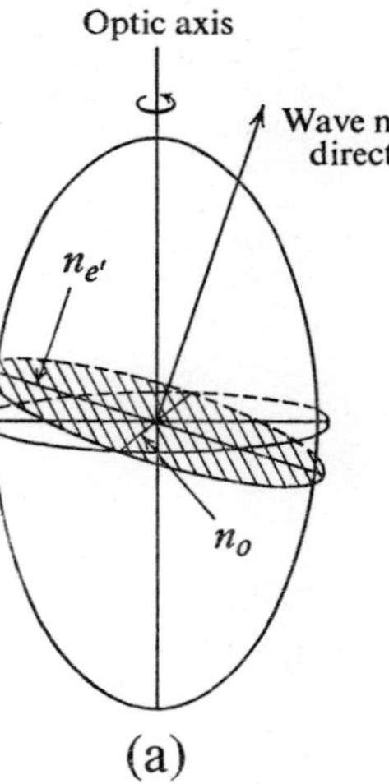

Fig. 10.1 The formation of an interference figure from a section of a uniaxial crystal normal to the optic axis.
a. The section of the indicatrix for one wave normal direction.
b. Light parallel to this wave normal focused by the objective at one point.
c. The position of the point on the interference figure due to light parallel to the wave normal direction.

effects to be seen in convergent light from this section. For any general wave normal direction, not only do the two permitted vibrations travel through the crystal with different speeds, but we must remember that they vibrate in perpendicular directions: the ordinary disturbance vibrates perpendicular to the plane of the optic axis and the wave normal, while the extraordinary disturbance vibrates in this plane (Fig. 10.1*a*). Hence for light waves giving rise to a particular point on the interference figure, the extraordinary and ordinary vibrations may be taken as being respectively radial and tangential to the interference fringe passing through this point on the image (Fig. 10.1*c*). This implies that there are four dark points around this fringe where the interference effect will not be seen, for there will be four positions for which the permitted vibration directions are parallel to those of the crossed polars. At these points, the conditions are similar to those which cause extinction of the interference effect in parallel light. Since such extinction positions occur for all equal retardation fringes on the same radii, we shall expect the interference figure to appear as in Fig. 10.2.

In white light, commonly used in this work, the concentric coloured fringe system is surmounted by a centred black cross, the arms of which are called *isogyres* or *brushes*; in practice the isogyres tend to broaden towards the edge of the image. If the stage is rotated, the figure is unchanged, for with this section we are rotating about the axis of revolution of the indicatrix. The number of orders of the interference scale which are visible depends on the optical system as well as the thickness and birefringence of the section; for a particular optical arrangement an increase either in thickness or birefringence increases the total retardation for light waves at the extremities of the figure, so that more of the interference scale is visible. In describing conoscopic image formation in 7.7, we saw that the inclination of wave normals giving rise to points on the edge of the figure was determined by the numerical aperture of the objective, which should be as large as possible to give the best angular spread. For most microscopes under optimum conditions, wave normals within the crystal inclined at about 30° to the microscope axis are just focused at the edge of the directions image, though the angle also depends on the optical properties of the crystal (see 10.5).

Interference figures different from those we have just described are sometimes obtained from basal sections of uniaxial materials. The most common type of abnormal interference figure is one in which the coloured sequence of the circular fringes does not follow the normal interference scale; this may be due to dispersion, body colour, etc. Occasionally some uniaxial crystal sections show a slight separation of the isogyres on rotation of the stage; this is often caused by stress effects which give the specimen a slightly biaxial character (see 10.4). One further anomaly is shown by thick basal sections of quartz, for which the centre of the field, normally the intersection of the isogyres, has only an illuminated

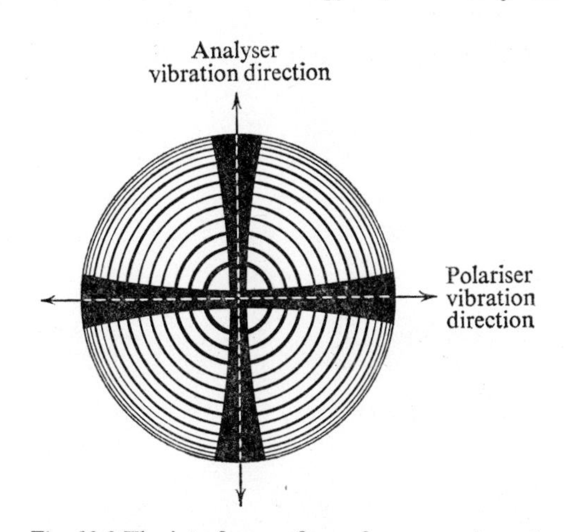

Fig. 10.2 The interference figure from a section of a uniaxial crystal perpendicular to the optic axis, crossed polars, monochromatic light.
Sixteen intensity minima are visible (due to thickness of section and/or high birefringence).
Note that although intensity variation along any radius is similar to that along a wedge, the scale is not linear; the angular radius of a ring is proportional to the square root of its order.

circular area; the size of this area and its colour depends on the thickness of the quartz. This behaviour is typical of materials which are optically active and which rotate the vibration direction of polarised light travelling along the optic axis through an angle dependent on the thickness and the wavelength (a fuller description of optical activity is given in Appendix D). It is also worth while to mention the false interference figures which can sometimes be seen even when there is no crystal on the stage; these have a faint black cross similar to the brushes of the basal uniaxial figure. They are due to the effect of the highly curved upper surface of the first lens of the objective upon the vibration direction of light from the polariser. It can be shown that when linearly polarised light is refracted at such a surface, the vibration direction is slightly rotated except for rays within the vertical sections of the lens parallel and perpendicular to the vibration direction of the polariser. Hence complete extinction occurs only parallel to the crosswires, and elsewhere in the field the rotation of the vibration direction provides a weak component which is transmitted by the analyser. There is little that can be done about such effects except to take care that they are not confused with genuine figures from crystal sections.

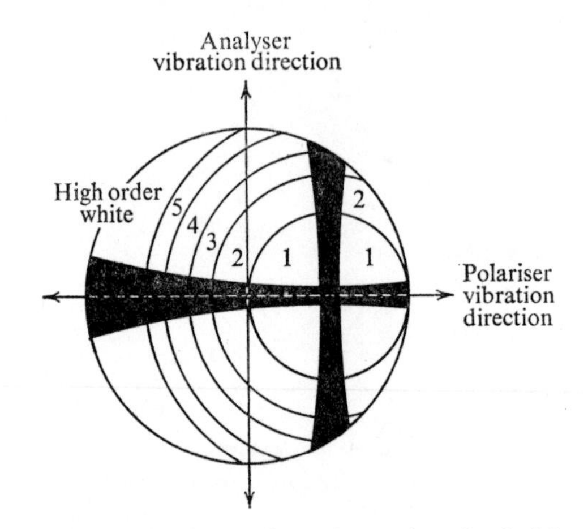

Fig. 10.3 Interference figure for section of uniaxial crystal inclined at small angle (~15°) to optic axis, crossed polars, white light.
The circular fringes marked on the diagram represent the divisions of the coloured fringes into orders by the sensitive violet.

So far our discussion has been restricted to basal sections normal to the optic axis, but in practice we may have to be content with other more general sections. We can begin to understand the features of general uniaxial interference figures by imagining what would happen as a basal section is tilted. (This is not usually practical with the normal high power objectives which have a short working distance; some medium power objectives have large enough apertures and working distances to permit the figures for slightly tilted sections to be obtained.) As the section is tilted, the optic axis becomes inclined to the axis of the microscope. Since the optic axis is at the centre of the equal retardation fringe system and the isogyres, the interference figure will show an offset view of the optic axis figure (Fig. 10.3); as the stage is rotated, the optic axis direction will describe a circular path around the centre of the directions image, so that the fringe system and isogyres move eccentrically around the field of view. If the inclination of the section exceeds the maximum angle of the cone of wave normals that can be received and focused by the objective, the optic axis direction at the centre of the black cross is not visible. Its approximate position can be deduced from the appearance

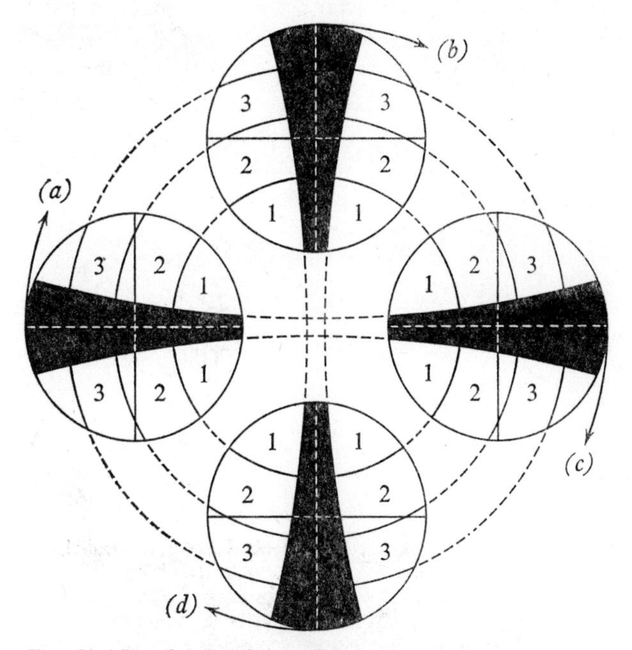

Fig. 10.4 Interference figures for section of uniaxial crystal inclined at a moderate angle (~40°) to optic axis, crossed polars, white light.
(*a*), (*b*), (*c*), (*d*) represent the figure at 90° intervals of rotation of the stage; the colour fringes are represented schematically as in Fig. 10.3.

of the isogyres which sweep through the field of view, always remaining parallel to the crosswires, as the stage is rotated (Fig. 10.4). With increasing inclination location of the optic axis becomes more difficult as the brushes occupy more of the field of view; the isogyres can become curved and the coloured fringe system noticeably loses its circular form. In the limit, we are considering the case where the optic axis is parallel to the stage. For such a section the coloured retardation fringes are usually very broad and indistinct; they are hyperbolic and symmetrically occupy four quadrants of the field of view. When the stage is rotated, the hyperbolic fringes rotate with it; but as a position where the optic axis becomes parallel to the vibration direction of the polars is approached, indistinct hyperbolic brushes enter the field from the quadrants containing the optic axis direction. In the extinction position, these form an indistinct black cross, which with further rotation breaks into hyperbolae; they vanish from the field of view on rotation of a few degrees. In the 45° position the centre of the field is occupied by an interference colour determined by the retardation of the section. This behaviour (Fig. 10.5) is typical of the *flash figure* obtained from any

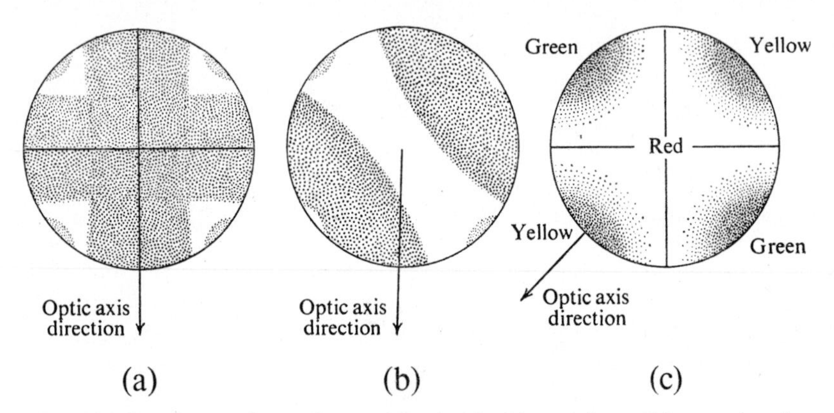

Fig. 10.5 Interference figures for section of uniaxial crystal parallel to optic axis, crossed polars, white light.
a. With optic axis parallel to vibration direction of analyser.
b. With optic axis inclined at small angle (~2°) to vibration direction of analyser; hyperbolic brushes leaving field in quadrants containing optic axis direction.
c. With optic axis inclined at 45° to vibration direction of analyser. Colours from centre fall down interference scale in quadrants containing optic axis direction, and rise in other two quadrants.

section containing the optic axis; this term is employed because in many cases one only observes a momentary darkening of the field four times in every revolution of the stage when the indistinct cross is formed. We shall not attempt to explain in detail the formation and behaviour of this kind of interference figure, but it is important that it should be recognised for it can be used to determine the orientation of the crystal section.

10.3 Practical use of uniaxial interference figures

The value of interference figures lies not only in the data which they give about the optical properties of a substance, but also in their use to identify and confirm the orientation of sections upon which measurements by different methods can then be made. A common example of the latter procedures involves the selection of a section from which the maximum birefringence ($n_e - n_o$) can be determined from interference colours in parallel light. It might be possible to pick out a suitable grain from the interference colours provided the crystals are of uniform thickness, but if there are variations in thickness (as for sieved grains) we may find that there are several possible grains with high order interference colours. Examination of their interference figures will resolve the problem, for the crystal that is required with its optic axis normal to the microscope axis must show a centred flash figure. Indeed the uniaxial flash figure is rarely used for any other purpose than orientation, but sections normal or nearly normal to the optic axis give interference figures which in themselves can tell us something about the properties of a material.

Suppose first that the section we are examining conoscopically gives the symmetrical optic axis figure; such a section is easily recognised, for it is isotropic for parallel light travelling along the axis of the microscope, and would be extinguished in all settings between crossed polars. For the optical system of a particular microscope, we can estimate the retardation at the edge of the field from the number of orders of the interference scale in white light; for low retardations, the colour will be in the first order and little of the ring system is visible and so on. Thus if sections are prepared to a standard thickness, the birefringences of different materials can be compared. Quantitative measurements of birefringence can be made if the optical constants of the microscope are known; however other methods are usually more accurate, and observations on interference figures are confined to rough comparative work. Careful examination of an interference figure can also tell us whether the crystal shows appreciable dispersion of the birefringence (see Chapter 11), but the simplest and most valuable determination is that of the optic sign of the uniaxial substance.

To find the optic sign, the effect of a compensator on the appearance of the figure is observed. In deciding what changes this will produce, we recall that the projections of the ordinary and extraordinary vibration directions are always respectively radial and tangential to the circular fringe passing through a point on the figure. When the compensator is inserted, it will cause an increase or a decrease in the total retardation at a particular point in the field depending on how its vibration directions are aligned with respect to those for the light arriving at the point. In two of the four quadrants of the image, the effective retardation will be increased, and in the other two it will be decreased. Suppose that we have a length-slow compensator and an optically positive crystal (Fig. 10.6*a*). In quadrants 1 and 3 the vibration directions for all points are such that slow vibrations in the section are more nearly parallel to the slow vibration direction of the compensator, and so the effective retardation is increased; conversely in the opposite quadrants 2 and 4 slow and

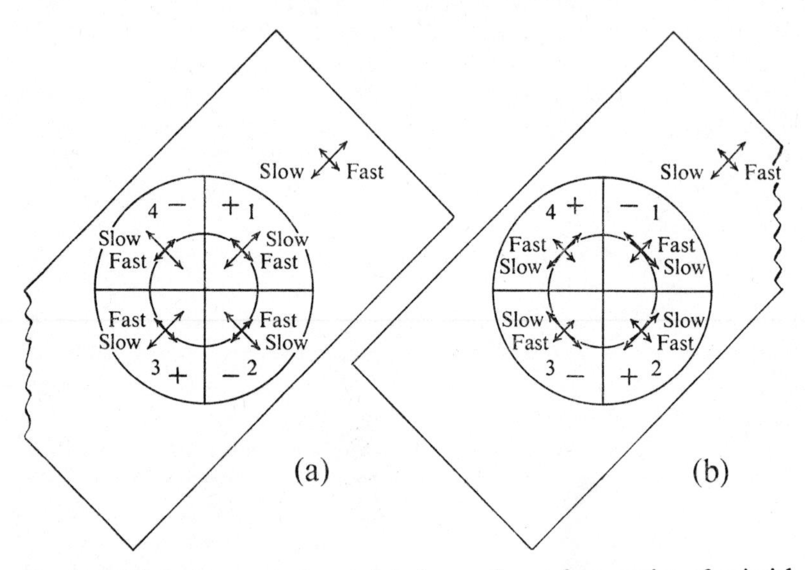

Fig. 10.6 Effect of compensator on interference figures from section of uniaxial crystal normal to optic axis.
a. Optically positive crystal ($n_e > n_o$).
b. Optically negative crystal ($n_o > n_e$).
The plus and minus signs show the quadrants where addition and subtraction of retardations take place.

fast vibrations in crystal and compensator are more nearly parallel, and so the effective retardation is reduced. With an optically negative crystal (Fig. 10.6*b*) the effects would be reversed, and quadrants 1 and 3 would show decrease in the effective retardation, while the total retardation in quadrants 2 and 4 would have increased by the insertion of the compensator.

Considering the effects of the three common compensating devices, the insertion of both the quarter wave and sensitive tint plates gives a discontinuous change which is uniform over the whole field. For positive crystals and a length-slow quarter wave plate inserted as in Fig. 10.7*a*, the black isogyres are replaced by a grey cross and the circular fringes are slightly displaced radially inwards for quadrants 1 and 3 and outwards for quadrants 2 and 4. Simultaneously two dark spots appear in the diagonals of quadrants 2 and 4 close to the centre of the image. These spots mark the positions at which complete compensation occurs, and make it easy to see the quadrants in which the effective total retardation is decreased; they will, of course, appear in quadrants 1 and 3 for

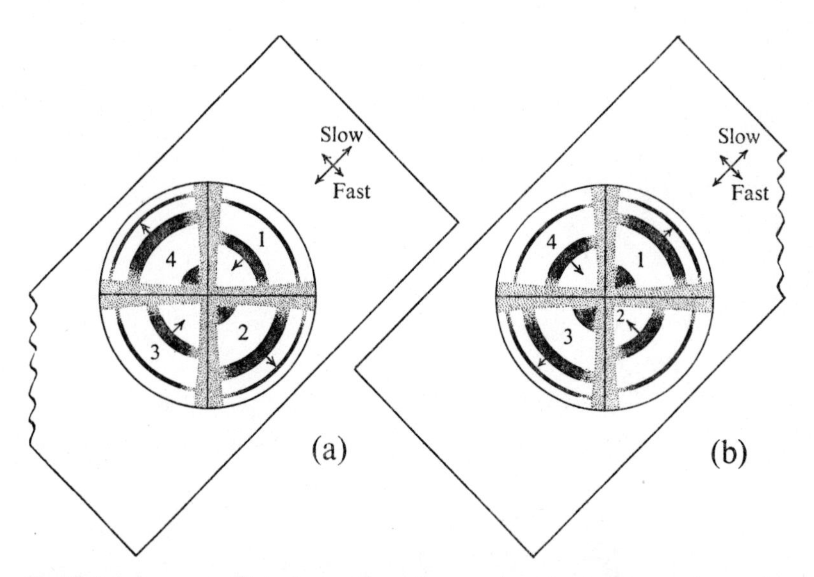

Fig. 10.7 Appearance of interference figure from section of uniaxial crystal normal to optic axis with quarter wave plate superposed; crossed polars, white light, the fringes shown are for the sensitive violet colours at the end of each order.
a. Optically positive crystal.
b. Optically negative crystal.
Note particularly the black dots corresponding to complete compensation in opposite quadrants near the centre of the figure.

negative crystals (Fig. 10.7*b*). The displacement of the rings is simply understood. Fixing our attention on one particular fringe of the original figure, e.g. the first order sensitive violet tint, this is observed at a certain radius because the optical path and birefringence for this direction of travel produce the necessary retardation. In quadrants where the total retardation has been increased by the insertion of the compensator, a second order colour will be seen at this point on the figure; thus the first order sensitive violet fringe must now be closer to the centre of the field of view. Conversely, in the two other quadrants, the first order violet fringe will have moved radially outwards from the centre as the total retardation is decreased by the compensator. Consequently the ring systems in adjacent quadrants are displaced relative to each other by twice the retardation of the compensator. The rings remain circular and gradually fade into the central grey cross. The sensitive tint plate is used

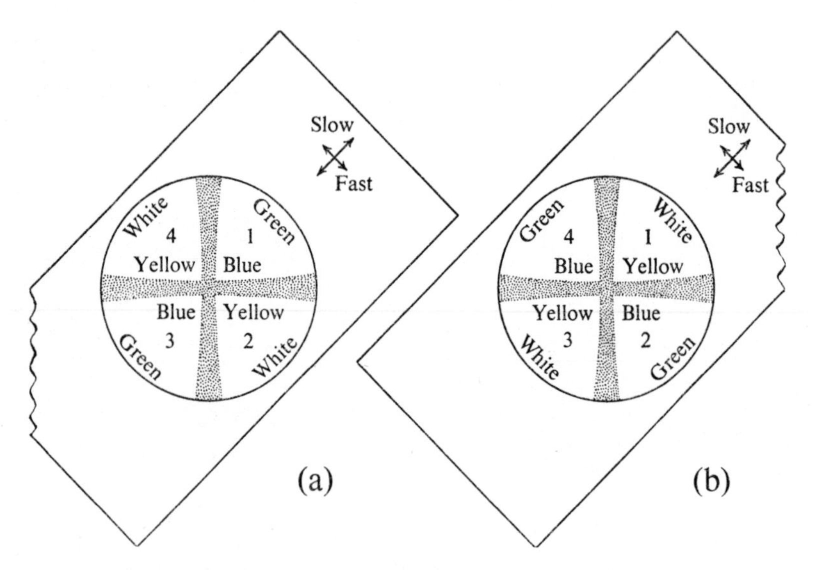

Fig. 10.8 Appearance of interference figure from section of uniaxial crystal normal to optic axis with sensitive tint plate superposed; crossed polars, white light. The section is of very low birefringence and the figure shows only low first order colours within the field before insertion of the compensator.
a. Optically positive crystal.
b. Optically negative crystal.

in the same way to produce comparable effects. With the plate inserted the isogyres will appear violet; from the scale of interference colours, we know that a small increase in retardation from that producing sensitive violet gives a second order blue, while a small decrease gives a first order yellow. The quadrants in which the retardation is rising when the tint plate is inserted may be found by looking at the image close to the centre of the isogyres where blue areas will be seen; in the opposite quadrants the retardation is falling and the same regions will be coloured yellow. The effects for both positive and negative crystals with a length-slow plate are shown in Fig. 10.8. When a quartz wedge is used as a compensator the effects are analogous to those described for the two plates, except that the wedge gives a non-uniform field; the rings move continuously as the increasing thickness of the compensator is pushed into the field. This radial displacement of the ring system is such that the movement will be towards the centre in those quadrants for which

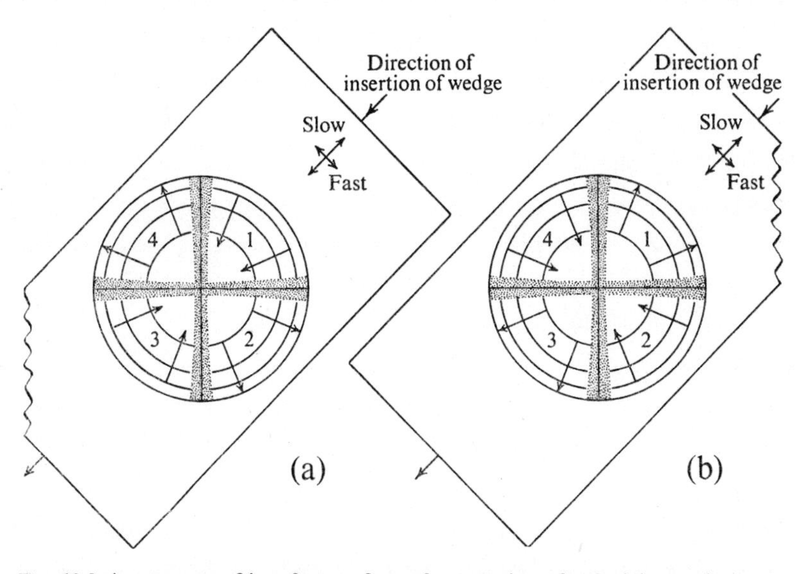

Fig. 10.9 Appearance of interference figure from section of uniaxial crystal norma to optic axis with quartz wedge superposed; crossed polars, white light. The fringes shown are for sensitive violet colours at the end of each order; the arrows denote the direction of movement of the fringes as the wedge is inserted.
a. Optically positive crystal.
b. Optically negative crystal.

the retardation is increased, and outwards from the centre in the quadrants for which the retardation is falling (Fig. 10.9).

The choice of simple compensator in making these tests is often one of preference, though the sensitive tint plate has obvious advantages if little or no part of the coloured fringe system is visible due to low birefringence of the crystal or a very thin section.

It will often happen that our section is not exactly normal to the optic axis. This can arise because in the examination of a collection of randomly orientated sections in parallel light between crossed polars we cannot find one which remains in extinction for all positions of the stage. If we then choose a section which shows a low order interference colour under these conditions, its orientation must be such that its normal is not too far displaced from the optic axis direction; such a section will give a slightly displaced optic axis figure. Even if the optic axis direction is not within the field of view, we shall be able to locate its position by following the movements of the isogyres as the stage is rotated. Once this is done, a quadrant is chosen whose orientation relative to the complete image is known and the test carried out with the compensator as before. The quartz wedge is particularly valuable when looking at inclined sections where we have only the movement of the coloured fringes as indications of changes in retardation. Interference effects from flash figures can be used for determination of the optic sign provided we can be certain of the quadrants in which the optic axis direction lies. If the section shows any recognisable crystallographic direction, it is usually simpler to use the compensating device and the interference colour in parallel light to determine the sign.

10.4 Interference effects for biaxial crystals

We should expect the appearance of interference figures from biaxial crystals to be a little more complex and varied than those from uniaxial substances. Nevertheless they must retain the two basic features in the colour fringes of equal retardation and the isogyres marking the loci of vibration directions parallel to those of the polars; the difficulty arises in visualising the form of the fringes and isogyres for the more general optical properties of biaxial crystals. The form of equal retardation fringes can be calculated and the shape of isogyres deduced from skiodromes (see Johannsen's *Manual of Petrographic Methods*), but without such a formal approach, we can deduce the appearance of the figure for some particular sections. We recall that biaxial optical properties were described in terms of the indicatrix, a triaxial ellipsoid in which the optic axes are symmetrically disposed in the α–γ section at a variable angle; depending on the sign of the crystal either γ or α is the bisector of the acute angle between the optic axes. Let us consider the interference figure for a section normal to the acute bisectrix.

Suppose that the crystal section is set so that the α–γ plane is parallel to one of the crosswires, i.e. in an extinction position in parallel light. When the interference figure is observed, provided that the optic axial angle is not too large, light travelling through the crystal parallel to either of the optic axes will be brought to a focus within the field of view. As before, with crossed polars, such points (known as the *eyes* or *melatopes*) will appear as dark spots symmetrically placed on the interference figure. Their separation in the field of view is a measure of the optic axial angle for a given optical system. By analogy with the uniaxial figure, we shall expect colour fringes marking paths of equal retardation to surround each optic axis, for as the light waves become more inclined to an optic axis the birefringence will increase. However, the fringes will not be exactly circular as the retardation will not vary uniformly around the inclined optic axis. Close to the 'eye', they are nearly circular, becoming approximately oval in shape, until further increase in retardation allows the formation of a single fringe, roughly in the form of a figure of eight, enclosing both optic axes; towards the margin of the field the fringes become almost elliptical (Fig. 10.10). The colour sequence in white light on moving outwards from an 'eye' will normally be that of Newton's colour scale. In addition to this fringe system, we shall expect isogyres to be superposed where the vibration directions for the light giving rise to a point on the directions image are parallel to those of the crossed polars. The prediction of vibration directions at any point on the figure is not so simple as in uniaxial cases. In addition to the use of skiodromes, it is also possible to deduce vibration directions from a form of the Biot-Fresnel construction given in Appendix A; in this a point on the figure due to a particular wave normal direction is joined to the melatopes, when the vibration directions are the internal and external bisectors of the angle so formed. In the present case, with the optic axial plane parallel to one of the microscope crosswires, it is clear that only points on the image on radii parallel and perpendicular to this plane can have vibration directions parallel to the polars. The isogyres form a central cross superposed on the colour fringes; the two brushes are differentiated in that the one containing the optic axes becomes narrower around the position of the melatopes (Fig. 10.10*a*). If the stage is now rotated so that the optic axial plane is no longer parallel to the crosswires, the melatopes and the colour fringes rotate unchanged, but the isogyres break into two hyperbolic brushes centred on the 'eyes', revolving in the opposite sense to the stage. The appearance of the figure in the symmetrical 45° position is shown in Fig. 10.10*b*; this is the orientation most usually employed in the examination of the interference effects.

Centred acute bisectrix figures such as we have just described are convenient in practice, but sections from which they can be obtained are often difficult to find; the orientation of the biaxial indicatrix need not bear any special relationship to the crystallographic axes or other reference directions (such as cleavages). Moreover, we cannot identify a suitable section by examination in parallel light with crossed polars, for it will show an interference colour, determined by the thickness and the birefringence, $(n_\gamma - n_\beta)$ or $(n_\beta - n_\alpha)$, which is not diagnostic.

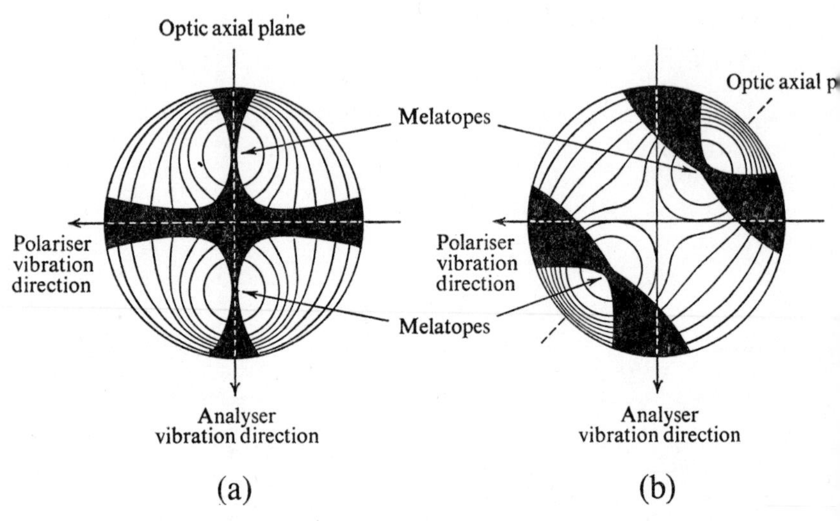

Fig. 10.10 The interference figure from a section of a biaxial crystal perpendicular to the acute bisectrix; moderate optic axial angle ($2V \sim 30°$), crossed polars, white light. The fringes are shown for the sensitive violet colours at the end of each order, though at the periphery of the field only high order whites will be seen.
a. Optic axial plane parallel to analyser vibration direction.
b. Optic axial plane at 45° to vibration directions of polars.

Unless a specially orientated section is cut, or there is some other means of recognising one normal to the acute bisectrix, we shall often have to be content with the interference figures from more general sections.

As for uniaxial crystals, we can get some idea of the figures for inclined sections by imagining what would happen if an acute bisectrix section is tilted about axes in its own plane, in particular the other two axes of the indicatrix. Consider first the effect of tilting about the third mean line normal to the optic axial plane, with the figure observed in the 45° position. As the acute bisectrix is inclined to the axis of the microscope we shall get an off-centred view of the acute bisectrix figure, still symmetrical about the trace of the optic axial plane; eventually the angle of rotation will be sufficient to bring one of the melatopes to the centre of the field of view, and we shall have the interference figure for a section perpendicular to an optic axis (Fig. 10.11*a*).

In this optic axis figure there is a single dark brush passing through the centre of the image. Often the other isogyre is not visible for its

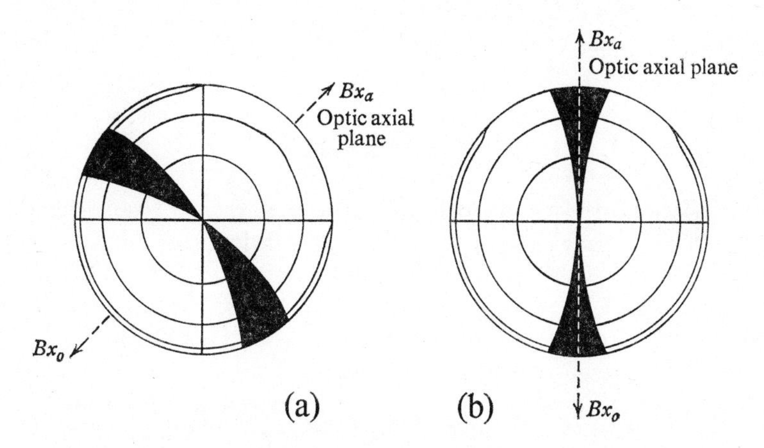

Fig. 10.11 The interference figure from a section of a biaxial crystal perpendicular to an optic axis; moderately large optic axial angle ($2V \sim 60°$), crossed polars, white light. The fringes are shown for the sensitive violet colours at the end of each order.
a. With optic axial plane at 45° to vibration directions of polars; note curvature of brush (a measure of $2V$) and convexity towards Bx_a.
b. With optic axial plane parallel to vibration direction of analyser.

inclination will not allow it to be focused within the usual directions image; though if the optic axial angle is small (less than about 30°) a second brush will be seen towards the edge of the field of view. The colour fringes are now nearly concentric circles about the eye of the figure. The curvature of the central brush is a measure of the size of the optic axial angle; its convex side is directed towards the acute bisectrix. When this optic normal section is rotated from the 45° position, the brush becomes straight while the colour fringes are unchanged (Fig. 10.11*b*). The optic axis figure is quite useful for most determinative work, and it is often far easier to find a suitable section than for a centred bisectrix figure. Between crossed polars in parallel light such a section would be isotropic and in extinction at all positions of the stage, though if we find one with a low order interference colour, its normal will not be far from the ideal optic axis direction.

Continuing now with further rotation of an acute bisectrix section about the third mean line direction, we shall at first see off-centred views of the optic axis figure in the 45° position. Eventually the remaining optic axis disappears from view, and the limiting position is approached in which the obtuse bisectrix is parallel to the axis of the microscope. It is to be expected that the obtuse bisectrix figure has similar characteristics to the symmetrical acute bisectrix figure. The colour fringes are similar in shape, though not so densely packed, but the points of emergence of the optic axes are well outside the field of view, so that no isogyres are visible in the 45° position. As with the acute bisectrix figure, if the stage is rotated so that the optic axial plane is parallel to the crosswires, a black cross is seen superposed on the colour fringes. But rotation of the stage towards the 45° position causes this diffuse cross to break into two hyperbolic brushes which vanish from the field of view after only a small rotation. The amount of angular rotation which causes the disappearance of the brushes from the field obviously depends on the size of the optic angle. For an obtuse bisectrix section, as $2V$ tends towards 90° so the angle of rotation necessary to remove the isogyres from the field will increase and the figure becomes increasingly difficult to distinguish from that of an acute bisectrix section; as $2V$ decreases towards zero, we are approaching uniaxial optical characteristics, and the appearance of the figure and its behaviour on rotation of the stage become similar to those of a flash figure. Indeed in practice it becomes increasingly difficult to decide whether a section is showing a flash or an obtuse bisectrix figure, particularly if the colour fringe system is not very visible, as is often the case.

We can now investigate briefly the rotation of an acute bisectrix section about the other axis of the indicatrix, the obtuse bisectrix direction. At first, off-centred views of the acute bisectrix figure in the 45° position are seen, the figures remaining symmetrical about a plane normal to the rotation axis. As the angle of tilt is increased so that the optic axial plane is too inclined to be visible, the figures which are presented show only a distorted but symmetric colour fringe system. In the limit the optic axial plane will be horizontal, and the third mean line (the vibration direction β) will be parallel to the axis of the microscope. The interference figure is now another flash figure similar to that described for uniaxial crystals. As the stage is turned, the poorly defined hyperbolic coloured fringes rotate, diffuse isogyres in the form of a cross momentarily darkening the field as the bisectrices become parallel to the vibration direction of the polars; this cross breaks into two hyperbolic brushes which vanish from the field in the quadrants containing the acute bisectrix after a slight rotation of the stage. The movements of the isogyres and the hyperbolic fringes are often difficult to see clearly, and all that is visible is a general darkening of the field at certain positions of the stage. Sections which give a biaxial flash figure can often be recognised in parallel light. Light travelling along the normal to the optic axial plane has the maximum birefringence ($n_\gamma - n_\alpha$) for the material, so that in parallel light with crossed polars a section of standard thickness shows the highest order interference colour possible for the substance.

We mentioned above the difficulty of distinguishing flash figures from obtuse bisectrix figures. Provided that the optic axial angle is not too small ($>$ about 10–15°), we can attempt to resolve this by measuring the rotation of the stage which causes the complete disappearance of the isogyres from the field. For a flash figure, this is less than 5° for the normal microscopic system; for an obtuse bisectrix figure, the angle will vary up to about 15° depending on the size of $2V$, but within the limitation above, it will usually be greater than 5°.

From this short account of biaxial interference figures, it will be realised that it is difficult to attempt a systematic account of the figures for more general sections; indeed it is not really necessary to describe asymmetric figures, for it is generally better to select a more suitably orientated section. If we have a collection of randomly orientated sections of the specimen, a preliminary examination between crossed polars in parallel light will usually allow the selection of those sections most nearly normal to an optic axis and most nearly of highest birefringence; these will allow the determination of most of the important optical characteristics, and can lead to the location of sections normal to the bisectrices, if these are required. However, there will be occasions when such a collection of randomly orientated sections is not available and little or no selection is possible, e.g. in a crushed powder of a material with an exceptionally good cleavage, so that all the crystal fragments lie on the microscope slide with the same direction parallel to the microscope axis. The restricted range of interference figures may now be difficult to recognise, though an experienced observer may be able to relate them to more symmetrical and useful images, especially if the optical properties of the specimen are partially known. Nevertheless there are times when no useful information comes from conoscopic study unless it is possible to change the orientation of the specimen; the subsidiary stages, used in thin section and powder work, which can be attached to the microscope stage for this purpose are described in Chapter 12.

10.5 Practical use of biaxial interference figures

As with uniaxial crystals, the use of biaxial interference figures is two-fold; they can be valuable in identifying and confirming the orientation of sections on which measurements are to be made by other techniques, and they inherently contain data on the optical properties of the specimen not obtainable from orthoscopic examination. We will restrict the discussion here to the latter, and allow the examples of optical problems in Chapter 12 to demonstrate the use of interference figures in the orientation of sections of biaxial crystals.

With an interference figure in the 45° position, the retardation of the section determines the interference colour seen at the centre of the field of view; if an optic axis is visible, the order of this colour can be determined by inspection, and is a comparative measure of the birefringence of sections of standard thickness. With a standard section which shows a centred bisectrix figure the number of orders of coloured fringes within the field is also a measure of the birefringence. But, as we should expect, accurate measurements of birefringence are made using compensators in parallel light, and interference figures give only a rough, comparative guide. Biaxial figures are, however, used for the determination of optic sign and for a reasonable assessment of the optic axial angle.

The optic sign can be determined by observing the changes in the figure when a compensator is inserted into the optical system, rather as was done with uniaxial crystals (see 10.3). Let us illustrate this by considering the effect of a length-slow quartz wedge upon the interference figure from an acute bisectrix section of an optically positive crystal set in the 45° position. If we restrict discussion to light waves whose normals lie in the optic axial plane, the vibration directions at each point on the figure are parallel and perpendicular to the diameter joining the melatopes (Fig. 10.12*a*). It must now be decided which of these vibration directions is fast and which is slow. Clearly the refractive index associated with light vibrating perpendicular to the optic axial plane is n_β, but that for the perpendicular component vibrating within the optic axial plane is variable. We can use the γ—α section of the

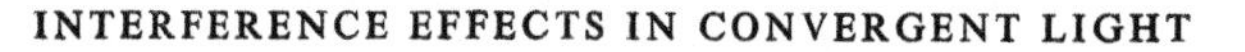

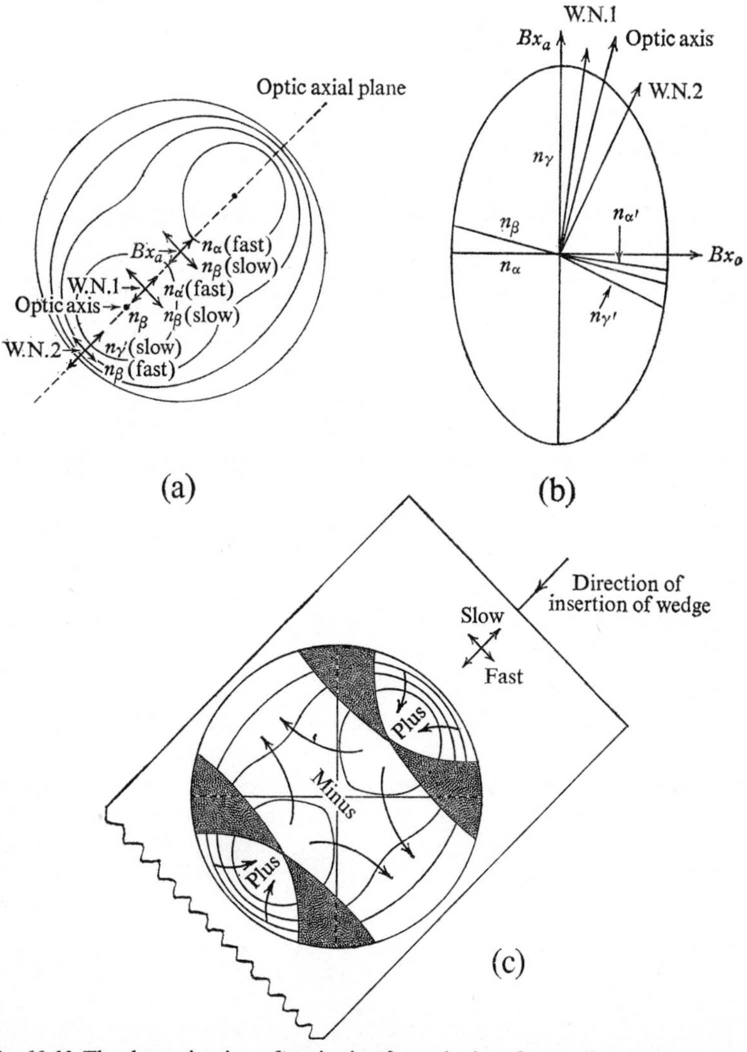

Fig. 10.12 The determination of optic sign from the interference figure of an acute bisectrix section of a biaxial material with positive optic sign; crossed polars, white light, 45° position. The fringes are shown for sensitive violet colours at the end of each order.
a. The fringe system and vibration directions within the optic axial plane.
b. The γ–α section of a positive biaxial indicatrix, showing the refractive indices for two general wave normal directions vibrating in the plane.
c. The appearance of the section with superposed wedge, the plus and minus indicate addition and subtraction of retardations and the arrows show direction of movement of fringes.

indicatrix to investigate this variation for the optically positive crystal with $Bx_a = \gamma$ (Fig. 10.12*b*). At the centre of the interference figure light travels along the acute bisectrix direction; the central section of the indicatrix perpendicular to this direction has semi-axes n_β and n_α. Obviously for light giving rise to this central point in the figure, the vibration direction parallel to the optic axial plane is fast (Fig. 10.12*a*). Moving along the optic axial plane from the centre of the field, points on the directions image are due to light inclined to the acute bisectrix. Initially the indicatrix sections have semi-axes of length $n_{\alpha'}$ and n_β, so that the fast and slow vibration directions are orientated as in the centre of the figure. With greater inclination further out in the image we come to the melatope, which corresponds to a circular section of the indicatrix of radius n_β. Beyond this point in the field, sections of the indicatrix show a semi-major axis ($n_{\gamma'}$) in the optic axial plane greater than the semi-minor axis (n_β) perpendicular to it. Thus beyond the optic axis position on the interference figure the relative speeds of the two vibrations are reversed; it is the vibration direction perpendicular to the optic axial plane which is now fast. When the length-slow wedge is inserted parallel to the optic axial plane, there is a decrease in the total retardation along the diameter between the centre of the field and a melatope, while beyond the eye to the edge of the field there is an increase in the total retardation. Similar changes in total retardation are produced by the compensator at points on the image displaced from the optic axial plane, so that for the field between the isogyres it is reduced, with increased retardation for the two other portions of the figure. Insertion of the wedge therefore causes the colour fringes to appear to move; in those parts of the field between the edge and the hyperbolic brushes they will appear to move inwards towards the eye, while in the rest of the field they will move outwards from the eye (Fig. 10.12*c*). The movement of the fringe system will be reversed for an optically negative crystal, as it would also have been if the wedge had been inserted perpendicular to the optic axial plane for a positive crystal.

Having established by this example how we can decide whether a compensating plate adds to or subtracts from the optical path difference at a point on the figure, there is no need to discuss the use of other simple compensators in detail; the visible effects of their insertion are analogous to those described for uniaxial crystals. As before the choice of compensator is generally dictated by the properties of the substance; the sensitive tint plate may be preferable if the colour fringes are barely visible within the field, and so on.

From other sections the optic sign can be determined by similar methods provided that the directions of the optic axial plane and the bisectrices can be established. The appearance of isogyres is most useful in this connection. If an isogyre can be observed in its straight position, the stage is then rotated through 45°; the brush will then be hyperbolic and its convexity indicates the acute bisectrix position (as is shown in Fig. 10.11 for an optic axis section, though, in general the brush will not be centred). If the isogyre vanishes from the field during rotation it is usually best to seek another more suitable section, though we can use a compensator plate with an obtuse bisectrix figure; it must then be remembered that similar observed changes are all in the opposite sense to those for an acute bisectrix section of the same material. The indistinct character of flash figures usually makes it preferable to seek a more suitably orientated section, though sign determination is possible under favourable conditions.

We can also use interference figures to obtain some estimate of the size of optic axial angles. When both the melatopes are visible, the size of the optic axial angle can be directly estimated. Clearly the most suitable sections are normal or almost normal to Bx_a, when both eyes are more likely to be within the field; their separation in the 45° position reflects the value of $2V$. For the optical system of most common microscopes, the total angular width of the field corresponds to about 60°, measured within the crystal, and the values of $2V$ up to this limit may be roughly estimated accordingly.

Strictly it should be recognised that the observed positions of the melatopes are only a measure of the *apparent optic axial angle* ($2E$), for waves travelling along optic axis directions in the crystal will be refracted on emerging from the section. Under normal conditions with a Bx_a section and a dry objective, the relationship between the true and apparent optic axial angles is given by $\sin E = n_\beta \sin V$, for light travelling along an optic axis direction has n_β as the appropriate value of the refractive index. We may equate E with the limit of the cone of light which can just be focused by an objective of a given numerical aperture, and work out the values of $2V$ for which the melatopes are at the extremities of the field of view. With an objective of $N.A. = 0{\cdot}82$, and the median value of $n_\beta = 1{\cdot}6$, the limit of $2V = 60°$; however, with more extreme values of n_β, the same optical system shows the melatopes just visible when $2V = 54°$ ($n_\beta = 1{\cdot}8$) and $2V = 72°$ ($n_\beta = 1{\cdot}4$). These variations are not too significant in terms of the accuracy of the rough estimation, but the method can be made quantitative. A particular optical system can be calibrated for a graduated ocular using standard materials; other measurements can then be made using the relation $\sin V = D/Mn\beta$, where D is the apparent distance between the melatopes on the eyepiece scale, and M is the Mallard constant for the optical system obtained during calibration.

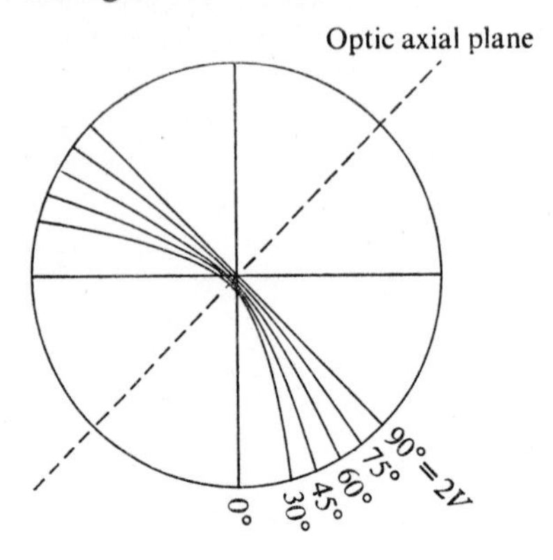

Fig. 10.13 Variation of curvature of brush with optic axial (2V) in interference figure of section of biaxial material normal to an optic axis direction in the 45° position. The curves are schematic only, and represent the centres of the brushes at each position; more details may be found in Wright's *Methods of Petrographic Microscopic Research*; when $2V<30°$, both isogyres appear in the field of view with a normal optical arrangement, and the angle can be estimated from their separation.

If only one eye is visible, as, for example, in an optic normal figure, we can roughly estimate the value of $2V$ from the curvature of the brush in the 45° position (Fig. 10.13). This diagram demonstrates that for large optic axial angles (85–90°), it becomes difficult to be certain of the convexity of the brush, and so locate the direction of the acute bisectrix. More accurate values of the optic axial angle can be made if the section or the crystal is mounted on some kind of tilting apparatus on the stage of the microscope which permits rotation of the specimen about an axis perpendicular to that of the microscope; we will defer consideration of such subsidiary stages until Chapter 12.

10.6 Exercises

1. Interference effects from orientated thick sections of uniaxial specimens:

Arrange the illumination of the microscope for conoscopic use, inserting the condenser and the high power objective.

(i) With a section of calcite ($n_o - n_e = 0{\cdot}172$) cut perpendicular to the optic axis, observe the interference figure between crossed polars both with the Bertrand lens inserted and by direct observation with the ocular removed. Observe the effect on the figure of (*a*) rotating the stage, (*b*) moving the section on the stage and (*c*) raising the body tube. Note the sequence of colours in the circular fringe system, and investigate the effect of rotating the polariser from its crossed position. Use other similar sections of calcite to observe the effect of thickness on the figure.

Confirm the optic sign of this material by using each of the testing instruments in turn; which is the most suitable?

(ii) Repeat (i) using a section of tourmaline (a complex alumino-silicate with $n_o - n_e \sim 0{\cdot}02$) cut perpendicular to the optic axis.

(iii) Repeat (i) using a section of quartz (a form of SiO_2 with $n_e - n_o = 0{\cdot}009$) cut perpendicular to the optic axis.

(iv) Repeat (i) using a section of beryl (a beryllium alumino-silicate with $n_o - n_e \sim 0{\cdot}007$) cut perpendicular to the optic axis.

(v) Repeat (i) using a section of apatite (a calcium fluor-phosphate with $n_o - n_e \sim 0{\cdot}004$) cut perpendicular to the optic axis.

(vi) Using the same section of calcite as in (i) observe the interference figure obtained by using a low power objective and removing the ocular. How does this figure differ from that seen in (i) with the high power objective? Observe the effect of tilting the section by lifting one edge from the stage.

(vii) Examine the section of calcite cut parallel to the optic axis in parallel white light to determine the fast and slow vibration directions, and hence the optic axis direction. Now observe the interference figure from this section and see that it has the characteristics of a flash figure. Determine the movement of the brushes with respect to the optic axis direction as the stage is rotated.

2. Interference effects from orientated thick sections of biaxial specimens:

With the microscope arranged for the observations of interference figures, examine the thick sections of three orthorhombic materials cut parallel to (100), (010) and (001) in each case.

(i) For aragonite (a form of $CaCO_3$) determine which sections show centred Bx_a, Bx_o and flash figures to confirm the optic orientation, given as $x = \beta$ $y = \gamma$, $z = \alpha$, by using suitable figures to determine the optic sign; use each of the testing instruments in turn, and decide which is the most suitable. For aragonite $n_\alpha = 1{\cdot}530$, $n_\beta = 1{\cdot}682$ and $n_\gamma = 1{\cdot}686$, with $2V_\alpha = 18°$. For the Bx_a section, note the apparent separation of the eyes, and number of orders of the interference colour scale between an eye and the centre of the field, as a reflection of these optical properties for this thickness of specimen.

(ii) Repeat (i) with the sections of barytes ($BaSO_4$) for which $x = \gamma$, $y = \beta$, $z = \alpha$, and $n_\alpha = 1{\cdot}636$, $n_\beta = 1{\cdot}637$, $n_\gamma = 1{\cdot}648$ with $2V_\gamma = 37°$.

(iii) Repeat (i) with sections of topaz ($Al_2(F, OH)_2\ SiO_4$) for which $x = \alpha$, $y = \beta$, $z = \gamma$, and $n_\alpha = 1{\cdot}607$–$1{\cdot}629$, $n_\beta = 1{\cdot}610$–$1{\cdot}631$, $n_\gamma = 1{\cdot}617$–$1{\cdot}631$, with $2V_\gamma = 48°$–$65°$.

3. Use of a biaxial interference figure from an oriented thick section to determine the orientation of the indicatrix:

A thick (001) section of a diopside (a member of the complex silicate pyroxene group) is provided; pyroxenes have good {110} cleavages, and (110):$(1\bar{1}0) \sim 93°$, with the obtuse angle between the x- and z-axes$\sim 106°$.

(i) Locate the fast and slow vibration directions. Use the crystallographic data above to determine which of these is parallel to the x- and y-axes.

(ii) Examine the slightly offset optic axis interference figure, and decide whether the optic axis plane is parallel or perpendicular to (010). Determine the optic sign, and the approximate value of the optic axial angle. From this information, estimate the orientation of the indicatrix with respect to the crystallographic axes.

4. Interference effects from fragments of a crystal powder:

Examine the cleavage fragments of a powder of barytes ($BaSO_4$). Notice that for some fragments the cleavage traces are perpendicular whilst for others they are inclined at about 80°.

(i) Determine which of the two types of fragment shows a centred interference figure. Try to decide what kind of interference figure this is.

5. Use of optical and crystallographic data to predict the appearance of an interference figure:

A crystal of the monoclinic material sphene ($CaTiSiO_5$) has the crystallographic constants $a:b:c=0{\cdot}755:1:0{\cdot}854$ $\beta\sim120°$, and is described optically as $y=\beta$, $z:\gamma=51°$ in the obtuse angle between the x- and z-axes, $n_\alpha=1{\cdot}910$, $n_\beta=1{\cdot}917$, $n_\gamma=2{\cdot}021$, with $2V_\gamma\sim25°$.

(i) Use this data to draw a sketch of the appearance of the interference figure formed in white light under normal microscopic conditions from a section 1000μ thick cut parallel to (102). Pay particular attention to the location of any melatopes, and the order of the interference colour visible in the centre of the figure.

CHAPTER 11

DISPERSION OF THE INDICATRIX

11.1 The general nature of wavelength dispersion

THE variation of optical properties expressed by changes in the size, shape and orientation of the indicatrix for a particular substance is known as dispersion. Although these changes can occur with temperature, the term *dispersion* is usually understood to mean the dependence of the indicatrix on the frequency (or wavelength) of light. We have already made several references to the effects of wavelength dispersion, and in this chapter it will be more systematically examined both from the viewpoint of its effect on the indicatrix and to clarify the implications of dispersion so far as practical observations are concerned.

The theory of dispersion is based on the assumption that the periodic electric field associated with light waves produces forced oscillations of the electrons of atoms of the transparent solid through which the electro-magnetic radiation is passing. These forced oscillations give rise to secondary electro-magnetic waves which interact with the primary waves to give the effects of dispersion. For transparent isotropic substances, dispersion means that the indicatrices corresponding to different colours form a group of concentric spheres. We can represent this kind of dispersion most conveniently by plotting the variation of refractive index against wavelength. For the majority of transparent materials, the refractive index values decrease as the wavelength gets longer, though the variation over the visible spectrum may not be large; a typical dispersion curve is shown in Fig. 11.1*a*. This relationship is known as *normal dispersion* and its form is expressed approximately by Cauchy's equation $n=A+B/\lambda^2$, where A, B are constants for a particular substance. For those materials for which there is an absorption band within the visible spectrum, the variation is quite different and is shown in Fig. 11.1*b*. The values of n cannot be determined in the absorption band, but at lower and higher wavelengths the variations follow the normal type of dispersion curve; however, the discontinuity at the absorption band ensures that the refractive indices at the long wave-length end of the spectrum are generally greater than those at the short wavelength end. This kind of relationship is known as *anomalous dispersion.*

Dispersion in isotropic substances can only have one of these forms and is usually studied by direct observations of the variation of n using monochromatic light. In anisotropic substances, in addition to the anomalous and normal dispersion just described, there are further possibilities. There is no reason why the variation of the different principal refractive indices should be the same, so that the shape as well as the size of the indicatrix can change with wavelength; moreover, in

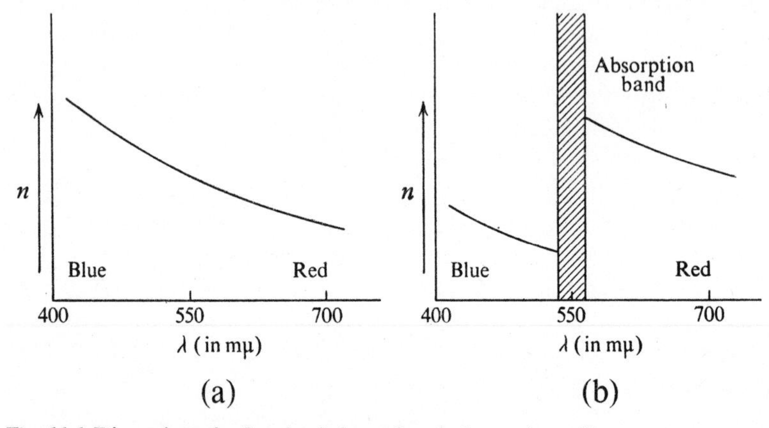

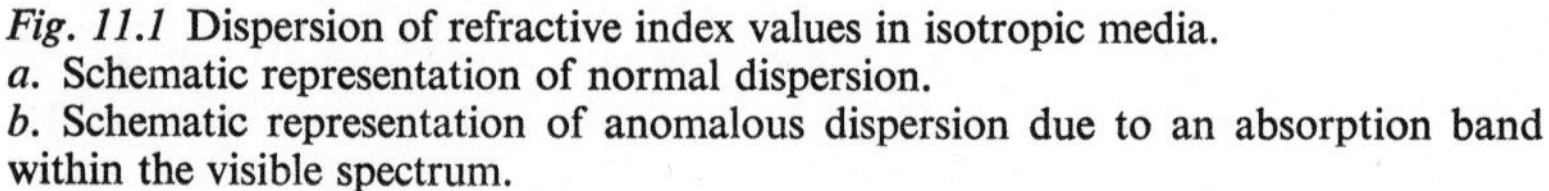

Fig. 11.1 Dispersion of refractive index values in isotropic media.
a. Schematic representation of normal dispersion.
b. Schematic representation of anomalous dispersion due to an absorption band within the visible spectrum.

lower symmetry crystals, where the symmetry control of the orientation of an indicatrix is relaxed, it is possible for its orientation, as well as its size and shape, to be dependent on the wavelength of the light. These additional possibilities allow dispersion of the indicatrix in anisotropic substances to become quite complex, and we must now carefully consider their implications for uniaxial and biaxial crystals.

11.2 Dispersion effects in uniaxial crystals

Optical properties of a uniaxial crystal are represented by an indicatrix which is an ellipsoid of revolution with axes proportional to the principal refractive indices of the crystal; the axis of revolution coincides with the main symmetry axis of the crystal. For a dispersive substance, there will be a family of these indicatrices corresponding to the different wavelengths, but for each member of the family the unique axis of revolution must be in the same direction; the optic axis directions must be the same for red and blue light (and all other wavelengths), due to the demands of crystal symmetry. However, even if we cannot have dispersion of the orientation of an indicatrix in uniaxial crystals, there still remain the two other kinds of dispersion shown in Fig. 11.2. In these, there is dispersion of the principal refractive indices, either without or with dispersion of the birefringence; in one case, the family of indicatrices has exactly similar shapes, whereas in the other both the size and the shape of the indicatrix can depend on wavelength.

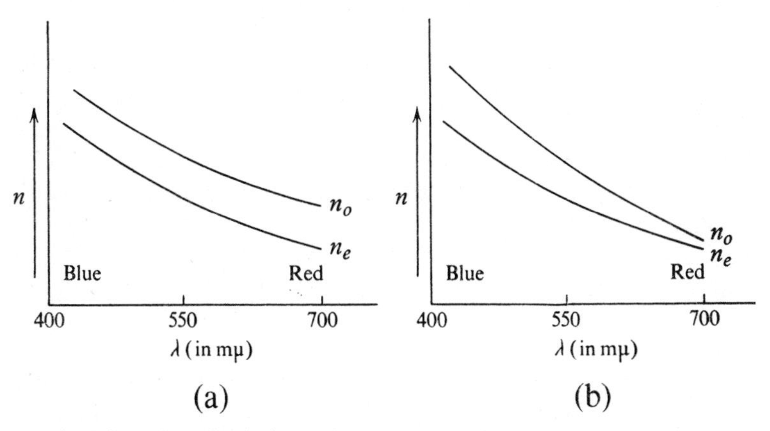

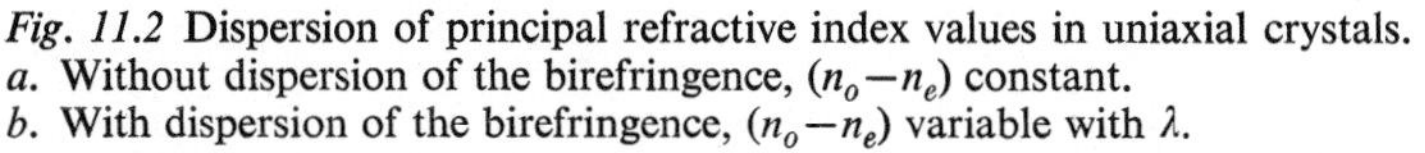

Fig. 11.2 Dispersion of principal refractive index values in uniaxial crystals.
a. Without dispersion of the birefringence, $(n_o - n_e)$ constant.
b. With dispersion of the birefringence, $(n_o - n_e)$ variable with λ.

For the majority of substances the overall dispersion is quite small, and there is no dispersion of the birefringence for all practical purposes; dispersion can only be investigated by accurate direct measurement of refractive indices at different wavelengths. For some materials, however, there is a significant dispersion of the birefringence. This can be detected not only by direct refractive index determinations but also by effects upon interference colours seen in white light. In 9.3 it was shown that the normal interference colour scale displayed by a quartz wedge was due to the complex complete and partial subtraction of various wavelengths at each point on the wedge. It was assumed that the optical path difference at each point is determined only by the thickness of the wedge, and that the birefringence is the same for all wavelengths; this condition is satisfied for quartz. If the wedge had been made of a material showing dispersion of the birefringence, the optical path difference at a particular point would depend on the wavelength; the complex complete and partial subtraction of the various wavelengths of white light would be different from those at corresponding points on the quartz wedge, and a different colour scale would be seen. We have already referred to dispersion as one of the causes of an anomalous interference colour scale; the precise sequence of colours along a dispersive wedge depends on the form of the birefringence variation. Very occasionally, the birefringence dispersion is such as to cause the curves for the principal refractive indices to cross in the visible spectrum; a crystal with these properties is isotropic for one wavelength, and of different optical sign on either side of this wavelength.

Apart from extreme examples, colour changes due to birefringence dispersion are quite slight, and anomalous interference colours are often difficult to recognise. Some caution must be exercised in ascribing to dispersion any abnormal interference colours from crystals with a strong body colour. Anomalous interference colours are best observed in the interference figure in convergent light, where the sequence of colours is displayed in the fringe system around the optic axis; since the vibration directions for light reaching any point on the figure are the same for all wavelengths, the anomalous ring system is seen together with normal black isogyres. Nevertheless despite the fact that the colour sequence as a whole is now visible, recognition of slight abnormalities resulting from moderate dispersions is difficult in practice and requires some experience.

11.3 Dispersion effects in biaxial crystals

The effect of dispersion of the indicatrix in biaxial crystals is necessarily more complex because not only have we those possibilities which exist for uniaxial crystals but also there is the additional possibility of dispersion of its orientation. In Chapter 4, we saw that the biaxial indicatrix was a triaxial ellipsoid whose principal axes have the values of the three principal refractive indices; as for uniaxial crystals the size and shape of this representation surface can vary with wavelength, but we must also consider the symmetry control over its orientation. The biaxial indicatrix has twofold symmetry about each of its principal axes, which will be expected to coincide with the direction of twofold symmetry axes where they exist in the biaxial systems. As described in 4.4, this can lead to relaxations over the control of the orientation of the indicatrix in the lower symmetry systems. In the orthorhombic system there are three mutually perpendicular symmetry axes, to which the axes of the indicatrix ellipsoid are parallel; for a dispersive material, the family of indicatrices for different wavelengths must all have their principal axes parallel to the three crystallographic axes. But in the monoclinic system, there is only one diad symmetry axis, and while one principal axis of the indicatrix will be parallel to this, the other two have the freedom to rotate into any position about this fixed direction; thus while one principal axis is parallel to the y-crystallographic axis for all wavelengths from blue to red, the other two are neither necessarily parallel to the other crystallographic axes nor are they necessarily in the same orientation for different wavelengths. For triclinic crystals even this control is relaxed, and the indicatrix is free to assume any orientation; in dispersive crystals, there can be different orientations of all three principal axes at different wavelengths. Thus in monoclinic and triclinic crystals, there can be some form of dispersion of the orientation of the indicatrix, or *dispersion of the bisectrices*, as it is often called. In these two systems, direct determination of the dispersion involves not only the measurement of the principal refractive indices as a function of wavelength, but also the variation of the bisectrices; this is usually done by locating the different extinction positions on orientated sections at different wavelengths. Effects of dispersion are often visible in interference phenomena, where they are most conveniently displayed in interference figures. We will examine the appearance of acute bisectrix figures for the three systems separately, as an illustration of how the problem may be treated.

As before, the dispersion curves of the three principal refractive indices can be of different forms, leading to changes both in size and shape of the indicatrix over the visible spectrum. Dispersion of the birefringence must give an anomalous scale of interference colours in white light, so that the sequence of coloured fringes surrounding each melatope must be abnormal. But the differences between the various dispersions of biaxial crystals are more readily visible from the appearance of the isogyres passing through the eyes of the interference figure. Dispersion of the birefringence in biaxial crystals implies that there must also be *dispersion of the optic axial angle*, for $2V$ depends on the relative magnitudes of the principal refractive indices (see 4.4). With independent dispersion curves, the size of the optic axial angle can vary; if it is greater for red light than for blue (or violet) light, this is conveniently noted $r > v$. The visible results of this kind of dispersion can be seen on the interference figures from acute bisectrix sections of orthorhombic crystals (Fig. 11.3). In addition to the anomalous fringe system, the melatopes and hyperbolic brushes are in different positions for different wavelengths due to optic axial dispersion; if $r>v$, as in the figure, the outermost isogyres will appear blue due to the removal of the red wavelengths. For moderate dispersions, the isogyres for the various colours overlap, so that, in practice, the general appearance in the 45° position shows a normal dark brush tinged blue on its concave side and red on its convex side; with the crystal in the extinction position the brushes are not coloured. We notice particularly that, in contrast with

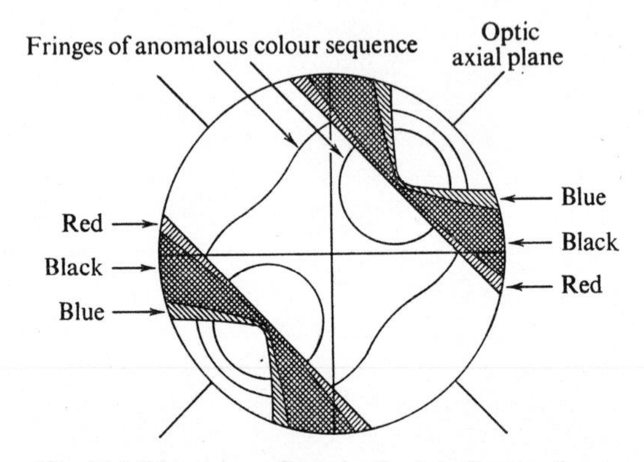

Fig. 11.3 Dispersion effects in the interference figure from a section of a biaxial crystal cut normal to the acute bisectrix; crossed polars, white light, 45° position. Dispersion of the birefringence leads to dispersion of the optic axial angle ($r>v$) and anomalous interference colours; note that the figure is symmetrical about both directions which bisect the crosswires.

dispersion effects from monoclinic and triclinic crystals, the interference figure retains a symmetrical appearance about diameters parallel and perpendicular to the optic axial plane. In most orthorhombic crystals, dispersion of the birefringence leads only to the typical figure just described but there are some biaxial materials for which this kind of dispersion produces rather more extreme effects. If n_β is not too different from either n_α or n_γ at one end of the spectrum, dispersion can cause the variation curves to cross in the range of visible wavelengths (Fig. 11.4*a*). At the blue end of the spectrum, the interference figure will show a moderate optic axial angle, but as the wavelength of the light is increased the size of this angle decreases until for a particular wavelength the crystal appears to be uniaxial; as the wavelength is increased further towards the red end of the spectrum, the melatopes again open out and interference figures resume a biaxial character (Fig. 11.4*b*), but the optic axial plane is now normal to its original orientation due to the interchange of two of the principal refractive indices (Fig. 11.4*c*). This phenomenon is called *crossed axial plane dispersion* (not to be confused with crossed dispersion to be described shortly); interference figures in

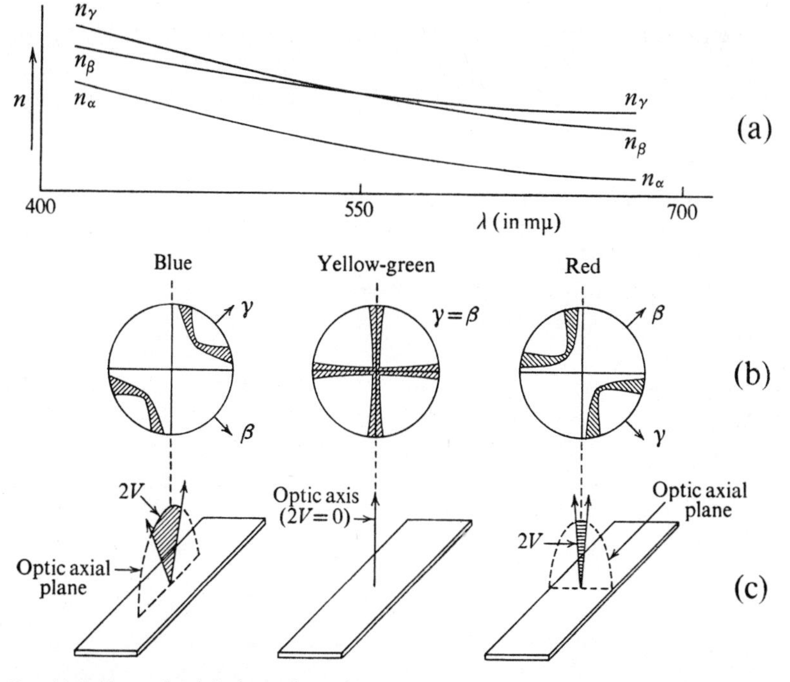

Fig. 11.4 Crossed axial plane dispersion.
a. Schematic illustration of curves showing dispersion of refractive indices; note that $n_\gamma = n_\beta$ at one point.
b. Sketches of interference figures for three different wavelengths, for $Bx_a(=\alpha)$ section; the ring systems are omitted.
c. Orientation of optic axial plane with respect to crystal section; note that crystal appears uniaxial at one wavelength.

white light are confused and difficult to interpret. The best known example of this kind of dispersion is the orthorhombic mineral brookite (a form of TiO_2) which has moderate values of $2V$ for red and blue light but with (001) and (010) as the optic axial planes for these two colours respectively; it behaves as uniaxial ($2V=0°$) for yellowish-green light. Dispersion can also cause the sign of a biaxial crystal to change; this is more likely to occur when n_β is about halfway between n_γ and n_α, so that the optic axial angle is about 90°. The independent dispersions of the principal refractive indices can then permit $2V_\gamma < 90°$ (optically positive) for some parts of the spectrum while for other wavelengths the crystal has $2V_\gamma > 90°$ (optically negative). These rather more unusual effects of dispersion of the birefringence are possible in all biaxial crystals; they are not limited to orthorhombic crystals.

We must now turn to monoclinic crystals, in which all the possible effects due to birefringence dispersion are supplemented by additional manifestations of the possible dispersion of the bisectrices. Since there is the limitation that one axis of the indicatrix must always be parallel to the diad symmetry axis, there will be only three distinct possibilities corresponding to each of the principal indicatrix axes being along this direction. If we consider first the case where the symmetry axis $y = Bx_a$, there can be dispersion of the other two bisectrices, Bx_o and the third mean line, so that with a section normal to the common acute bisectrix, the optic axial plane can be rotated about the common fixed direction (Fig. 11.5*a*). In the interference figure the melatopes and isogyres for red and blue light will appear as shown schematically in Fig. 11.5*b*, assuming some dispersion of the optic axial angle. The effects are best seen for normal dispersions, with the interference figure in the 45° position, by inspection of the isogyres; the colour scheme in white light is shown in Fig. 11.5*c*. This effect is called *crossed dispersion*, and it will be noted that the colour distribution is consistent with the common symmetry axis direction parallel to the acute bisectrix normal to the figure. In the second case with $y = Bx_o$, there can be dispersion of Bx_a and the third mean line, leading to rotation of the optic axial plane about the obtuse bisectrix (Fig. 11.6*a*). Taking a section normal to the acute bisectrix direction for a wavelength in the middle of the spectrum, the isogyres for red and blue light, in the 45° position, will be laterally displaced from the centre of the field, so that assuming some dispersion of the optic axial angle they will appear as in Fig. 11.6*b*; in the region of the isogyres the colour scheme in white light is illustrated in Fig. 11.6*c*. This type of dispersion is known as *horizontal* or *parallel dispersion*, and we notice that it has a colour distribution consistent with a symmetry line perpendicular to the common fixed direction, as expected from the geometry of the indicatrices. Finally, a monoclinic crystal can have $y = T.M.L.$, with dispersion of both the acute and obtuse bisectrices, allowing the optic axial planes for all colours to be common (Fig. 11.7*a*). Again, taking a section normal to the acute bisectrix for the middle of the spectrum, and assuming some dispersion of the optic axes, the

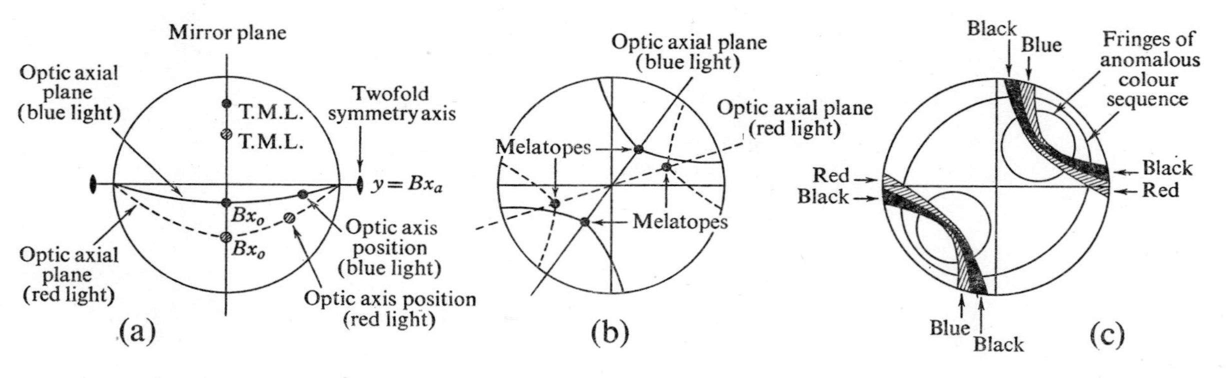

Fig. 11.5 Crossed dispersion for a monoclinic crystal with $y = Bx_a$.
a. Stereographic representation of orientations of indicatrices for red and blue light ($r > v$)
b. Diagram showing the position of optic axial planes, melatopes and isogyres for red and blue light for an interference figure in the 45° position from a section normal to the common Bx_a direction.
c. Schematic representation of the interference figure in white light; note that colours are consistent with twofold symmetry axis normal to section.

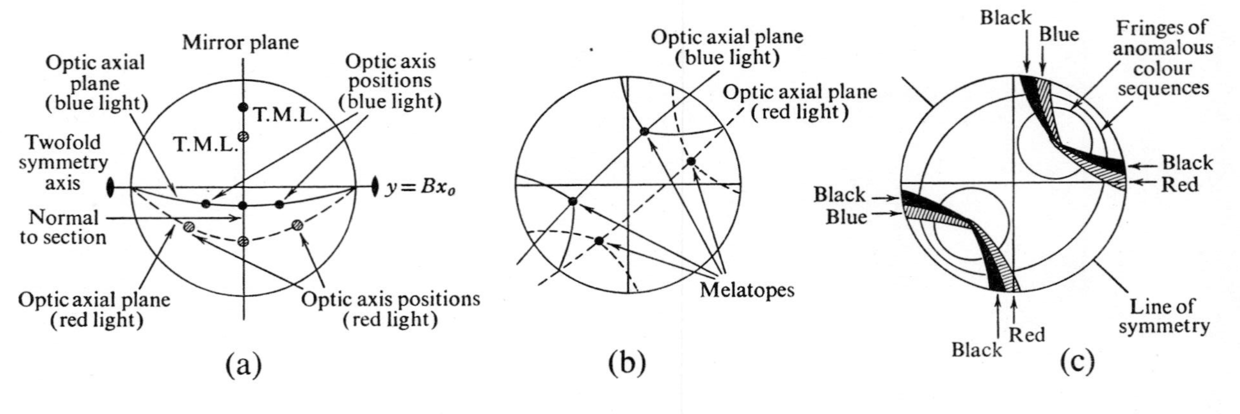

Fig. 11.6 Horizontal dispersion for a monoclinic crystal with $y=Bx_o$.
a. Stereographic representation of orientations of indicatrices for red and blue light ($r>v$).
b. Diagram showing the position of optic axial planes, melatopes and isogyres for red and blue light for an interference figure in the 45° position for a section normal to Bx_a for yellow light.
c. Schematic representation of the interference figure in white light; note that colours are consistent with line of symmetry shown.

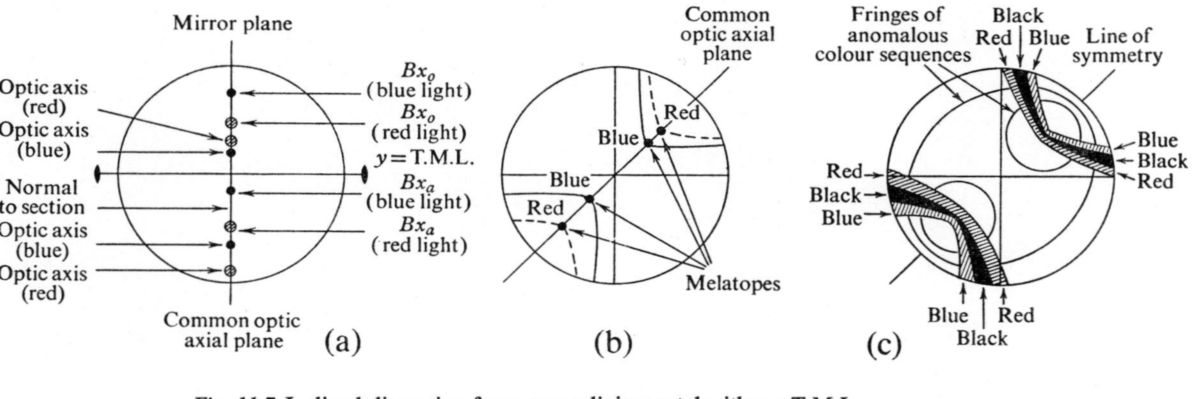

Fig. 11.7 Inclined dispersion for a monoclinic crystal with $y=T.M.L.$
a. Stereographic representation of orientations of indicatrices for red and blue light ($r>v$).
b. Diagram showing the position of the common optic axial plane, melatopes and isogyres for red and blue light for an interference figure in the 45° position for a section normal to Bx_a for yellow light.
c. Schematic representation of the interference figure in white light; note that colours are consistent with line of symmetry shown, and that sequences of colours can depend on amount of dispersion of optic axes and bisectrices.

isogyres are asymmetrically displaced, although the melatopes for red and blue light still lie on the same diameter of the figure (Fig. 11.7*b*). The colour sequences around each of the isogyres depend on the positions of the optic axes. If the situation is that shown in Fig. 11.7*b*, the colour scheme of Fig. 11.7*c* will be seen in white light. If, however, the dispersion of the optic axial angle is so great that one blue isogyre is outside the red on one side of the field, and nearer to the centre on the other side of the field, the colour sequence around one isogyre would be reversed. Such effects are typical of *inclined dispersion*; this time the colour sequence in white light is consistent with a symmetry line on the interference figure parallel to the common optic axial plane, as expected from the orientation of the indicatrices. It is also possible that under special conditions the effects of optic axial and bisectrix dispersion combine to allow the melatopes and isogyres for red and blue light to be coincident for one brush; this isogyre will appear black without any colour fringes, though, of course, the other brush will show coloured fringes due to the dispersion. Any of these three types of dispersion allow the recognition of monoclinic symmetry in a substance, for they owe their origin to the limited dispersion of orientation of the indicatrix permitted by the monoclinic crystallographic symmetry. It must be emphasised again that monoclinic crystals can also show the types of dispersion, e.g. birefringence, crossed axial plane, etc. possible in higher symmetry crystals, which can lead to similar effects (e.g. anomalous interference colours or change of optic sign) in monoclinic crystals.

Finally, in triclinic crystals, the last remaining control over the orientation of the indicatrix is relaxed, and with different wavelengths there can be completely arbitrary orientations of the indicatrix. With such irregular dispersion of the optic axes and the bisectrices, it is unlikely that an acute bisectrix figure will show any symmetry in any dispersive colour fringes visible in the region of the isogyres in white light.

11.4 Exercises

1. Dispersion of the birefringence in a uniaxial crystal:

Examine the interference figure from a basal section of apophyllite (a rare hydrated sheet silicate mineral with tetragonal symmetry). Use monochromatic light of several wavelengths by inserting filters, and white light. Note particularly the appearance of the circular fringe system. What does this indicate about the nature of birefringence dispersion for this material?

2. Dispersion effects in biaxial crystals:

Observe the interference figures as in (1) for the following sections:

(i) Dispersion of the optic axial angle: use an (010) section of thomsonite (an orthorhombic member of the complex alumino-silicate zeolite group), paying particular attention to the appearance of the isogyres in the 45° and parallel positions. Confirm that $r>v$ for this material.

(ii) Crossed axial plane dispersion: use a (100) section of brookite to confirm the properties described in 11.3.

(iii) Inclined dispersion: use a thick section of gypsum cut from the crystal of 4.6, Exercise 3 so as to symmetrically bevel the edge formed by the (111) and $(1\bar{1}1)$ faces. Examine the offset optic axis figure to confirm that gypsum shows inclined dispersion with $r>v$.

(iv) Horizontal dispersion: use a section of orthoclase (a member of the complex alumino-silicate feldspar group) cut perpendicular to the x-axis. Examine the slightly offset acute bisectrix figure to confirm that this material shows horizontal dispersion with $r>v$.

(v) Crossed dispersion: use an (010) section of borax (a hydrated borate of sodium). Examine the acute bisectrix figure to confirm that borax shows crossed dispersion with $r>v$.

3. Effect of dispersion on extinction angles in a biaxial crystal:

An (010) section of a monoclinic material gives an interference figure which shows marked crossed dispersion; measurements in monochromatic light show that $2V_\alpha$ is 40° for red light and 30° for blue light. On the same section extinction measurements on to the traces of {110} cleavages show that $z:\gamma$ (in the obtuse x–z angle) is 20° for red light and 30° for blue light.

(i) Another (hk0) section is cut inclined at 10° to (010). Determine the difference in extinction positions for red and blue light for this section.

(ii) Repeat (i) for a second (hk0) section inclined at 20° to (010).

CHAPTER 12

MICROSCOPIC PRACTICE

12.1 General introduction

So far we have been concerned with the essential techniques of optical determination using the polarising microscope, and we have not considered in any detail how these techniques could be applied to any practical problem. At the outset, it must be stressed that it is impossible to define any universally applicable approach, for the best method depends on the nature of the specimen, both in its optical constants and its mode of occurrence. Clearly experimental procedures could be different when a specimen shows a large well-crystalline habit from what they would have to be if the same specimen formed only tiny poorly crystalline fragments; there would also be some changes in technique depending on whether we have thin sections or a powdered aggregate of crystal fragments. Apart from the nature of the specimen, there are several basically different kinds of problems that can be tackled by optical work, and these, too, may be approached in different ways; a complete optical determination of a new material may not be carried out by the same steps as, say, the less demanding identification of constituents in a mixture in which only certain substances of known properties can be present. This chapter is only intended to act as a guide to the application of optical techniques, so as to provide a basis which can be modified and adapted to fresh problems in the light of experience. It is set out in four sections; the first is concerned with the preliminary observations on the specimen which would be made whatever the problem; the second describes the ancillary specimen stages often needed in optical work on anisotropic crystals; the third deals with the distinction of the various subdivisions of optical properties, and sets out, in so far as it is possible, the procedures for the complete determination of a specimen within one of these subdivisions; finally some illustrative exercises are described in detail in the hope that, taken together with practical exercises, they will help the inexperienced student to attain the dexterity needed for the most advantageous resolution of optical problems.

The initial examination of any specimen does not require the techniques of optical study that we have described from Chapter 7 onwards; it is most important that we learn to make an examination of the general nature of our specimens, for the key to microscopic work lies just as much in careful observations of this kind as it does in more refined techniques. Sometimes the material for microscopic work is provided as small grains; these can have varying degrees of regularity in shape (perhaps showing the development of crystalline faces) or can be completely irregular. Sometimes the specimen is only available in thin section, as in mineral examination in rock sections; in this case, we shall be fortunate if the slice only contains sections of the test material, and we must first familiarise ourselves with the appearance of the specimen sections so that they can be recognised among any foreign grains. Both types of specimen have their advantages and disadvantages; a grain powder allows greater freedom of manipulation of individual crystals, though, even in a sieved material, the optical path may differ from one grain to the next; a slice of standard thickness has the same predetermined optical path length for all grains, but the individual grains are permanently mounted.

For either of these forms of specimen preparation, we begin the preliminary examination by careful observation of individual crystals. The mount (either a thin section or some grains in an immersion liquid, see 8.1) is placed upon the microscope stage illuminated by roughly parallel ordinary white light and examined using a medium–low power objective (on some microscopes it is difficult to remove the polariser, but this is a nuisance only if the specimen is pleochroic). We will look first at *crystal shapes in liquid mounts.* When crystals grow freely from solution crystalline forms are often developed, and these can be a guide to their symmetry. Unequal development of symmetry related faces during growth can be confusing (e.g. the ideal cube can often appear as a rectangular parallelopiped, which might be taken for an orthorhombic crystal), and so confirmation of the symmetry in some other way is always desirable; any edge angles should be accurately measured to help to resolve ambiguities of deformed growth, but symmetry determination on morphological evidence alone is full of pitfalls for the inexperienced (see Phillips, *An Introduction to Crystallography*). Some indication of twinning is given by the occurrence of re-entrant edge angles, though this can be confused by parallel and other forms of oriented aggregated growth. If crystals of the specimen have been obtained from a crushed and sieved powder, it is very unlikely that they will show the same regular development of forms as crystals grown from solution; nevertheless depending on the properties of cleavage and fracture for the material, its crushed fragments can show a variety of shapes. A *cleavage* reflects a tendency of the crystal to break along planes of some structural significance parallel to possible crystal faces, whereas a *fracture* merely denotes an irregular parting under stress. With no good cleavage, the grains can be completely irregular in outline, while more regularity of shape will be exhibited by a specimen that possesses several good cleavage planes which define the fragments

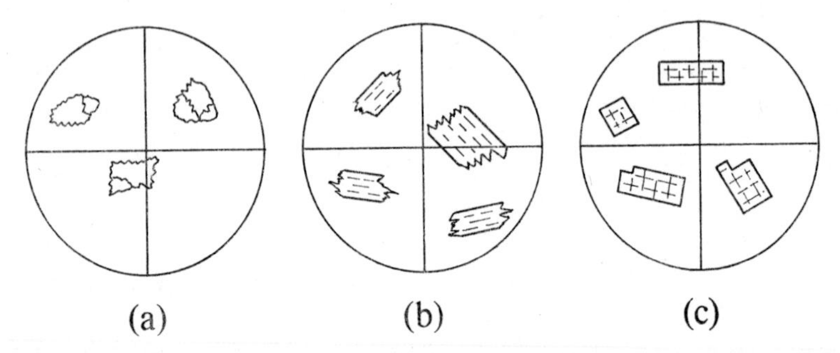

Fig. 12.1 Effect of cleavage upon the shape of crushed fragments.
a. Monoclinic crystal with {010} cleavage; irregular outline of fragment and terraces parallel to the single cleavage.
b. Tetragonal crystal with {010} cleavage; fragments have parallel edges and cleavage traces due to two equivalent cleavage directions, edges and traces parallel to z-crystallographic axis.
c. Cubic crystal with {010} cleavage; fragments have regular outline (parallelopipeds or distorted cubes) due to three equivalent cleavage directions, edges and traces parallel to crystallographic axes.

produced by crushing. Indeed the general appearance of fragments of a crystal powder is critically dependent on the particular cleavage planes of the specimen and its symmetry. If a monoclinic crystal has a perfect {010} cleavage the crystalline fragments will be flat cleavage plates of rather irregular outline (Fig. 12.1*a*). If the specimen is, say, tetragonal with a similar {010} cleavage, this would imply that the equivalent (100) planes are also cleavage planes, so that the crystal powder will contain two equivalent types of cleavage flake, with pairs of parallel edges formed by one cleavage intersecting the plane of the other; these edges denote the direction of the z-crystallographic axis (Fig. 12.1*b*). Finally, if our specimen were cubic with {010} cleavages, the crushed fragments will be in the form of cubes (or more likely, rectangular parallelopipeds) outlined by the three equivalent cleavage planes; the edges are parallel to the three crystallographic axes (Fig. 12.1*c*).

Cleavage planes are always planes of structural and crystallographic significance, so that the edges of powdered fragments formed by their intersections are zone axes (sometimes, as above, the crystallographic axes); they are often used as reference directions for optical measurements, and any angular relationships of grain edges should always be carefully measured. The quality of a cleavage can be judged by the regularity of its occurrence both on the outline and on traces of the cleavage within the body of the fragment. Regular edges on crushed grains can also be caused by planes of parting (i.e. planes of weakness in the crystal), though these differ from cleavage edges in that parallel traces are not found within the body of the crystal, nor do they occur so regularly or so frequently. Such a plane of parting could, for example, be the composition (or contact) plane of a twinned crystal; fracture along this plane of weakness will leave a regular edge on each of the separated subindividuals, but there can be no similar traces within the subindividuals. The general shapes of crushed fragments can sometimes be suggestive of the crystal symmetry of the specimen, though this indication should always be confirmed in some other way. The edges and faces of crystal fragments are invaluable in defining crystallographic reference directions but they can sometimes be troublesome in certain aspects of optical work. In particular the shape of the fragments will determine the way in which they lie upon the slide, and significant departure from the ideal roughly spherical form can restrict the orientations which they display; for example, elongated prismatic crystals all tend to lie with their lengths parallel to the microscope stage, so that it will not be possible to use this mount to examine the propagation of light parallel to the prism axis.

Similar observations are made when *the specimen is provided in thin section.* Occasionally oriented sections are cut from a large single crystal whose development allows the orientation to be chosen. More often the slice produces sections through randomly orientated microscopic grains of the test material. Sometimes regular grain outlines are recognisable; these are said to denote *euhedral* crystals, and edge angles can be measured, though unless the zone axis for the faces is perpendicular to the section the values will only be projections of the true angles between the faces. More often the aggregate has grown under constraint, as in many rocks, and it is unlikely that recognisable crystalline forms will have been able to develop. Even so, the *habit* (or general relative development of crystalline forms) can often be seen, and the general appearance of crystals deduced from the various cross-sections as acicular (needle-like), tabular (flattened), etc. Otherwise a lack of any pronounced habit leads to irregular cross-sections of crystals which are described as *anhedral.* In thin section cleavages play little part in determining external shapes, but their presence may often be detected by examining the interior of grains; as the section is prepared, grinding causes the cleavage planes to open up to intersect the surface in sets of parallel lines. (In practice the cleavage planes must be normal or nearly normal to the surface, or their intersections will not be clearly visible, as most microscope objectives have only a limited depth of focus.) Multiplicity of cleavage planes, due either to symmetry or several distinct cleavage directions can cause a grain to show two or more sets of differently orientated *cleavage traces*; as with edge angles, the angles between cleavage traces must not always be identified with the characteristic crystallographic angle between cleavage planes. The plane of a section of a particular grain will be arbitrary and the trace on its surface of intersection by a cleavage depends on the orientation of the section; cleavage traces are not necessarily zone axes for the crystal. Nevertheless, when the grain sections are carefully chosen these cleavage traces can act as the reference directions for many optical observations.

In addition to crystal shape and cleavage directions, the preliminary examination may reveal other specimen features which should be fully investigated, increasing the magnification and resolution of the microscope as necessary. These may include *the quality of the appearance* of the crystals (completely translucent, cloudy, etc.), any colour, inclusions of foreign material and any other unusual qualities shown by the specimen. Nearly all these aspects of the appearance of a specimen are better displayed in thin section where they are not confused by masking effects due to surface irregularities of grains. *The observation of colours* needs particular care, for the shade varies with the length of the optical path in the specimen (5.1). Most determinative tables list colours for thin sections of standard thickness, though these may be markedly different from the colours seen for powdered grains of the same materials. Whenever a specimen is coloured, we must also keep a careful watch for the effects of pleochroism. It is worth while concluding the preliminary examination by inserting the polariser, and noting whether any crystals show a change in absorption as the stage is rotated; there can be no attempt to specify absorption properties at this point, for this must await subsequent investigation of the nature of the optical properties.

At the conclusion of the preliminary examination the observations of crystalline forms, habit, cleavage, etc. may provide some indications as to the general optical character of the specimen, but detailed examination must now be made by the techniques described and illustrated by exercises in earlier chapters. The application of these microscopic methods to any problem depends on an ability to control the experimental conditions, in particular the directions of light propagation within the crystals. For anisotropic materials we need to be able to select those sections of the specimen which will yield significant observations and measurements, and much of the work in an optical study must be directed to this end. In 12.3 we will discuss the outlines of procedure on the assumption that all possible orientations of grain sections are available and that the problem is to decide which particular sections are to be examined by the various techniques. But this is not always the case, for the nature of some specimens can restrict the orientations which grains can assume; as we have seen, this difficulty can be particularly acute for powdered fragments of specimens with good cleavages, for the cleavage flakes will all lie in the mounting liquid with their normals parallel to the axis of the microscope. When necessary such restrictions in specimen orientation can be overcome by attaching subsidiary stages to the stage of the microscope; these permit limited but substantial variations in the orientation of the normal to any grain. Their use can provide enough general orientations of nearly any specimen to facilitate most optical determinations, and we shall describe them briefly before turning to the outlines of procedure.

12.2 Subsidiary stages

On the whole, there is less need for an auxiliary device to reorientate an individual grain in a thin section than when the specimen is a powder of separate crystal fragments. Nevertheless there are occasions when it is essential to pass parallel light through a given grain in a thin section in various directions; and an auxiliary device, the *universal stage*, is attached to the microscope stage. This subsidiary stage is designed to permit rotation of the thin section about a number of mutually perpendicular axes. Most modern universal stages have five different axes, though some older designs have only four; the whole stage can, of course, be rotated about the microscope axis by movement of the microscope stage, and this provides an additional axis of rotation. The disposition of the rotation axes for a five axis stage is shown schematically in Fig. 12.2*a*. With the movements of the stage set in their zero positions, there are three rotation axes parallel to the microscope axis, numbered A_1,

A_3, A_5 from the innermost to the outermost; A_5 is the movement of the microscope stage, for it is convenient to consider it together with the axes of the subsidiary stage. Two other axes are horizontal and parallel to the microscope stage, A_0, allowing inclination of the A_1 axis, and A_4, allowing inclination of the A_3 axis; the last axis, A_2, is also parallel to the microscope stage, but perpendicular to A_0 and A_4, and it is arranged

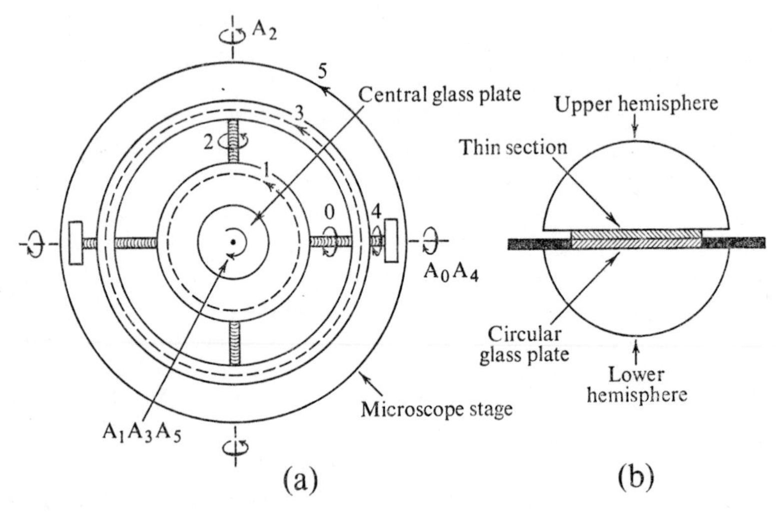

Fig. 12.2 Essential features of the universal stage.
a. The axes of a five-axis stage.
b. The mounting of the specimen between glass hemispheres at the centre of the stage.

to permit inclination of the A_0 axis. Clearly rotations about these axes are not all independent, and new settings on outer axes change the inclinations of all inner axes to the microscope axis, for instance movement about the A_4 axis must change the directions of all axes with lower subscripts, though their relative orientations remain perpendicular; independent settings of tilt can be made on each axis and are read on graduated scales. In four-axis stages, the A_0 movement is usually omitted, though this has some practical disadvantage. The thin section is placed on a circular glass plate at the centre of the stage and two glass 'hemispheres' are locked in position one above the section and one below the glass plate (Fig. 12.2*b*); all contacts between hemispheres, section and glass plate are made with a liquid having the same refractive index as the glass. This rather complex arrangement is needed because when the section is tilted, refraction of light obliquely incident on the various boundaries causes displacement of the image; ideally the hemispheres are so arranged that together with the specimen and plate they form a sphere which eliminates this displacement as the various axes of the stage are rotated. This means that all components of the sphere (including the grains of the specimen) should have the same refractive index, but this is clearly impracticable. Usually there must be some small corrections to angular readings with the stage to allow for deviations due to refraction at the crystal-hemisphere boundaries, though they can be minimised by having sets of hemispheres of different refractive indices for use with different specimens. For a given specimen, limitation of the tilts about the various axes to values less than those permitted by the mechanical construction can be imposed by total reflection at large angles due to the refractive indices at different boundaries.

With the complex system of interrelated rotation axes, the efficient use of the universal stage requires a systematic use of the various adjustments. A considerable literature has grown up around the use of these stages for various optical problems. Most of the techniques depend on the recognition and orientation of optical symmetry planes in parallel light, for it will be realised that the standard universal stage is not well suited for conoscopic work. The presence of the upper hemisphere only permits the use of low-medium power microscope objectives with long working distances. To observe satisfactory interference figures either the size of the hemispheres must be drastically reduced or special high power objectives of large numerical aperture but relatively long working distances must be designed; in many modern instruments a reasonable compromise between these two conditions does allow conoscopic use, but the specialised optical equipment is not a standard component of most microscopes and universal stages. However, all universal stages allow the orientation of optical symmetry planes using parallel light and crossed polars, and this remains their most essential function. By an optical symmetry plane we mean a symmetry plane of the indicatrix; for a uniaxial crystal there are an infinite number of such planes parallel to the optic axis, and one normal to the unique axis of the indicatrix while biaxial crystals have three such perpendicular symmetry planes. Let us illustrate the use of the universal stage by using it to locate and orientate the optic axis for grains of a uniaxial crystal section.

When the thin section is parallel to the microscope stage with all rotation axes at their zero settings, the optic axis for any given crystal is probably inclined to the microscope axis; we will represent this direction for a particular crystal on a stereographic projection normal to the microscope stage (Fig. 12.3*a*). In parallel white light between crossed polars, the grain will show some interference colour. The crystal is rotated on the A_1 axis into an extinction position (Fig. 12.3*b*). If the crystal remains in extinction when subsequently rotated about the

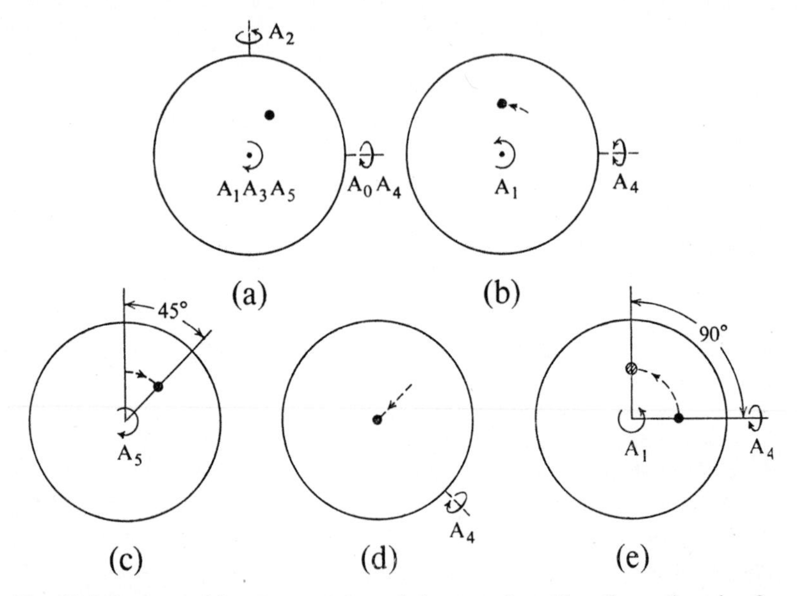

Fig. 12.3 Stereographic representation of the steps in setting the optic axis of a uniaxial crystal parallel to the microscope axis. All projections are perpendicular to the microscope axis, crossed polars E–W and N–S.
a. Initial general position of optic axis with axes of the universal stage.
b. Rotation into extinction by A_1; extinction remains with rotation of A_4.
c. Rotation through 45° by A_5 (microscope stage); crystal not extinguished.
d. Rotation into extinction by A_4; optic axis vertical.
e. Alternative extinction position after initial rotation by A_1; crystal not extinguished on A_4, but further rotation of 90° on A_1 sets crystal into position of (*b*).

horizontal A_4 axis, it must mean that an optical symmetry plane containing the optic axis is now perpendicular to the A_4 axis. With A_4 now returned to its zero position, the microscope stage is rotated through 45° about axis A_5 (Fig. 12.3*c*); the crystal will again show an interference colour. We can now rotate about A_4 until the crystal is in extinction again; this sets the optic axis direction parallel to the axis of the microscope (Fig. 12.3*d*), a fact which we can confirm by observing that the grain remains in extinction as the microscope stage is rotated by A_5. There are two snags in this simple procedure. First, it is possible that the crystal will not remain in extinction when rotated about A_4. This implies that when an extinction position is achieved by the initial rotation about the A_1 axis, the optic axis is neither parallel nor perpendicular to the A_4 axis; Fig. 12.3*c* shows that the remedy is simple, for a further rotation of 90° about A_1 must always bring the optic axis normal to A_4, when we can proceed as before. The second difficulty

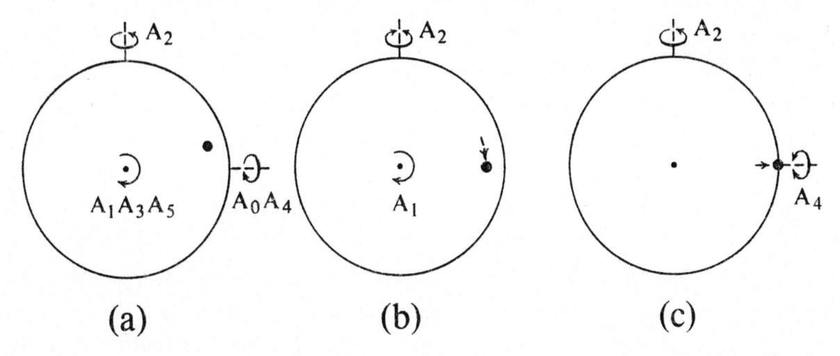

Fig. 12.4 Stereographic representation of the steps in setting the optic axis of a uniaxial crystal perpendicular to the microscope axis. All projections are perpendicular to the microscope axis, crossed polars E–W and N–S.
a. Initial general position of optic axis with axes of the universal stage.
b. Rotation into extinction by A_1; extinction remains with rotation of A_2.
c. Rotation of A_2 until crystal remains extinguished for rotations of A_4; optic axis parallel to A_4.

arises from the mechanical limitation on the maximum rotation about the A_4 axis, usually 60–70°; if the optic axis is inclined at too large an angle to the normal to the section, it will not be possible to rotate A_4 enough to bring it parallel to the microscope axis. We must then seek a more favourably oriented grain in the section, though the original crystal could be used to set the optic axis direction horizontal. This can be done in the following way. When the crystal has been extinguished by rotation about A_1 (Fig. 12.4*a*, *b*), the effect of rotation about A_2 is observed. If the crystal remains in extinction it must mean that an optic symmetry plane containing the optic axis is normal to A_2 (Fig. 12.4*b*); if rotation about A_2 causes the grain to come out of extinction, the optic axis is neither parallel nor perpendicular to A_2, but can be set normal to A_2 by a further rotation through 90° about A_1. With the optic axis located as in Fig. 12.4*b*, the section is rotated about A_2 until subsequent rotation about the A_4 axis leaves the crystal extinguished. The circular section of the indicatrix is now vertical with the optic axis parallel to A_4 (Fig. 12.4*c*).

This brief illustration of the relatively simple adjustment of a universal stage to orientate sections of uniaxial crystals emphasises the importance of a systematic approach to the use of the movements provided by the stage. The orientation of biaxial crystals is a more complex operation, and details of this and other more complicated universal stage methods will be found in the references in the bibliography. The most efficient application of universal stage methods to a particular problem is guided by experience, and the techniques are best acquired by practical demonstrations using the instrument. In the present context we merely wish to draw attention to its existence and capabilities, recognising that it is a precision-made expensive accessory which is not always available to students, and which is by no means always necessary for the routine investigation of thin sections. Although the universal stage can be adapted to undertake the investigation of separate crystal fragments, subsidiary stages of much simpler construction can be used for this purpose. We can often roll grains of an irregular or roughly cylindrical shape around in the liquid of an uncovered mount by manipulation with a needle, but the variation in orientation is limited, especially if the grains all have a particular habit; sooner or later it will be necessary to employ some kind of subsidiary stage to permit systematic and controlled changes in grain orientation, and elementary stages for this purpose should be part of the standard equipment of an optical laboratory.

Most subsidiary stages used for the orientation of crystal fragments have only one axis of rotation which lies in the plane of the microscope stage; they are often known as *spindle stages*. The complex system of axes of a universal stage is not required, for the freedom to handle separate grains permits the mounting of a fragment on the axis of the spindle stage to be chosen to suit a particular problem. With the spindle stage the crystal can be rotated about two perpendicular axes; one of these movements is provided by the spindle axis, while rotation of the microscope stage provides the other (Fig. 12.5*a*). Elementary spindle stages can be improvised very easily. A flat base of some material such as brass or Perspex with a central circular hole is attached to the microscope stage by the spring clips that normally hold the specimen mount in position. The spindle on which the crystal is mounted can be a fine metal rod (or needle) or a glass rod; the spindle needs some kind of knob at one end to allow easy adjustment of rotation. The spindle must then be mounted so that its axis is in the plane of the microscope stage. A rudimentary bearing can usually be fashioned from a cork or rubber bung permanently attached by a strong adhesive to the base. It is convenient for the bearing to be constructed to allow the crystal to be attached to the pointed end of the spindle by a suitable adhesive remote from the stage, so that the spindle may be placed in its bearing without

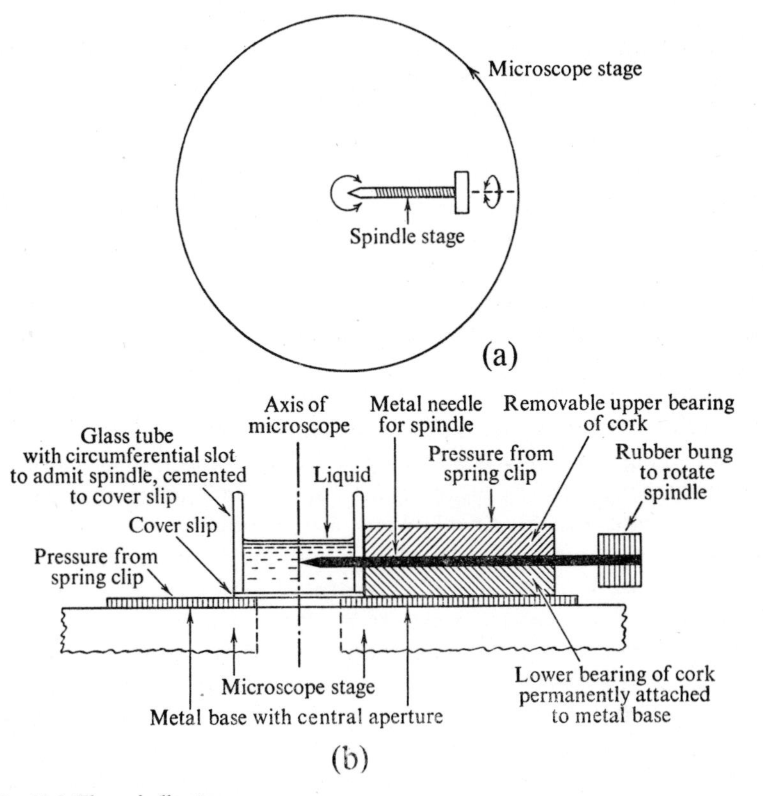

Fig. 12.5 The spindle stage.
a. The movements provided by a spindle stage.
b. The construction of an elementary spindle stage; a section parallel to the microscope axis.

disturbing the setting of the crystal, for example, the bearing block of cork or rubber is split with the upper half removable. While the morphology of a crystal can be observed satisfactorily in air, most optical measurements require the crystal to be immersed in a refractive index oil. A small immersion cell should be devised to fit on the base of the stage; this can usually be improvised from microscope slides, cover glasses or glass tubing. A simple cell and spindle stage are shown in Fig. 12.5*b*.

This simple spindle stage can be used to locate optical symmetry planes and other important optical directions by observations in parallel light between crossed polars, but as with the universal stage, useful conoscopic observations are not possible with standard microscope objectives. Moreover, the student will soon find that it is advantageous to be able to make measurements of the angular rotation of the spindle. In a detailed examination of crystal fragments a more refined version of a spindle stage is often a necessity; while these are not an essential accessory for each microscope, they should be available as required. Many forms of spindle stage have been designed, often for particular purposes, for instance to allow controlled temperature variation of the liquid within the cell; each design has its particular virtues and defects. We shall describe a recent model by Roy, which retains many of the features of other designs; it has an additional advantage in that it allows observation of satisfactory interference figures using normal high power microscope objectives. The essential parts are set out diagrammatically in Fig. 12.6. As usual, the apparatus is clamped to the microscope stage by a locking screw. It has a main spindle by which the crystal can be rotated through 360° by the main knob during preliminary adjustment; when the most suitable orientation range has been located, a coupling device connects a second shaft which allows the rotation of the spindle to be read to 3′ of arc on a steel protractor graduated at 1° intervals through 180°. At the other end of the main spindle is a detachable threaded head for mounting the specimen. This head has two perpendicular slides which carry a ball joint with a pointed tip; a glass fibre to mount the crystal is cemented to this tip. The slides and ball joint allow lateral and tilting adjustments needed for the accurate setting and centring of the crystal. The crystal itself is mounted at the extremity of the glass fibre after a preliminary examination on a separate microscope to roughly select the desired orientation (the ball joint allows deviations of 10–15° in setting to be corrected); various cements (dental cement, Durofix, carpenter's glue) have been recommended for attaching the crystal to the fibre, and it is important that the one chosen should not be attacked by the liquids in which the crystal is to be immersed. After some orientation adjustment and centring of the crystal on the microscope axis, the specimen is immersed within an oil cell brought up on to the microscope stage. With this design all adjustments have to be undertaken with great care and precision, for the oil cell is an opensided

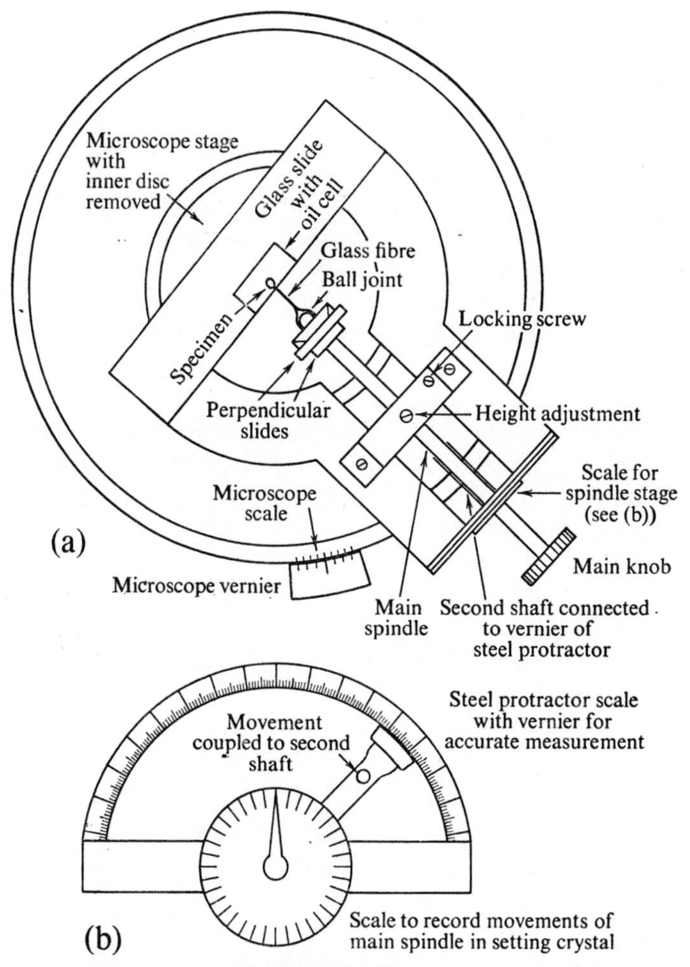

Fig. 12.6 An improved spindle stage by Roy.
a. The general feature of the stage in position on the microscope.
b. The scales used for recording movements of the crystal around the spindle axis.

cavity only 1·25 mm high in which the liquid is retained by surface tension; it is the small height of this cell which allows objectives of relatively large aperture and small working distances to be used with the stage.

As an illustration of the use of a spindle stage we will describe the determination of the optic axial angle of a biaxial crystal by this instrument.

The most advantageous setting of the crystal fragment has the optic axial plane normal to the spindle axis so that there can be direct measurement of $2V$ from the interference figure as the spindle is rotated. In a preliminary examination the most suitable crystal fragment is picked out and mounted on the glass fibre at the end of the spindle in approximately the correct orientation. Together with centring adjustments, the orientation of the crystal is corrected by movements of the ball joint after the head has been screwed on to the main spindle; setting of optical symmetry planes can be carried out by methods similar to those used with a universal stage. In the present problem, however, the final adjustments to the orientation of the optic axial plane are made from the interference figures with the microscope arranged for conoscopic use; when these are complete, the acute bisectrix is brought parallel to the axis of the microscope by rotation of the spindle. The accurate protractor scale is then coupled in, and the interference figure set into the 45° position by rotation of the microscope stage. Rotation of the spindle axis brings each of the melatopes in turn to the centre of the microscope field, so that the angular rotation is a measure of the angle between these directions. It is important to realise that this angular rotation will only be a direct measure of $2V$ if the liquid in the immersion cell has refractive index n_β for the crystal. If this is not so, there will be refraction of the light waves travelling along the optic axis direction in the crystal at the liquid-crystal interface so that (Fig. 12.7)

$$\sin V = {}_c n_l \sin E_l = n_l/n_c \sin E_l$$

Only if $n_l = n_c$, i.e. the refractive index of the liquid is that of light travelling along the optic axis direction, will $V = E_l$; otherwise a correction must be made for this refraction. Under optimum conditions, the accuracy in the determination of $2V$ by the spindle stage is quite high, about $\pm\frac{1}{2}°$; this direct observation is far better than calculation from the values of principal refractive indices (4·4).

12.3 Outlines of a general procedure

Having carefully characterised the appearance of the specimen as in 12.1, we must discover whether the material is optically isotropic or anisotropic. To do this we can examine a number of differently orientated sections[1] in parallel white light between crossed polars; those which are

[1] The term 'section' here and elsewhere in this description of a general procedure of optical examination refers only to planes normal to microscope axis, without prejudice to the type of specimen; the term 'thin section' will be specifically used to denote this form of specimen.

isotropic are readily recognised for they remain in extinction at all positions of the microscope stage (9.2). If all sections are isotropic then the material must be isotropic; in practice, it is necessary to guard against the possibility that sections presented by an anisotropic specimen are all in the same orientation so that an optic axis is parallel to the microscope axis. For this reason, it is usually as well to check suspected isotropic character by conoscopic examination between crossed polars; if

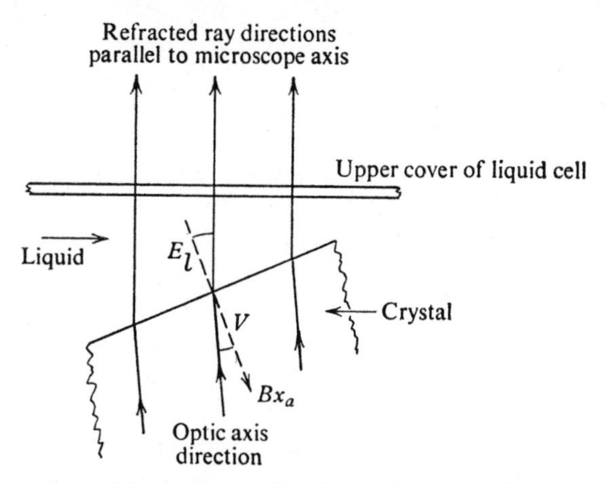

Fig. 12.7 Refraction at liquid-crystal interface for light travelling along the optic axis direction of biaxial crystal flake. Section parallel to optic axial plane, normal to spindle axis.

the crystal is truly isotropic there will be no interference effects, whereas if it is anisotropic an interference figure of some kind will be seen (10.2, 10.4). Having confirmed *an isotropic specimen* there is little further to be done except to record its refractive index (8.1), using variation methods (8.4) to study any dispersion (11.1).

When *the specimen is anisotropic* nearly all sections will show some interference colour in parallel white light between crossed polars; should all sections have the same orientation as suggested in the previous paragraph, it will be necessary at the conclusion of the preliminary examination to use one of the subsidiary stages of 12.2. The colour for each section will be determined by its birefringence and thickness, and will be extinguished four times in a complete revolution of the stage (9.2) though any section exactly normal to an optic axis will remain dark in any orientation. The optical techniques described in earlier chapters require the use of sections in particular orientations, and for anisotropic crystals an important part of any optical examination involves the selection of suitable sections. But before we turn to this selection, *the preliminary examination between crossed polars* to show isotropic or anisotropic character may also reveal other specimen properties important in a detailed investigation. In particular it can tell us whether individual grains of the specimen are homogeneous or not, i.e. whether the sections are of separate single crystals of uniform properties. For example, it is not uncommon for crystals of a specimen to contain smaller fragments of a foreign material, either caught up during a complex crystallisation process or perhaps subsequently precipitated from the host crystal during the later stages of crystallisation; these crystallites can vary in size and be randomly or regularly orientated with respect to their host crystal. The presence of these crystallites of different optical properties can often be detected between crossed polars, even if they have not been resolved in the earlier microscopic examination; a random or regular extinction of all the fragments within a particular host crystal reveals their orientation relationship. Again in the crystallisation of complex solid solutions, often under non-equilibrium conditions, crystals can be formed with slight systematic composition changes at different points in an apparently homogeneous macroscopic crystal; the core of such a crystal might be, say, iron rich, while approaching the periphery of the grain the iron concentration gradually falls. In such *zoned crystals*, the variable composition means that the optical properties can change slightly but progressively with chemical constitution. The effect of zoning is often seen with crossed polars when an apparently homogeneous grain fails to extinguish uniformly throughout. Perhaps the commonest type of crystal inhomogeneity is twinning, a phenomenon shown by very many crystalline substances, and which does not involve any chemical inhomogeneity. *A twinned crystal* is composed of two or more subindividuals of identical composition in fixed relative orientations to each other according to the twin law; the particular twin law depends on the substance and perhaps also on the conditions of crystal growth. Once again examination between crossed polars often allows the subindividuals of a twinned crystal to be recognised. A particular section of a twinned crystal will have two permitted vibration directions for each subindividual; in favourable sections the twinned crystal can show one (or more, if the twinning is multiple) region in extinction at one position of the microscope stage sharply separated across the contact plane(s) from other twinned region(s) still showing the appropriate interference colour (Fig. 12.8). The presence of twinning can be particularly useful if the twin law is known, for the sharp boundaries between the subindividuals can act as reference directions (like cleavage traces) for optical measurements. In practice irregularities in grain surfaces often make the detection and description of crystal inhomogeneities very much more difficult for powdered specimens than for thin sections.

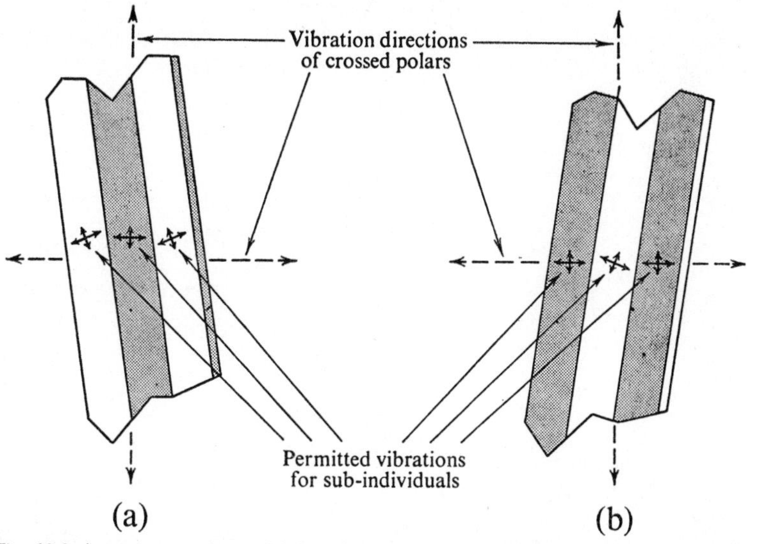

Fig. 12.8 Appearance of a multiple twinned crystal between crossed polars, parallel white light.
a. One orientation of sub-individuals in extinction; the other showing interference colour across contact plane.
b. Rotation of crystal so that second orientation of sub-individuals is in extinction.

After noting the occurrence of any inhomogeneities, we must now decide *whether our anisotropic specimen is uniaxial or biaxial*; this involves the use of interference figures. In Chapter 10, we saw that there are characteristic differences between the figures from uniaxial and biaxial crystals, but we need to select our sections most advantageously. For all anisotropic crystals the most useful sections for detailed optical work are perpendicular to important directions of the indicatrix, the principal axes or optic axes. Of these sections, the easiest to recognise are normal to optic axes, for they are isotropic. The earlier examination in parallel light and crossed polars will have enabled us to locate such a section, or, at least, one which is very close in orientation and shows a very low order interference colour. With this section, the interference figure will show either a uniaxial optic axis figure with circular colour fringes and straight brushes in all positions (10.2) or a biaxial optic axis figure with its fringe system and isogyres which become curved in the 45° position (10.4). Now the uniaxial or biaxial character of the specimen is established, and the subsequent procedure depends both on this and what further optical data is sought.

For *a uniaxial specimen*, the problem can range from the mere determination of the optic sign through to a complete determination including any dispersion or pleochroism. We will continue with a

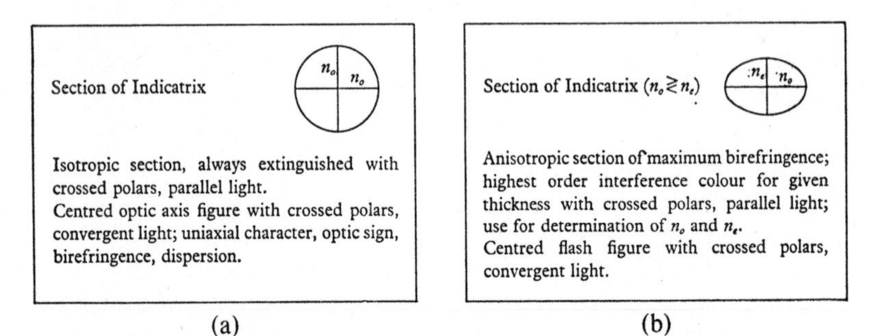

Fig. 12.9 Properties of important sections of uniaxial crystals.
a. Normal to optic axis.
b. Containing optic axis.

procedure for a complete determination from the point at which the optic axis figure establishes the uniaxial nature of the specimen. This same interference figure can be examined with a compensating plate to give the optic sign (10.3); if any rings are visible they may give some idea of the birefringence if the thickness of the section is known (10.3); the sequence of colours will tell us if there is appreciable dispersion of the birefringence (11.2). If the section is exactly perpendicular to the optic axis, its relief will give a measure of the value of n_O relative to the mounting medium, but for a complete optical determination it is now essential to choose a second orientated section; we need a section which contains the optic axis (Fig. 12.9). This section has maximum birefringence ($n_e - n_O$), and for a given thickness will show the highest order interference colour between crossed polars in parallel white light. While thin sections have grains of uniform thickness, the fragments of a sieved powder will inevitably have slightly differing optical paths which can confuse selection of the correct orientation. The only certain confirmation comes from the interference figure of the section; a correctly orientated grain shows a centred flash figure (10.2).

Having located the second important section, we can complete the optical measurements on the uniaxial specimen. First we can establish which of the two permitted vibration directions for this section is fast using a testing instrument to compensate the interference colour (9.4). Since the optic sign has already been determined, we know whether the ordinary disturbance is fast or slow, and hence we deduce which vibration direction corresponds to the ordinary waves; with a thin section of known thickness we could at the same time obtain the birefringence ($n_e - n_o$). We can now determine the principal refractive indices n_o and n_e to any desired accuracy by immersion methods (8.1). The crystal is set into extinction so that its permitted vibration directions are parallel to those of the polars; when the analyser is removed, light passes through the section vibrating parallel to one of the principal vibration directions; observation of relief, etc. in this position allows the particular principal value to be measured. After the section has been rotated through 90°, the other principal refractive index can be determined. When dispersion studies are required similar experiments can be carried out with the same section using monochromatic light, and, if possible, some form of double variation apparatus (8.4). The only remaining determination for this uniaxial crystal is made if the preliminary examination of 12.1 revealed any pleochroism (5.2). The colours of the dichroic scheme are those seen in white light when the section and polariser are set to measure the principal refractive indices; the face colours are observed in unpolarised light.

In setting out this scheme of procedure for uniaxial crystals we have only needed to locate two critical sections either by searching for them among a collection of randomly orientated sections or by using one of the subsidiary stages described in 12.2. We have neglected any additional data, e.g. the location of significant crystallographic directions in the preliminary examination, often available in practice, which can help in the selection of the sections. Even when we choose to neglect such pointers, a determination cannot be regarded as complete until all observations have been linked together to provide a coherent whole.

We will return now to a general procedure when the interference figure from an optic axis section reveals that *the specimen is biaxial.* Again, we will follow through the stages of a general investigation. Inevitably all observations become slightly more difficult for we are concerned not only with the determination of the principal axes of the indicatrix, but also with its orientation with respect to crystallographic directions, i.e. with the determination of the crystal system and the choice of crystallographic axes for the material. In this kind of work, it is essential that full advantage is taken of any ancillary information about the specimen that may be available; no additional data that arises during the optical studies can be neglected if the observations are to be carried out in the most expeditious manner. Starting from the interference figure from a section normal to an optic axis, this can be used to give the optic sign, an assessment of the optic axial angle, and if the thickness of the section is known, some idea of the birefringence (10.5); it can also tell us if the specimen shows significant dispersion, and this may provide a clue as to the symmetry of the material (11.3). At this stage, note should be taken of the orientation of the optic axial plane (as shown by the figure) with respect to any reference direction of the section (cleavage trace, etc.). When a section is exactly perpendicular to an optic axis, it can be used to obtain a value of n_β to any desired accuracy by the immersion methods of 8.1; measurement of n_β in this way is often to be recommended for it can be difficult to locate other suitable sections. Having obtained as much data as possible from this section, we must locate other suitable orientations. The important sections of a biaxial crystal are those perpendicular to the three principal axes of the indicatrix (Fig. 12.10). In general, without any help from ancillary data, the only one of these which can be systematically sought is that perpendicular to the third mean line, for it has the maximum birefringence ($n_\gamma - n_\alpha$) for the specimen. In thin section, this means that we must choose the grain showing the highest order interference colour in white light; powdered specimens again allow some ambiguity of choice due to the variable lengths of optical paths in different grains. The correctly orientated section should show a centred flash figure in convergent white light with crossed polars (10.4), and this should be used to confirm the validity of our choice.

Having found this section we can ascertain which of the two vibration directions is fast by examining the effect of a compensator upon the interference colour (9.4). This distinguishes the vibration directions associated with n_γ (slow) and n_α (fast); if the thickness of the section is known the birefringence ($n_\gamma - n_\alpha$) can also be measured. The immersion methods of 8.1 are used to determine n_γ and n_α separately; measurements are carried out with the polariser inserted so as to permit the transmission of light vibrating parallel to each of the two vibration directions in turn. Dispersion curves for principal refractive indices are best obtained using double variation apparatus (8.4). So far, we have determined the size and shape of the indicatrix by methods very similar to those used for uniaxial crystals; we could even attempt to fix the absorption axes and pleochroic scheme, though some caution is necessary as the indicatrix and absorption axes do not always coincide (5.3). By using the subsidiary stages of 12.2, an accurate determination of $2V$ can be made. Nevertheless at this point biaxial crystals present a further

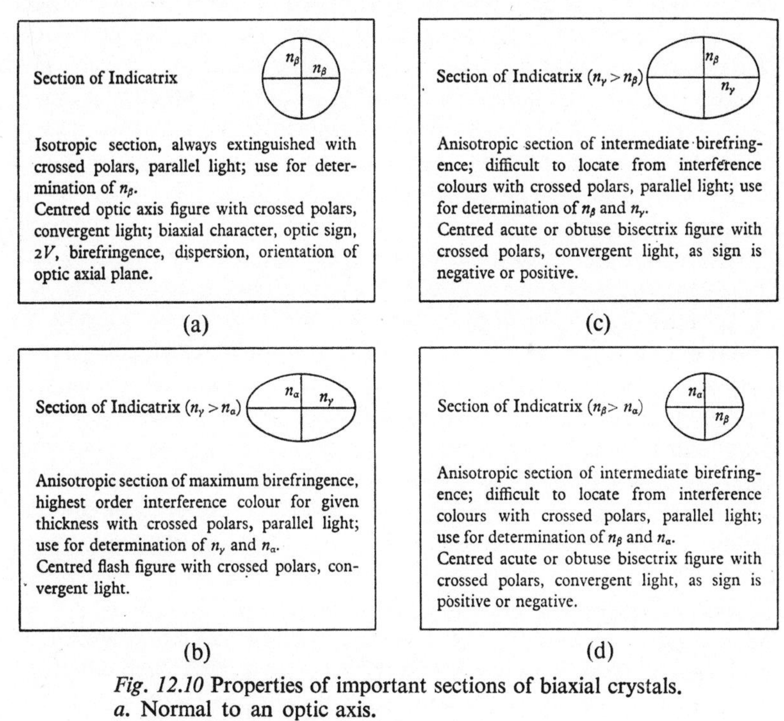

Fig. 12.10 Properties of important sections of biaxial crystals.
a. Normal to an optic axis.
b. Normal to the third mean line.
c. Normal to principal vibration direction α.
d. Normal to principal vibration direction γ.

problem in that the orientation of the indicatrix with respect to crystallographic directions remains.

The problem of *the orientation of the biaxial indicatrix* is twofold, involving first the determination of the symmetry system and the choice of crystallographic axes, and second the establishment of the relation between these axes and those of the indicatrix. The first part of this problem is the most difficult; for any new materials, it is not soluble by optical methods alone. Optical work can provide some clues as to whether the biaxial specimen is orthorhombic, monoclinic or triclinic.

Setting aside any morphological indications, the nature of any dispersion (11.3) and the variation of extinction angles in principal zones (see the illustrative example on an amphibole in the next section) can in favourable conditions tell us to which symmetry system the specimen belongs. Apart from these relatively uncommon circumstances, the crystal symmetry of an unknown specimen must always be determined or confirmed by X-ray methods. Even if the symmetry could be unambiguously assigned by optical examination alone, the conventional choice of crystallographic reference axes can only be made when the form of the unit cell of the atomic arrangement has been investigated by X-ray diffraction. Suitable X-ray methods lie outside the scope of this book but are well documented in the references in the bibliography. For the present purposes, once they have been used to determine the symmetry and choice of axes for our specimen, we must identify and relate some visible reference direction to this choice so that subsequent optical measurements can be referred to this direction; in most cases this reference direction will be a cleavage trace or crystal edge. For specimens with no visible reference directions, as for completely irregular grain fragments, the relationship between optical and crystallographic directions becomes much more difficult to specify; it is sometimes necessary to carry out X-ray and optical examinations on the same grain. Of course, in some optical problems, the crystallographic significance of a visible reference direction is already known, and an independent X-ray examination is unnecessary.

Once the location of the crystallographic axes is made, we can relate them to the orientation of the indicatrix. The permissible orientations of the indicatrix in the three biaxial crystal systems have been described in 4.4, and we will briefly discuss each system separately. Individual procedures must be adapted to suit particular specimens and much will depend on the nature of the visible reference directions, but the general problem may be formulated for each system. For orthorhombic specimens, the sole problem is to determine the axis of the indicatrix that is parallel to each of the three perpendicular crystallographic axes. Provided that a suitable reference direction is visible on the two orientated sections, this presents no difficulty; that normal to the optic axis allows the orientation of the optic axial plane, while the vibration directions of γ and α within this plane are displayed by the section normal to the third mean line. With monoclinic crystals, the problem is a little more complicated, and we have to decide which of the principal axes is parallel to the diad symmetry axis, and the orientation of the other two axes in the (010) plane. The optic axial plane can be parallel or perpendicular to (010); with a suitable reference direction, these possibilities can often be distinguished by the observation of the optic axial plane using the section normal to an optic axis. When this plane is parallel to (010), $\beta = y$; when it is perpendicular to (010) either α or γ is parallel to y, and the determination of optic sign, and the direction of Bx_a from the interference figure can help to decide which is appropriate. The angular position of the other two principal axes with respect to the x and z axes usually depends on the choice of a section parallel to (010). When $\beta = y$, this is relatively straightforward for the selected section of maximum birefringence is in this orientation; with the optic axial plane perpendicular to (010), the selection is more difficult for an (010) section shows the intermediate birefringences $(n_\gamma - n_\beta)$ or $(n_\beta - n_\alpha)$.

There can be no recommended systematic procedure for any search depends on the properties of a particular specimen; essentially we must use all the known facts about the specimen to find a section with a centred acute or obtuse bisectrix interference figure (an example is given in the next section). Once the (010) section has been found, its permitted vibration directions are parallel to principal axes of the indicatrix; measurement of extinction positions of the slow and fast vibrations (9.5) gives the relationship of the indicatrix and crystallographic axes. For triclinic crystals, the complete lack of correspondence between crystallographic and indicatrix axes nearly always makes it essential that their relationships are established by measurements on selected crystals using the subsidiary stages of 12.2.

Inevitably this description of the orientation of the indicatrix for biaxial crystals must seem to lack precision, for it is obvious that no systematic procedure can be recommended. Experimental methods depend very much on the nature of individual problems, and the student must learn by experience how a particular determination is best undertaken. To this end, the next section contains some illustrative examples of optical problems which encompass much of the generalisation which has been set out in this section; it is followed by some practical exercises which will help to give further experience in the application of the optical techniques.

12.4 Some illustrative examples

This section is devoted to the description of a number of optical determinations which illustrate how particular problems can be undertaken. The progress of each example is recorded stage by stage, though details of experimental procedure are gradually omitted as they become more familiar with each successive problem. Naturally we start with simpler exercises on uniaxial crystals and move on to the more difficult and varied problems of work with biaxial crystals; the illustrations contain many of the commoner types of optical problem, and use both thin section and powdered specimens. They can be repeated with the same or similar materials by the student as practical exercises.

(a) The determination of the principal refractive indices of a uniaxial specimen with well developed, microscopic crystals

The specimen comprises a few elongated fragments of calcite, which have well developed crystalline forms visible even to the naked eye. The tiny crystals are immersed in a liquid of refractive index 1·54 to make an uncovered mount; preliminary microscopic examination is made under low-medium magnification (30–50×) in parallel unpolarised white light. All grains have the same appearance, and their shape is shown in Fig. 12.11*a*; even when teased with a needle and rolled about their lengths, the appearance is unchanged. Clearly these calcite crystals show hexagonal prisms and bipyramids. Although this morphological description cannot unambiguously establish the symmetry class, calcite must belong to either the trigonal or the hexagonal symmetry system, and is therefore optically uniaxial. The crystals show no colour or inhomogeneity of any kind. With the polariser inserted, the crystals have no change in absorption properties as the microscope stage is rotated.

Even after this brief examination of the initial mount, the next step is clear. With a uniaxial specimen, we need a section parallel to the optic axis on which to measure the principal refractive indices. The calcite crystals lying on prism faces in the mount provide just such sections; confirmation of this orientation can be obtained from the centred flash figure shown by each crystal in convergent light. Reverting to parallel light, the extinction positions for prism faces are investigated; as expected, they are parallel and perpendicular to the length of the face. With a crystal in extinction the analyser is removed, so that light vibrating parallel to the length of the crystal is transmitted (Fig. 12.11*b*); the crystal shows a moderate relief, and a Becke test indicates that the refractive index is less than that of the liquid. The stage is then rotated through 90° so that the incident light now vibrates parallel to the other principal vibration direction (Fig. 12.11*c*); there is now high relief, and the refractive index is greater than that of the liquid. Since the optic axis is parallel to the length of the crystal, $n_o > 1{\cdot}54 > n_e$, so that calcite is optically negative with a fairly large birefringence. We now pursue higher accuracy in the values of n_o and n_e by immersing the crystals in lower and higher refractive index liquids; uncovered mounts facilitate the transfer of crystals, which are carefully dried and cleaned between

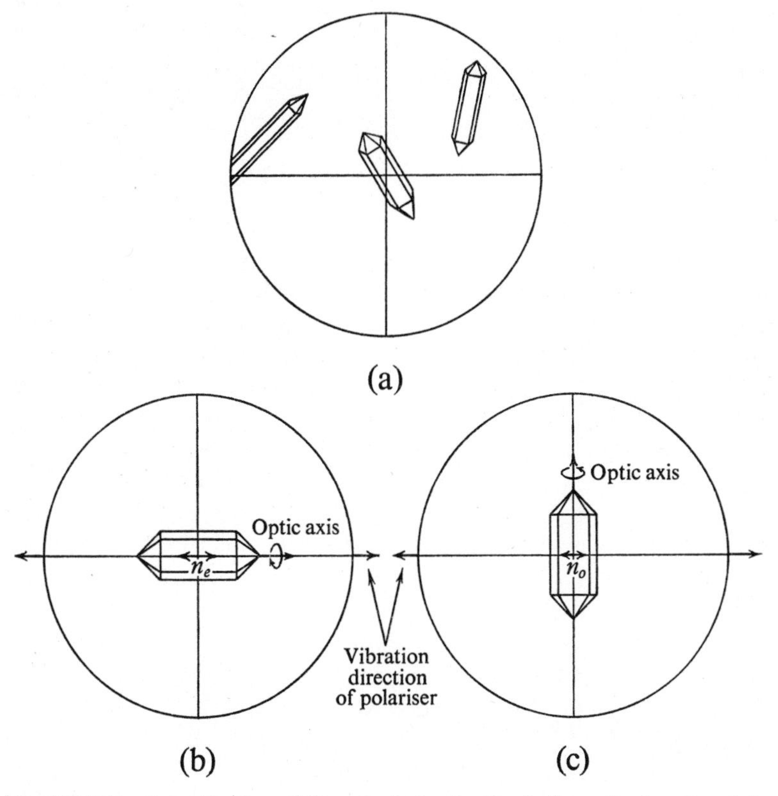

Fig. 12.11 The determination of the principal refractive indices of prismatic calcite crystals.
a. General appearance.
b. Orientation of crystal to determine n_e, polariser inserted.
c. Orientation of crystal to determine n_o, polariser inserted.

each immersion. When light is vibrating parallel to the length of the crystal, n_e is bracketed between 1·48 and 1·49 with very similar relief in each of the mounts; when light is vibrating perpendicular to the length of the prism, an almost complete match is obtained in a liquid of refractive index 1·66. Hence the principal refractive indices of calcite are determined as n_o=1·66 and n_e=1·48$_5$.

(*b*) *The determination of the optical properties of a uniaxial specimen from a thin section through a polycrystalline aggregate*

A thin section of a quartzite rock is permanently mounted on a slide with a cement of refractive index 1·54, and appears completely transparent to the naked eye. Preliminary microscopic examination in unpolarised light is rather uninformative and reveals that there are no inclusions, no foreign crystals, nor apparently any cleavages; some rather irregular traces are faintly visible in places, but these are probably due to slight fragmentation of the section along boundaries between individual quartz grains during grinding. No significant change occurs with the insertion of the polariser, but when the analyser is also introduced in the crossed position the appearance changes markedly to that usually shown by a section through a random aggregate of anisotropic crystals. Each of the interlocked grains in the slice shows an interference colour, but the position of the colour in the interference scale depends on the orientation of the section through each grain; the boundaries of individual crystals within the aggregate are clearly defined by the colour changes across them (Fig. 12.12). For the standard 30μ quartzite section the interference colours of different grains range from grey-blues of various shades to an occasional slightly yellowish white; there are also one or two grains which appear to be effectively isotropic. In all cases the extinction is sharp, but the permitted vibration directions for any grain are arbitrary; individual crystals show no sign of any kind of inhomogeneity.

The range of interference colours from the 30μ section is limited to the first order; if the aggregate is truly random the maximum birefringence of quartz must be rather low. We need to find, first, a section as nearly normal to the optic axis as possible; this requires a little more care than usual, for the low maximum birefringence means that sections of 30μ thickness inclined at considerable angles to the optic axis show the grey interference colours which often provide slightly offset but satisfactory sections for more birefringent materials. From a more or less isotropic crystal, an interference figure shows a slightly off-centred black cross, whose arms remain straight on rotation of the stage (*n.b.* the section is too thin to show noticeable effects of the optical activity of quartz described in Appendix D); owing to the low birefringence, no pronounced coloured fringe system is visible. In addition to confirming the uniaxial nature of quartz, this figure may be used to determine the optic sign with a sensitive tint plate; quartz is optically positive with $n_e > n_o$. Since the relief of this crystal is very low, n_o is about 1·54.

The second important section of uniaxial quartz is one which contains the optic axis, so that it has the maximum birefringence and shows the highest order interference colour (yellowish white). The two permitted vibration directions for light passing through this section are

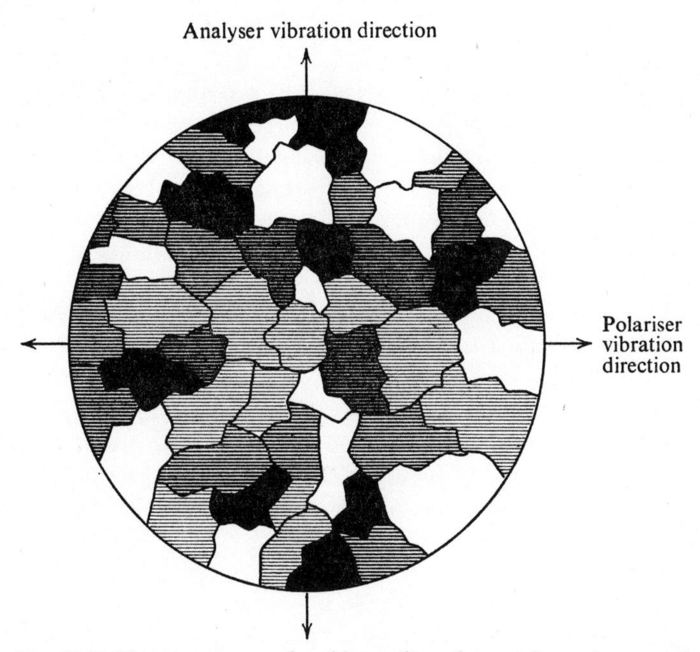

Fig. 12.12 The appearance of a thin section of quartzite rock; crossed polars, parallel white light. The boundaries of the separate quartz grains are distinguished by the interference colours which range from black through greys to a yellowish white.

associated with the principal values n_o and n_e, but since the thickness of the section is known, it is worth while measuring the birefringence ($n_e - n_o$). Since there is no ambiguity about the order of the yellowish white interference colour, the value $n_e - n_o \sim 0{\cdot}010$ can be read directly from the Michel-Lévy chart. We now have approximate values of the principal refractive indices, and more accurate determination can only be made if this grain is cut from the section. It can, of course, be used *in situ* to confirm the deductions so far by comparison measurements relative to the mounting cement. To do this, it is necessary to determine which of the permitted vibration directions is the ordinary (fast);

it is difficult to achieve complete compensation with a wedge owing to the low total retardation, but a quarter wave or sensitive tint plate works satisfactorily. We conclude from this investigation that quartz is uniaxial, optically positive, with $n_o \sim 1{\cdot}54$, $n_e \sim 1{\cdot}55$.

(c) The determination of the dichroic scheme of a coloured uniaxial specimen present in a thin section

The problem is to investigate the absorption properties of a variety of tourmaline (a complex alumino-silicate mineral group) in a thin section of a rock containing other minerals. The general properties of members of the tourmaline group are known; prismatic crystals are uniaxial, of negative sign, with refractive indices within a restricted range. Even to the naked eye, the coloured grains of the thin section stand out from the transparent minerals quartz and feldspar which are also present. Initial microscopic examination shows that most sections of the coloured crystals are elongated with rather irregular terminations, though an occasional cross-section appears to have a roughly hexagonal outline. The only other coloured minerals known to form in significant amount in the assemblage of this rock-type have good cleavages; careful examination of all coloured grains reveals no cleavage traces suggesting that only tourmaline crystals are present in this specimen. The colours range from a deep olive green to pale brown for various grains. With the polariser inserted, rotation of the microscope stage causes colour changes for most crystals, and demonstrates the pleochroism of the tourmaline.

The determination of absorption properties of a uniaxial crystal follows an analogous procedure to the last example; once again we must locate a section containing the optic axis direction. In the previous example we searched for this systematically by finding grains which show the highest order interference colours; this method is no longer entirely reliable as the body colour of the crystal may mask the interference effects to give an anomalous colour sequence. It is probably safer to try to work from the previous knowledge of tourmalines concerning their prismatic habit. Sections through prismatic crystals show a roughly equi-dimensional outline normal to the optic axis, with increasing elongation as the inclination to the optic axis decreases. When examined over a polariser, the occasional crystal of equi-dimensional cross-section shows little or no colour change on rotation; the appearance of the grain remains a dark green. Turning to the most elongated grains, the ordinary vibration direction must be perpendicular to the length, and with light vibrating in this direction we can obtain one colour of the dichroic scheme; as expected, all crystals show the dark green colour in this position. When these same elongated crystals are rotated through 90° above the polariser, their colours are variable from straw yellow to deeper browns; this range of intensities and colours can occur because the crystal sections are at differing inclinations to the optic axis. A section which contains the optic axis direction is one in which there is the greatest change in absorption during the rotation of the stage above the polariser. Ideally it would be best to confirm the correct orientation of the chosen crystal by seeing that it shows an approximately centred flash figure in convergent light, but in practice it is not always possible to obtain enough transmitted light to be able to see the ill-defined interference effects. We conclude that this variety of tourmaline has the absorption formula $O \gg E$, while the axial colours are O, dark green; E, straw yellow; the corresponding face colours are green and brown.

(d) The determination of the principal refractive indices of a crushed powder of a biaxial specimen

The specimen provided is a small quantity of crushed and sieved colourless fragments of anhydrite (β-$CaSO_4$). An exploratory covered mount is made in a liquid of refractive index 1·57, and the microscopic appearance of the powder shows that the crystal fragments are all regularly shaped in the form of rectangular parallelopipeds. All grains show traces of mutually perpendicular cleavage planes; they are colourless and are apparently homogeneous. With crossed polars all crystals appear anisotropic, and have straight extinction parallel to their edges. While eliminating any suspicion of cubic symmetry, these observations also make the possibility of tetragonal (uniaxial) symmetry very unlikely. The most probable explanation of the shape of the fragments is that anhydrite is orthorhombic (biaxial), and has three distinct perfect pinacoidal cleavages.

Normally the biaxial character could be confirmed by a suitable interference figure, but in this problem there is some advantage in first carrying out rough refractive index determinations for the crystals in the mount. These show that three distinct cleavage fragments can be recognised (Fig. 12.13): (*a*) some grains have one refractive index matching the liquid with the other only slightly greater; (*b*) some grains, although they have one refractive index almost exactly matching that of the liquid, have rather higher relief than those of type (*a*) when the light vector is parallel to the other vibration direction; (*c*) crystals of the third group have one refractive index slightly greater than the liquid and the other distinctly greater, as in (*b*). The observations are in accord with suspected orthorhombic symmetry and pinacoidal cleavages of anhydrite. We can obtain further confirmation from the interference figures shown by the three kinds of cleavage fragment; type (*a*) shows a centred

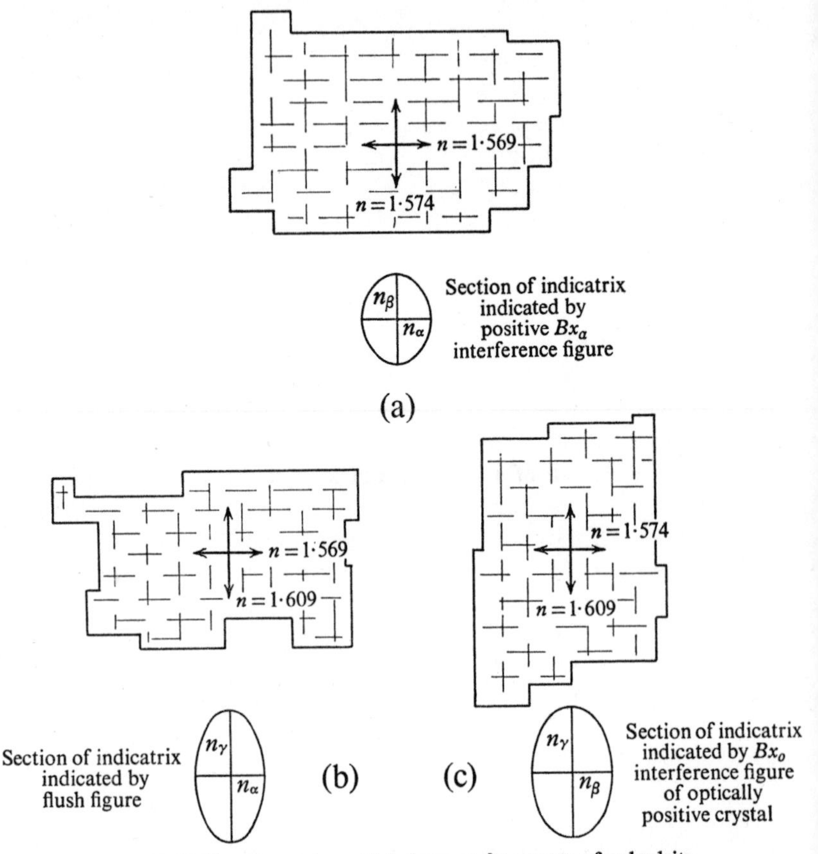

Fig. 12.13 The three pinacoidal cleavage fragments of anhydrite.

optically positive acute bisectrix figure ($2V_\gamma \sim 40°$), type (*b*) shows a centred flash figure and type (*c*) a centred obtuse bisectrix figure; there is slight indication of dispersion. From this one mount, we deduce that for orthorhombic anhydrite, the principal refractive indices are observable from the three cleavage fragments, n_α, n_β from (*a*), n_α, n_γ from (*b*) and n_β, n_γ from (*c*); estimating values from the reliefs, we obtain $n_\alpha \sim 1{\cdot}57$, $n_\beta \sim 1{\cdot}57_5$ and $n_\gamma \sim 1{\cdot}60$. Further definition of the indicatrix can be obtained by examining the three cleavage fragments in a single variation apparatus to give $n_\alpha = 1{\cdot}569$, $n_\beta = 1{\cdot}574$ and $n_\gamma = 1{\cdot}609$ (all to $\pm 0{\cdot}001$); the optic axial angle is measured using a spindle stage as $2V_\gamma = 42°$ (these are the values used for anhydrite in 3.3).

(e) The determination of the optical orientation of an orthorhombic specimen using thin sections

Three thin sections of celestine ($SrSO_4$) are provided cut parallel to (100), (010) and (001) for this orthorhombic material; celestine has cleavages described as {001}, perfect, and {110}, nearly perfect, with the angle $(110):(1\bar{1}0) = 76°$. Since celestine is known to be orthorhombic the problem is to decide which of the three principal axes of the indicatrix is normal to each of the three orientated sections. In all orientation work, it is essential to identify crystallographic reference directions in the plane of each section; for celestine cleavage traces provide these directions, and their occurrence on the three sections must be carefully examined. The (100) section shows one set of parallel cleavage cracks, for both planes of cleavage intersect the section in traces parallel to the *z*-axis (Fig. 12.14*a*); the same is also true of the (010) section (Fig. 12.14*b*). The (001) section, however, shows two inclined sets of traces (Fig. 12.14*c*); the angle between the traces is measured as about 75°, so they must represent the intersections of the {110} cleavage planes with the section. For this section, the bisectors of the obtuse and acute angles between the traces must be the directions of the *x*- and *y*-axes respectively.

We can now proceed with the orientation of the indicatrix. Direct determination of principal refractive indices as in the previous problem is not practicable. Although all three principal values are appreciably greater than the mounting cement (1·54), visible changes in relief are not discernible as each of the sections is rotated over the polariser, indicating a relatively low maximum birefringence. However, we can determine the fast and slow vibration directions for each section by examining the effect of a compensator on the interference colour. For both the (100) and (010) sections, the fast vibration direction is parallel to the cleavage traces, which can only be so if $z = \alpha$. The (001) section can now be used to determine whether or not light vibrating parallel to the *x*-axis is slow relative to that vibrating parallel to the *y*-axis; since it is found that the light vector is slow when parallel to the *x*-axis, we conclude that $y = \beta$ and $x = \gamma$. Alternatively, or for confirmation, this orientation can be derived from interference figures. The (100) and (001) sections show

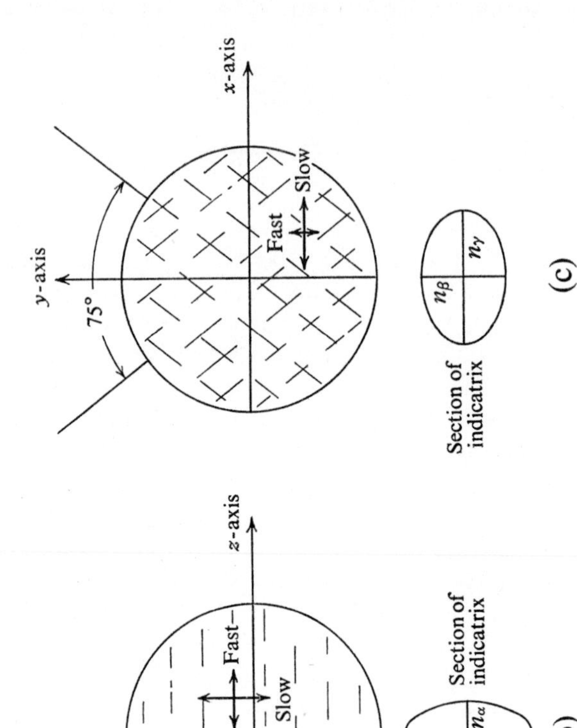

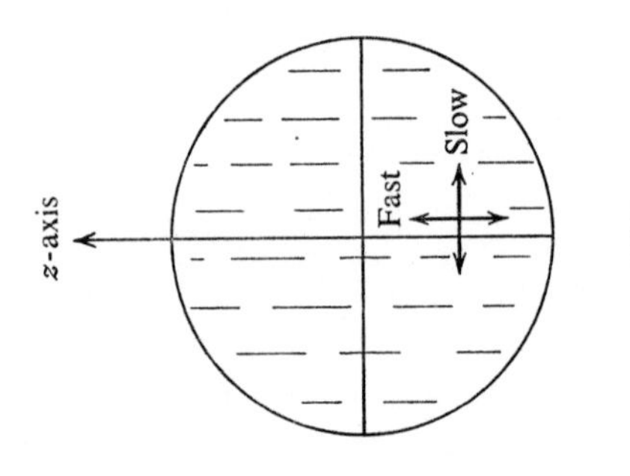

Fig. 12.14 The determination of the optic orientation of celestine: (*a*) (100) section; (*b*) (010) section; (*c*) (001) section.

centred bisectrix figures; that from the (100) section is an optically positive acute bisectrix figure, showing that $2V_\gamma$ is about 50° in an optic axial plane perpendicular to the cleavage traces.

(*f*) *The determination of the optic orientation of a monoclinic specimen in thin section*

The specimen provided is a thin section through an aggregate of small needle-like crystals of an amphibole (a well known silicate mineral group); the elongated crystals in the aggregate are more or less parallel to one another, and the thin section is cut roughly parallel to their common direction. So far as our problem is concerned, essential data are that minerals of the amphibole group have either orthorhombic or monoclinic symmetry and that acicular crystals are always elongated parallel to the *z*-axis. Preliminary microscopic examination of the specimen shows that is contains only thin elongated sections of amphibole crystals; from the nature of the aggregate and the properties of amphiboles, the sections are roughly parallel to the *z*-axis, which is directed along their length. The crystals are coloured and show pleochroism with colours ranging from a pale yellowish green to a dark green; although not primarily a concern of the problem in hand, this absorption is relevant in that it may complicate other observations.

We must first decide whether the particular variety of amphibole has orthorhombic or monoclinic symmetry. We know that in biaxial crystals the essential orientation of the indicatrix differs in the three systems, and this can lead to characteristically different optical properties. In particular the variation of extinction angles measured on to a crystallographic axis around principal zones can differ in the three systems. So far as our problem is concerned, the stricter symmetry control of the indicatrix in orthorhombic crystals means that any section parallel to the *z*-axis must show straight extinction on to this direction; a random collection of such sections, although of differing birefringences, will always show parallel extinction (Fig. 12.15*a*). If our specimen is monoclinic, the only symmetry control on the orientation of the indicatrix is about the *y*-axis, so that sections parallel to the *z*-axis will only show straight extinction if they are also parallel to the *y*-axis; all other sections of this kind will show oblique extinction, the angle on to the *z*-axis being variable up to a maximum depending on the inclination of the section to the *y*-axis. A random collection of sections as displayed by our specimen will show variable interference colours, and predominantly oblique extinction (Fig. 12.15*b*). (The argument may be

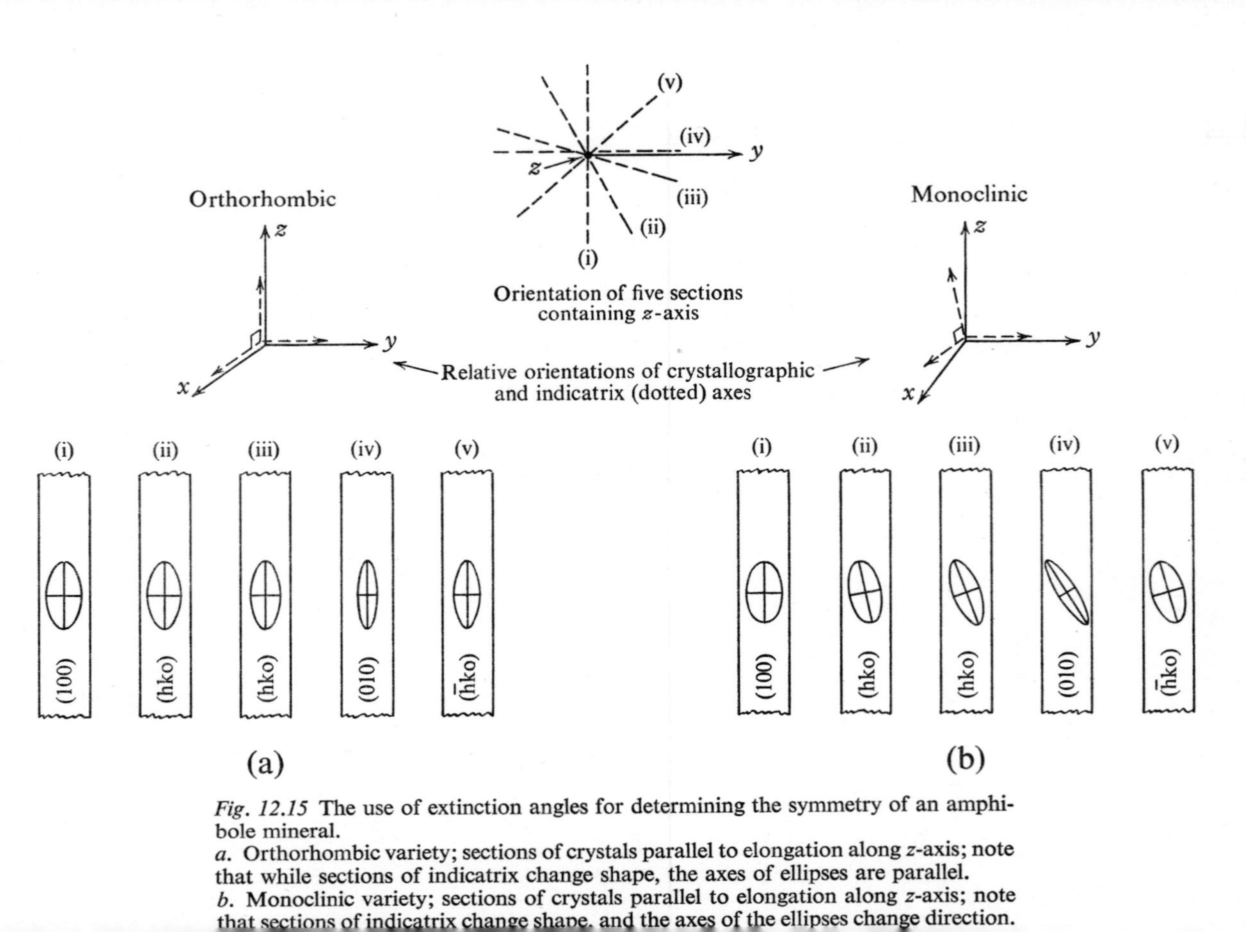

Fig. 12.15 The use of extinction angles for determining the symmetry of an amphibole mineral.
a. Orthorhombic variety; sections of crystals parallel to elongation along z-axis; note that while sections of indicatrix change shape, the axes of ellipses are parallel.
b. Monoclinic variety; sections of crystals parallel to elongation along z-axis; note that sections of indicatrix change shape, and the axes of the ellipses change direction.

extended to triclinic crystals, where the random sections will show exclusively inclined extinction.) In the present specimen the amphibole sections show a mainly oblique extinction of variable angle, with only an occasional parallel extinction; our specimen is therefore a monoclinic amphibole.

In order to fix the orientation of the indicatrix about the y-axis, we need to identify an {010} section containing the x- and z-axes. In general, the principal axis of the indicatrix normal to this section can be the direction of γ, β or α, so that the section can show maximum or minimum birefringence, as well as some intermediate value. A study of interference colours is not very helpful; for the amphibole specimen, it would be complicated by the effects of pleochroism. It is rather better to extend the argument above about the orientation of the indicatrix to realise that we should expect an {010} section to have a maximum value of the extinction angle. On its own, this method is not entirely reliable, for some optical properties can lead to extinction angles of the same magnitude for prismatic sections inclined at appreciable angles to (010); the correct choice of section can be confirmed if it shows a centred interference figure. For the amphibole, a suitable selection shows a centred flash figure, indicating that $y=\beta$, with the optic axial plane parallel to (010). For this section, the extinction angle from the slow vibration direction on to the length is 16°; thus $z:\gamma=16°$. There remains a certain ambiguity in this last observation which cannot be resolved in the present optical work, for there is no reference direction which can tell us whether the direction of γ is in the acute or obtuse angle between the x- and z-axes.

(g) *The complete determination of a powdered monoclinic specimen which is a member of a solid solution series*

The sieved powder of separated, colourless fragments has already been recognised from its occurrence and an initial optic examination as a hyalophane, a member of the relatively rare potassium-barium feldspar mineral series. The problem is to determine as completely as possible the optical properties of this monoclinic material so that they may be compared with those of the few other members of this solid solution series which have been described. Previous work on hyalophanes has shown that they have relatively good {001} and {010} cleavages, that the optic axial plane is perpendicular to (010), and that the refractive indices are within the range 1·51–1·55. Microscopic examination of a mount made with a liquid of refractive index 1·53 confirms that the powder contains cleavage flakes with parallel sides, but there are no other significant optical features. From the earlier data, the parallel edges on either kind of cleavage flake must be in the direction of the x-axis.

Using the arguments on the effect of the orientation of the indicatrix

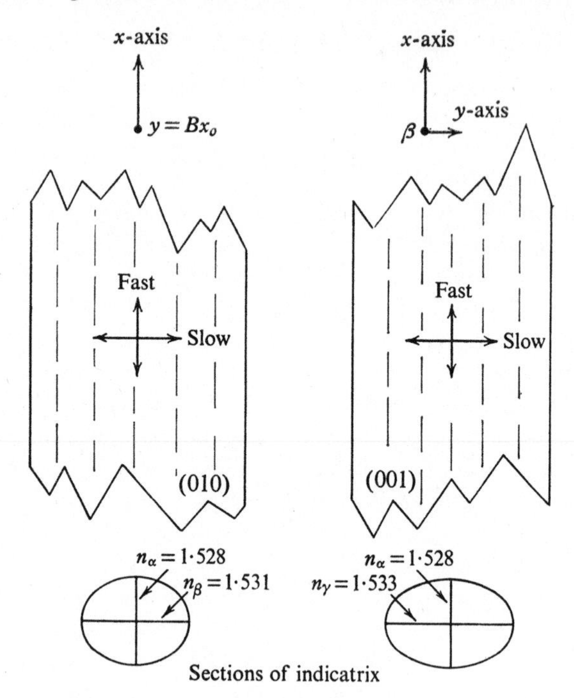

Fig. 12.16 The properties of the {010} and {001} cleavage flakes of a variety of hyalophane.
Note that owing to the parallelism of the x-axis and a principal (α) vibration direction, both flakes show straight extinction on to the x-axis, and allow the determination of all three principal refractive indices.

on extinction angles in principal zones set out in the previous example, we should expect to distinguish the two kinds of cleavage flake; the {001} flakes should show straight extinction, while {010} flakes should have inclined extinction on to the x-axis. Unfortunately for this hyalophane, all cleavage flakes show straight extinction (Fig. 12.16). There are two possible interpretations of this unexpected observation. Either this variety of hyalophane is unusual in that it does not show the expected {010} cleavage, or at this composition in the solid solution series, it so happens that one axis of the indicatrix is parallel to the

x-axis. This dilemma can be resolved by the observation of interference figures. With the optic axial plane normal to (010), an {010} flake shows a centred acute or obtuse bisectrix figure, depending on the orientation of the indicatrix and optic sign; from data on other hyalophanes $y = Bx_o$. {001} cleavage flakes of monoclinic crystals do not usually show centred interference figures, though if the specific orientation of the indicatrix suggested by the parallel extinction is correct, we can expect a centred flash figure for such sections of our hyalophane. Two types of interference figure are distinguished for our specimen, confirming that both kinds of cleavage flakes are present in the powder; those with identifiable flash figures are taken as {001} flakes, while all those that show obtuse bisectrix figures are regarded as {010} flakes.

For both {001} and {010} cleavage flakes, it is found that the fast vibration direction is parallel to the x-axis; as $y = Bx_o$, this implies that the orientation of the optically negative crystal is $y = \gamma$, and $x \| \alpha$. Using a variation method, we can now proceed to the determination of the principal refractive indices. From an {010} section the fast and slow vibration directions give $n_\alpha = 1{\cdot}528$ and $n_\beta = 1{\cdot}531$ respectively; similar measurements on an {001} flake provide the values of $n_\alpha = 1{\cdot}528$ (fast) and $n_\gamma = 1{\cdot}533$ (slow). (It should be noted that but for the fortuitous orientation of the indicatrix, the fast vibration direction would have yielded $n_{\alpha'}$, an intermediate value.) Although $2V_\alpha$ can be calculated from the principal refractive indices, the value will be very inaccurate, and it is best measured directly. The third mean line is normal to an {001} section providing a convenient orientation for mounting on a spindle stage to permit rotation of the bisectrices; the negative sign of the crystal is confirmed, and the optic axial angle measured as 66°.

We conclude from this investigation that the optical properties of this variety of hyalophane are: $n_\alpha = 1{\cdot}528$, $n_\beta = 1{\cdot}531$, $n_\gamma = 1{\cdot}533$ (all to $\pm 0{\cdot}001$); $y = \gamma$, $x : \alpha = 0°$ (it is not determined whether β lies within the acute or obtuse angle between the x- and z-axes); optically negative, with $2V_\alpha = 66°$ ($\pm 2°$).

12.5 Exercises

The following examples are only a selection of those which can be devised to help the student improve his optical techniques. The selection covers the range of topics within this book and includes both practical and theoretical examples, stressing that both aspects of optical studies are essential ingredients of the experience demanded in the most efficient solution of optical problems. The exercises are progressive and are based on those found suitable in moderately large classes.

1. Refractive index determination:

Use a powder containing small cleavage rhombohedra of calcite to confirm that the refractive indices for light travelling normal to a rhombohedral face are $n_o=1{\cdot}66$ and $n_{e'}=1{\cdot}56_7$ (as in Fig. 3.10).

2. Study of a recrystallised material:

Recrystallise ammonium dihydrogen phosphate ($NH_4H_2PO_4$) from water. Use these crystals to determine as much as you can about the optical properties of this substance.

3. Study of a thin section:

Scapolite (a complex alumino-silicate) is a constituent of the limestone rock slice provided; it is colourless, has moderate birefringence and is untwinned. After identifying the scapolite grains, use them to determine as much as you can about the optical properties of this substance. Try to decide the nature of the cleavages.

4. Recognition of a powdered material:

All five carbonates listed below are trigonal with good $\{10\bar{1}1\}$ cleavages. A crushed powder of one of these materials is provided; use the optical properties to identify the carbonate.

$CaCO_3$	$n_o=1{\cdot}658$, $n_e=1{\cdot}486$
$CaMg(CO_3)_2$	$n_o=1{\cdot}679$, $n_e=1{\cdot}500$
$MgCO_3$	$n_o=1{\cdot}700$, $n_e=1{\cdot}509$
$MnCO_3$	$n_o=1{\cdot}816$, $n_e=1{\cdot}547$
$ZnCO_3$	$n_o=1{\cdot}850$, $n_e=1{\cdot}625$

5. Refractive index determination from measurements on an oriented general section:

A section cut parallel to the (212) face of a crystal of the tetragonal material X shows the traces of good {110} cleavages. The slow vibration direction is inclined at 14·75° to one of these traces in the acute angle between them, and the refractive indices for the section are measured as 1·378 and 1·383. Determine the values of the principal refractive indices of X.

6. Recognition of the components of a powdered mixture:

The powder supplied contains two or more of the salts whose optical properties are listed below. Use these properties to decide which salts are present.

K_2SO_4	Orthorhombic symmetry:	$n_\alpha=1{\cdot}494$, $n_\beta=1{\cdot}495$, $n_\gamma=1{\cdot}497$
$K_2S_2O_8$	Triclinic symmetry:	$n_\alpha=1{\cdot}461$, $n_\beta=1{\cdot}470$, $n_\gamma=1{\cdot}566$
$K_2S_2O_6$	Trigonal symmetry:	$n_o=1{\cdot}455$, $n_e=1{\cdot}515$
$K_2S_3O_6$	Orthorhombic symmetry:	$n_\alpha=1{\cdot}493$, $n_\beta=1{\cdot}564$, $n_\gamma=1{\cdot}602$
$K_2S_4O_6$	Monoclinic symmetry:	$n_\alpha=1{\cdot}590$, $n_\beta=1{\cdot}606$, $n_\gamma=1{\cdot}644$

7. Use of extinction angles in biaxial crystals:

The two thin sections provided are of tremolite asbestos and chrysotile asbestos, both complex silicates which occur as fibrous materials elongated along the z-axis; one has orthorhombic and the other monoclinic symmetry.

Decide which has monoclinic symmetry, and determine the characteristic maximum extinction angle for this material.

8. The optical properties of a well-developed biaxial crystal:

A well-developed crystal of aragonite (the orthorhombic variety of $CaCO_3$) has $a:b:c=0{\cdot}6224:1:0{\cdot}7206$; the crystal was used for the determination of refractive indices by the minimum-deviation method (see Appendix C.1). When monochromatic light entered through the face (110) and left through the face $(1\bar{1}0)$, the angles of minimum deviation were measured as 44° 12′ and 62° 12′; when the faces (011) and $(01\bar{1})$ were used the angles were 87° 27′ and 89° 09′.

For this wavelength, determine the principal refractive indices, the optic orientation, the optic axial angle and sign of aragonite.

9. Construction of a wedge:

A wedge of 1° angle is cut from the aragonite crystal of (8) above with its flat base parallel to (001). What is the distance between the first and second dark bands when the wedge is viewed between crossed polars in parallel NaD light ($\lambda=590$mμ)? How should the wedge be cut so as to have the slow vibration along its length? Describe what happens as the polariser is rotated relative to the analyser.

10. The optical properties of a biaxial crystal from an oriented thick section:

Morphological studies of a well-developed crystal of diopside (a member of the complex alumino-silicate pyroxene group) confirms that it has monoclinic symmetry, with $a:b:c=1{\cdot}092:1:0{\cdot}589$, $\beta=105°\ 50'$.

A section was cut perpendicular to the acute bisectrix, and examination of the interference figure showed that the optic axial plane bisects the acute angle (72·25°) between the traces of the {110} cleavages. The principal refractive indices were measured by immersing the section, after polishing, in a bath of liquid ($n=1{\cdot}742$) on a Kohlrausch refractometer (see Appendix C.2). With the optic axial plane vertical, values of 78° 28′ and 74° 40′ were recorded for the critical angles; with the optic axial plane horizontal, values of 78° 28′ and 75° 20′ were obtained. Use this information to determine as much as you can about the optical properties of diopside. How would you attempt to resolve any ambiguities that remain?

11. The pleochroic scheme of a biaxial material:

A thin section of a rock contains crystals of green hornblende (a member of the complex alumino-silicate amphibole group) in various orientations. It is known that hornblendes have monoclinic symmetry, with good {110} cleavages and $(110):(1\bar{1}0)\sim56°$; the optic axial plane is (010), $z:\gamma\sim15°$ and a large negative optic axial angle. Use this information to identify grains in various orientations so as to determine the pleochroic scheme for this hornblende.

12. The determination of a member of a solid solution series:

Olivines have orthorhombic symmetry and are members of a solid solution formed ideally between Mg_2SiO_4 and Fe_2SiO_4. Use the crushed and separated powder of an olivine to determine its optical properties as accurately and as fully as possible. Compare your results with those for other members of the series (see Deer, Howie and Zussman *Rock Forming Minerals*, Vol. 1) and estimate the composition of your specimen.

13. A general study of a biaxial material:

Crystals of the biaxial substance Y are always elongated parallel to the z-axis. A section 290μ thick cut parallel to (100) shows an almost centred positive acute-bisectrix interference figure with three rings about each melatope in NaD light ($\lambda=590\text{m}\mu$), and from which $2E$ is determined as 95°. Other {hk0} sections show both fast and slow vibrations along their lengths in different cases, while an (010) section has a centred obtuse bisectrix interference figure.

If $n_\alpha=1{\cdot}586$, what are the approximate values of n_β and n_γ, and to what symmetry system does Y probably belong?

14. Study of a recrystallised material:

Recrystallise potassium chlorate ($KClO_3$) from water; the material will show mainly {001} plates bounded by faces of the form {110}, with (110) : $(1\bar{1}0)\sim 80°$. Determine the optical properties of $KClO_3$, as fully as you can both by using the plates themselves and by mounting fragments of them on a spindle stage.

Occasional crystals show lamellar twinning. Try to locate such a twinned crystal by crushing recrystallised plates to provide more general orientations. Attempt to relate the twin law to the optical and crystallographic features of the original plates, by making a detailed study of an individual crystal using a subsidiary microscope stage.

APPENDIX A

THE INDICATRIX AND ITS PROPERTIES

A.1 The uniaxial indicatrix

In 4.3 we defined the optical indicatrix as a spatial plot of the variation of refractive index as a function of vibration direction. For a uniaxial crystal, the indicatrix was described as a single-surfaced ellipsoid of revolution similar in shape to the extraordinary ray velocity surface, with properties that allow the prediction of refractive indices (and vibration directions) for any general wave normal direction of propagation in the crystal. We shall now justify the description and properties of this representation surface for uniaxial crystals assuming that such crystals have ray velocity surfaces as in 4.1.

There are two disturbances, ordinary and extraordinary, associated with a general wave normal direction in the uniaxial crystal. Initially we will direct our attention to the extraordinary waves, which travel so that the ray direction is inclined to the wave normal. Fig. A.1 shows a principal section through a uniaxial extraordinary ray velocity surface containing the optic axis direction and the ray direction. The semi-axes of the ellipse are OY′, the maximum (or minimum) extraordinary velocity, and OZ′, the minimum (or maximum) extraordinary velocity; since OZ′ is the optic axis direction, OZ′ $=v_o$, the ordinary velocity, while OY′ $=v_e$, with the optic sign determining whether $v_o>v_e$, or vice versa. OR′ is the direction of the extraordinary rays we are considering; the associated wave fronts are parallel to the tangent to the surface at R′, so that ON′, normal to these wave fronts, is the wave normal direction. In this general direction, there is a distinction between the ray and wave velocities; we recall from 4.2 that in practical measurement it is the wave velocity which is significant, so that ON′ $=v_{e'}$. Now let us construct another surface similar in shape to the extraordinary ray velocity surface but with inversely related semi-axes. The principal section of this second ellipsoid of revolution is exactly the same as the original ray velocity surface except that its semi-axes are inversely related so that OY $=1/$OZ′ $=1/v_o$, and OZ $=1/$OY′ $=1/v_e$. For the second surface, we can produce OR′ to OR, draw the tangent RQ on which lies the point N at the intersection of ON′ produced (Fig. A.1). Subsequently we can draw the radius OP parallel to RQ, and the tangent PQ, which will be parallel to the radius OR.

The radii OR and OP are called conjugate radii of the larger ellipse, and together with the associated tangents form a parallelogram OPQR.

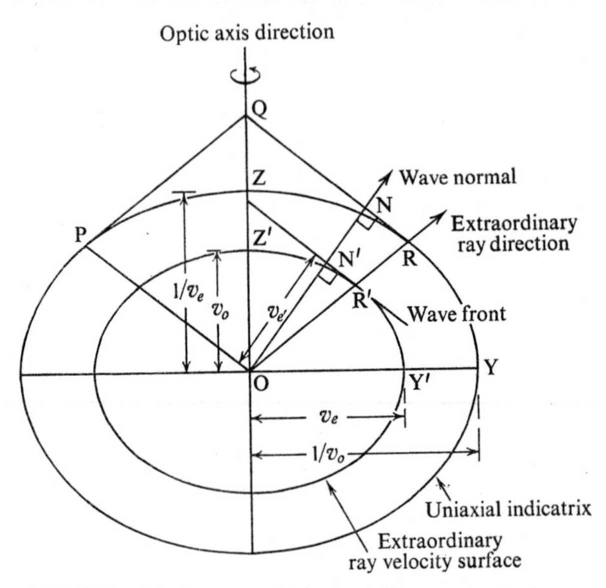

Fig. A.1 Relationship between the extraordinary ray velocity surface and the indicatrix for a uniaxial crystal.

Now it is a geometrical theorem that the area of this parallelogram is constant irrespective of the directions of its sides, so that it is equal to the area of the rectangle formed when the conjugate radii are the semi-axes of the ellipse; we can equate this to the area of OPQR expressed as the product of base and height, so that

$$\mathrm{OY.OZ = OP.ON}$$

$$\mathrm{OP = OY.OZ/ON}$$

but since the figures are similar

$$\mathrm{ON/ON' = OY/OY'}$$

so that $$\mathrm{OP = OY'.OZ/ON' = 1/ON'} = 1/v_{e'}$$

(since we defined $\mathrm{OZ = 1/OY'}$).

Thus far the discussion has been purely geometrical, but we must now consider the implications for the second ellipse. The second surface was defined so that its axes were reciprocals of v_o and v_e; it is therefore an ellipsoid of revolution for which the unique axis is proportional to the maximum (or minimum) extraordinary refractive index (n_e), and for which the radius of the circular section is proportional to the ordinary refractive index (n_o). The geometry above has shown that a property of this surface is that a radius OP, perpendicular to the wave normal ON and lying in the principal section containing ON and the optic axis direction, is the reciprocal of $v_{e'}$; it follows that the radius OP is proportional to the extraordinary refractive index ($n_{e'}$) for this wave normal direction. But what significance has OP? We know that it is in the plane of the wave front perpendicular to ON, and that it lies within a principal section; it must therefore represent the permitted vibration direction for an extraordinary disturbance travelling along this wave normal direction. If we recapitulate the deductions so far, an ellipsoid of revolution with n_e as the axis of revolution, n_o as the radius of the circular section, has the property that a radius parallel to an extraordinary vibration direction is of length $n_{e'}$, the value of the associated refractive index.

The indicatrix may thus be said to be a spatial plot of the extraordinary refractive index with vibration direction, but we must now consider whether it also serves to describe the ordinary disturbance in the same way. For any general wave normal direction ON, there will always be an ordinary disturbance as well as the extraordinary; the ordinary waves move perpendicular to the wave normal, so that ON is the ray direction, with vibration directions always normal to the principal section in the plane of the wave fronts. This implies that whatever the direction of ON, the ordinary vibration direction is perpendicular to it and lies in the central circular section of the ellipsoid of revolution; thus the refractive index of the ordinary waves travelling along ON is n_o. We have now demonstrated that the indicatrix represents a spatial plot of refractive index as a function of vibration direction.

We have incidentally during this argument also demonstrated the basic property of the indicatrix that if the common wave normal direction in the crystal is known, the vibration directions (and associated refractive indices) can be deduced; for it is a geometrical property of an ellipsoid of revolution that any central section (other than that normal to the revolution axis) is an ellipse. An elliptical central section perpendicular to a general wave normal direction must have one of its semi-axes lying within the circular section; depending on the optic sign, this radius of the ellipse (n_o) must be greater or less than all other radii, and so must be either the semi-major or semi-minor axis. Clearly the other semi-axis will be perpendicular to this direction, i.e. it will be the radius whose length is $n_{e'}$. Therefore, as we stated in 4.3, the two axes of the central elliptical section of an indicatrix perpendicular to a wave

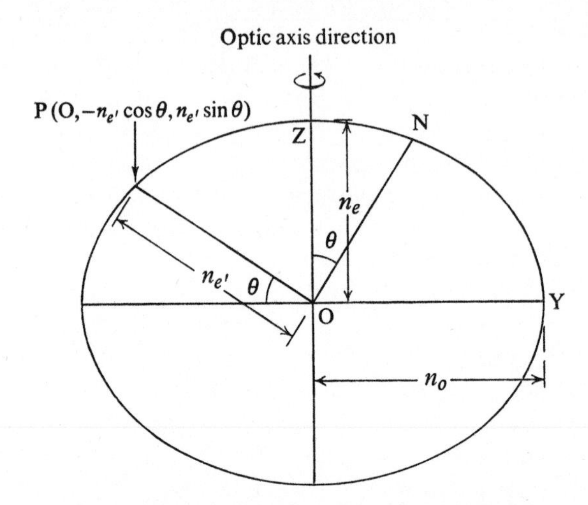

Fig. A.2 Principal section of a uniaxial indicatrix.

normal direction define the two permitted mutually perpendicular vibration directions, whilst the length of the semi-axis is, in each case, proportional to the appropriate refractive index.

The equation of the uniaxial indicatrix can be written

$$x^2/n_o^2+y^2/n_o^2+z^2/n_e^2=1.$$

We can use this equation to evaluate $n_{e'}$ for any general wave normal direction. In Fig. A.2, ON is the general wave normal inclined at an angle θ to the optic axis direction in the yz plane, OP is the radius of the ellipse perpendicular to ON, so that from the properties of the indicatrix OP$=n_{e'}$; the coordinates of P are therefore $(0,-n_{e'}\cos\theta, n_{e'}\sin\theta)$. Substituting these coordinates in the equation of the indicatrix

$$n_{e'}^2\cos^2\theta/n_o^2+n_{e'}^2\sin^2\theta/n_e^2=1$$

so that
$$1/n_{e'}^2=\cos^2\theta/n_o^2+\sin^2\theta/n_e^2.$$

This equation can be put in the form

$$1/n_{e'}^2-1/n_o^2=(1/n_e^2-1/n_o^2)\sin^2\theta.$$

Provided that the birefringence is small, we may write

$$n_{e'} - n_o \doteqdot (n_e - n_o) \sin^2 \theta$$

an equation which can be used for calculating the birefringence for any direction inclined to the optic axis direction provided the maximum birefringence is known.

We can use this equation for the birefringence to determine the curves of equal retardation which appear in the interference figures from uniaxial crystals described in 10.2. If we consider the retardations for total destructive interference giving the dark concentric circles of an optic axis figure with monochromatic light of wavelength λ, the path difference introduced between the ordinary and extraordinary waves in passing through a thickness t is

$$n\lambda = t(n_{e'} - n_o) \doteqdot t(n_e - n_o) \sin^2 \theta.$$

If t is constant, and θ_n is the angular inclination of waves giving rise to the nth dark ring,

$$\sin^2 \theta_n = n\lambda / t(n_e - n_o)$$

so that at small angles, the angular radius of a ring is proportional to the square root of its order. In practice, of course, t increases with the inclination of wave normals to the optic axis, so that the actual increase in angular radius with order is rather smaller.

A.2 The biaxial indicatrix

In 4.4 we showed that the logical development of the indicatrix concept to cover optically biaxial properties needed only a generalisation of the representation surface to become a triaxial ellipsoid. This shape, specified by three principal refractive indices n_γ, n_β and n_α, has two circular sections, whose normals are the two optic axis directions. The general properties concerning the prediction of vibration directions for a particular wave normal direction are essentially the same as those for a uniaxial indicatrix, and it is not proposed to prove them here; proofs may be found in Fletcher's original treatise on the indicatrix mentioned in the bibliography. The relationships between wave normals and ray directions are not so readily apparent for the triaxial ellipsoid as they are for the uniaxial indicatrix. The more important relations may be determined by the following constructions, whose justifications are also to be found in Fletcher's work.

In the most practical problem that it is sometimes necessary to solve, *the two ray directions associated with a given wave normal* must be determined. Essentially this construction is based on properties of the indicatrix illustrated in Fig. A.3*a*. ON is the wave normal direction, and OP is the associated vibration direction perpendicular to it, PQ is the normal to elliptical section PT in this plane, and OR (perpendicular to PQ) is the ray direction; the ray velocity along OR is inversely proportional to PQ. We can demonstrate these relationships in the use of the

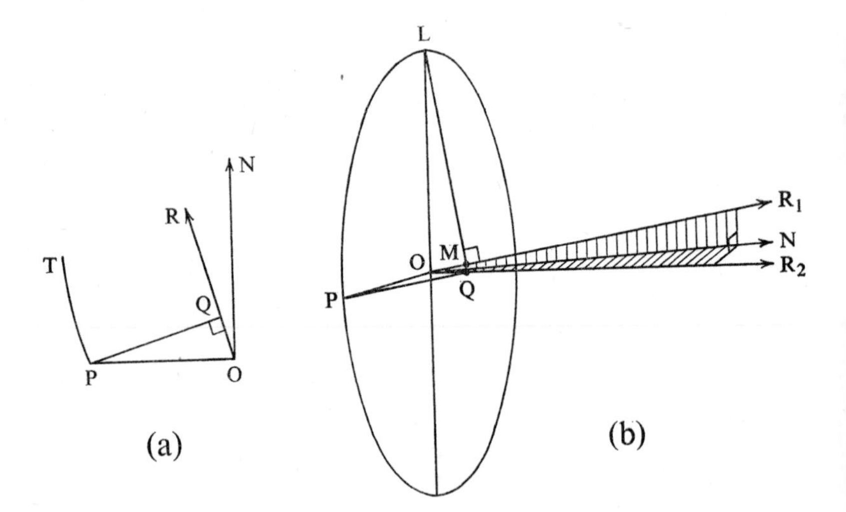

Fig. A.3 Construction to find the two ray directions associated with a given wave normal direction.
a. Essential properties of the indicatrix (see text).
b. Elliptical section of indicatrix perpendicular to a wave normal ON.

indicatrix to solve our problem. In Fig. A.3*b*, ON is the wave normal direction shown together with the elliptical section of the indicatrix perpendicular to it; OP and OL are the semi-axes of this ellipse, and the permitted vibration directions for the given wave normal direction. PQ and LM are the normals to the indicatrix at P and L, and OR_1, OR_2 perpendicular to these normals are the ray directions associated with ON. The geometrical properties of any triaxial ellipsoid are such that OP, PQ, OR_2 and ON are co-planar, as are OL, LM, OR_1 and ON. Similar principles are used in the related construction to find the *two wave normal directions associated with a given ray direction.* Now we must find two mutually perpendicular normals to the indicatrix which are also perpendicular to the ray direction. The tangent cylinder to the ellipsoid (Fig. A.4) parallel to the ray direction OR touches the indicatrix around an elliptical section for which all normals are perpendicular to OR. The problem now is to find the four normals to this ellipse which intersect OR. The four points on the ellipse giving rise to these normals are not, in general, the ends of the semi-axes, and they may be found in the following way. A section of the tangent cylinder perpendicular to OR will be an ellipse whose semi-axes are UV and UW. To locate the

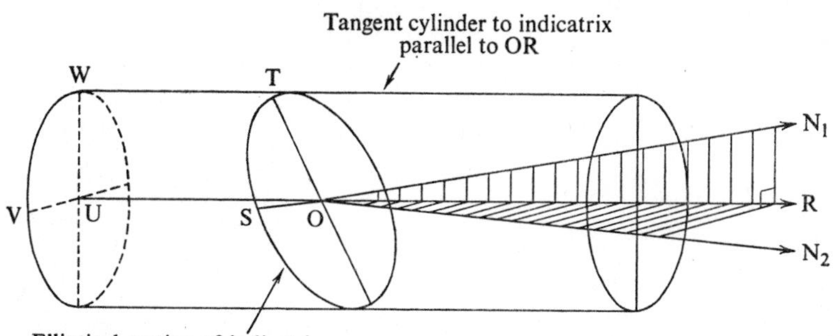

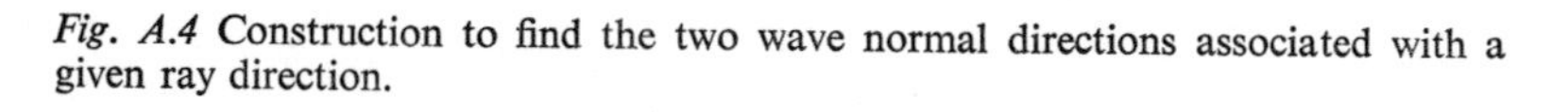
Fig. A.4 Construction to find the two wave normal directions associated with a given ray direction.

normals to the indicatrix section which intersect OR, we must find the radii OS and OT which are co-planar with UV and UW respectively. The two wave normals associated with OR are then ON_1, in the plane TOR perpendicular to OT, and ON_2, in the plane SOR perpendicular to OS.

While these two constructions are not perhaps of great practical importance, it is of considerable value to have a construction which allows *the prediction of the permitted vibration directions for a given wave normal.* In principle, we know that we have to find the major and minor axes of the elliptical section of the indicatrix perpendicular to the wave normal, but it is useful to have a simple method of achieving this without resorting to complex analysis. This can be provided by some form of the Biot-Fresnel construction involving a stereographic projection of the optical elements. The essentials of this construction can be seen in Fig. A.5*a*; we need to locate the semi-axes of the general elliptical section normal to ON. Now this section will be intersected at four points on the surface of the ellipsoid by the circular sections of the indicatrix; P, P′ are the intersections with one circular section, Q, Q′

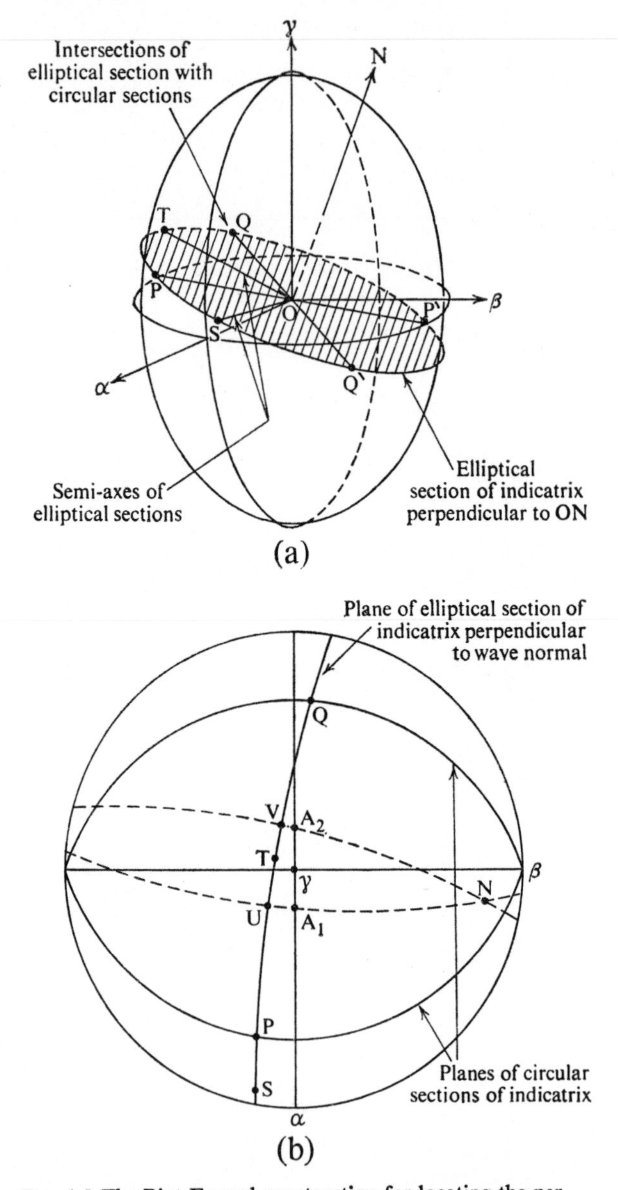

Fig. A.5 The Biot-Fresnel construction for locating the permitted vibration directions for a given wave normal.
a. The geometry of the construction shown on the indicatrix.
b. Adaptation of the construction for use on a stereogram; the dotted great circles represent the planes containing the optic axes and the wave normal used in the alternative form of the construction.

the intersections with the other. This means that OP, OQ, etc. are not only radii of the ellipse but also of the circular sections; they must therefore be of equal length. It is a geometrical property of any ellipse that radii of equal length are symmetrically inclined to its major and minor axes, so that we can find the semi-major and semi-minor axes OS and OT, the permitted vibration directions, by bisecting the angle POQ internally and externally. The transference of this geometrical construction to the stereogram is shown in Fig. A.5*b*. The principal axes of the indicatrix are denoted by γ, β and α, while N represents the direction of the wave normal and A_1 and A_2 locate the two optic axes. The central section of the indicatrix perpendicular to the wave normal is represented by the great circle of which N is the pole, and the circular sections of the indicatrix are shown as the great circles of which A_1 and A_2 are the poles. P and Q at the intersections of these great circles denote the directions of the radii of equal length, so that S and T, the external and internal bisectors of the angle PQ, show the permitted vibration directions. This construction can be put into a different form if we realise that since Q is at the intersection of great circles denoting planes perpendicular to A_1 and N, it must represent a line normal to the plane A_1N; similarly P must represent the direction of a line normal to the plane A_2N. We now draw the great circles through N and the poles of the optic axes to intersect the great circle representing the plane of the ellipse at U and W; since PT=QT and QU=PV=90°, then UT=VT. Thus, in the alternative form, the Biot-Fresnel construction states that the two planes which intersect in a wave normal and which each contain an optic axis meet at an angle which is internally and externally bisected by the permitted vibration directions for the wave normal direction; we used this form when discussing the occurrence of isogyres in biaxial interference figures in 10.4. It will also be noticed that when $2V=0°$, i.e. the crystal is uniaxial, one vibration direction is always on the primitive of the stereogram (the ordinary) whilst the other (the extraordinary) is always 90° away but at differing positions on the stereogram depending on the wave normal direction.

In a graphical form the Biot-Fresnel construction is most useful for predicting extinction angles, perhaps to confirm the behaviour of a test material; these can be calculated (see Johannsen's *Manual of Petrographic Methods*), but often the accuracy of a stereographic projection is sufficient. Suppose that we wish to check the experimental measurements (referred to in 9.5) that the extinction angles for a particular section of an orthorhombic crystal measured between the slow vibration direction and the traces of the {110} cleavages in the plane of the section are +20° and −60°; we might wish to do this to confirm the optical properties of the substance. Fig. A.6 shows a stereogram on which are plotted the optical and crystallographic data. N represents the wave normal for the parallel light incident normally on the crystal section between crossed polars; thus the great circle of which N is the pole represents not only the elliptical section of the indicatrix but also the

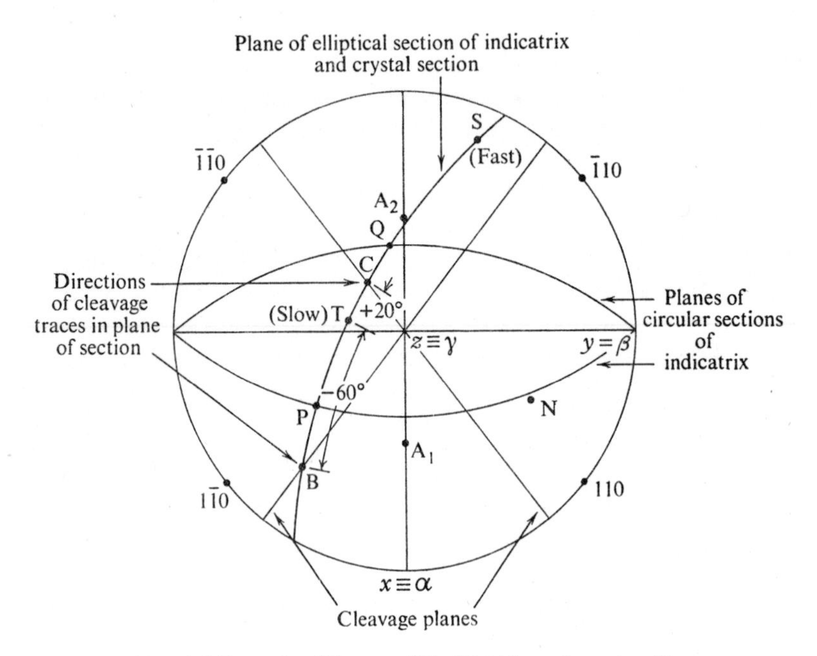

Fig. A.6 Example of the use of the Biot-Fresnel construction.

plane of the crystal section. The Biot-Fresnel construction is carried out as described above to locate S and T, the permitted vibration directions. We must now decide whether T is fast or slow. This is simply done if we remember that the indicatrix shows the variation of refractive index as a function of vibration direction. The vibration direction represented by T is obviously closer in direction to γ (the slowest possible vibration direction for the crystal) at the centre of the stereogram than is that represented by S, so that we may deduce that T is the slower vibration direction. Alternatively we realise that in Fig. A.6 the great circles showing the planes of circular sections of the indicatrix represent the loci of vibration directions for which the refractive index is n_β. As the vibration direction T lies in that sector of the stereogram defined by these great circles which also contains the slowest vibration direction γ, it must be the slower vibration direction; conversely the vibration direction S, which lies outside this sector, must be the faster. We must now insert the reference directions, the cleavage traces. The poles of {110} are plotted from the crystallographic data, and the great circles of which these points are the poles represent the cleavage planes; B and C are at the intersections of these great circles with that representing the section plane, so that they denote the directions of the cleavage traces in the plane of the section. Thus CT and BT are the extinction angles that have been described, $+20°$ and $-60°$ respectively. A practical point that arises concerns the visibility of the cleavage traces; owing to the limited depth of focus of microscope objectives, the traces will only be seen if their intersections are normal or nearly normal to the plane of the crystal section; these angles are represented on the stereogram by the angles between the great circles at A and B, and unless these are greater than about 70°, it is unlikely that the traces will be visible.

From general properties of the biaxial indicatrix we can turn to more detailed consideration of its geometry. The equation of the biaxial indicatrix can be written

$$x^2/n_\alpha^2+y^2/n_\beta^2+z^2/n_\gamma^2=1.$$

This surface has two circular sections whose normals lie in the x–z (or α–γ) plane. We can relate the angle between the optic axes ($2V_\gamma$) to the principal refractive indices n_γ, n_β and n_α quite simply. Fig. A.7 shows the α–γ section of the indicatrix with the traces of the circular sections, and optic axis directions. The radius OP lying in the circular section is of length n_β, and so the coordinates of P are ($-n_\beta \cos V_\gamma$, O, $n_\beta \sin V_\gamma$). If these are substituted in the equation of the ellipsoid above

$$n_\beta^2 \cos^2 V_\gamma/n_\alpha^2+n_\beta^2 \sin^2 V_\gamma/n_\gamma^2=1=\cos^2 V_\gamma+\sin^2 V_\gamma$$

so that $$\tan^2 V_\gamma(1-n_\beta^2/n_\gamma^2)=(n_\beta^2/n_\alpha^2-1)$$

i.e. $$\tan^2 V_\gamma=(1/n_\alpha^2-1/n_\beta^2)/(1/n_\beta^2-1/n_\gamma^2)$$

which can be approximated for most purposes to

$$\tan^2 V_\gamma \doteqdot (n_\gamma-n_\beta)/(n_\beta-n_\alpha).$$

Both these results have been quoted in 4.4 and used there to express the optic sign of a biaxial crystal in terms of principal refractive indices.

We can also use the equation of the triaxial ellipsoid to evaluate the refractive indices appropriate to a general wave normal direction. More often it is important to know the birefringence (n_1-n_2), and this is given by the approximate relation

$$(n_1-n_2) \doteqdot (n_\gamma-n_\alpha) \sin\theta \sin\theta'.$$

where θ and θ' are the angles between the wave normal and the two optic axes; the equation reduces to that given in A.1 for the particular case of uniaxial crystals. The derivation of this expression for the birefringence is rather tedious; details will be found in Johannsen's *Manual of Petrographic Methods*. This equation can be used to investigate

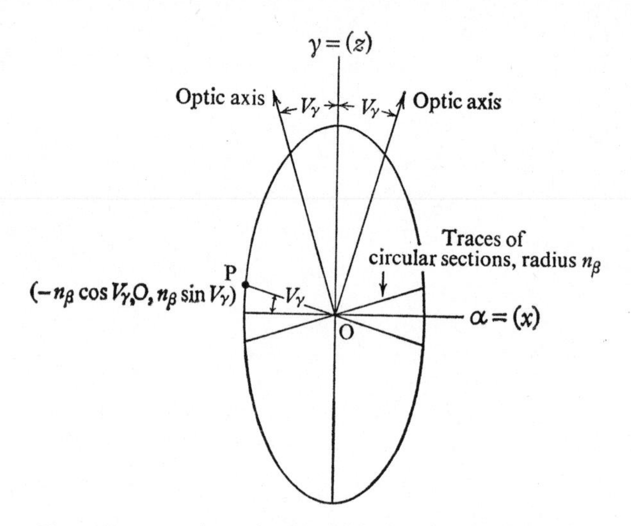

Fig. A.7 γ–α section of a biaxial indicatrix containing the optic axes.

the complex shapes of the equal retardation surfaces seen in section on the interference figures from biaxial crystals. To illustrate this, we will consider only a section of thickness t normal to the acute bisectrix; the equation of the interference minima between crossed polars is

$$n\lambda = t(n_1-n_2) \doteqdot t(n_\gamma-n_\alpha) \sin\theta \sin\theta'.$$

If θ, θ' are small, then t will not vary much so that we can approximate this relationship to

$$n\lambda = k\theta\theta' \text{ (where } k \text{ is a constant).}$$

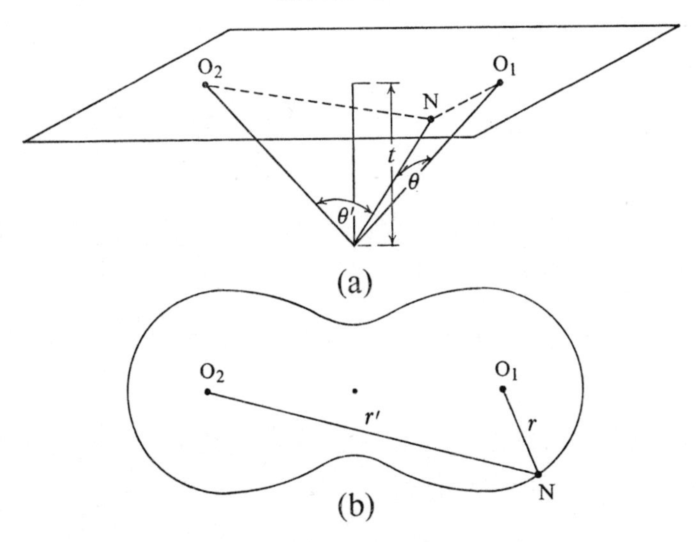

Fig. A.8 Equal retardation fringes for biaxial crystals.
a. Section plane of retardation surfaces for a section of thickness t normal to Bx_a.
b. The appearance of the section of one surface for a particular retardation; this is one fringe of equal retardation in an interference figure.

The form of this curve for a particular fringe is illustrated in Fig. A.8, where O_1 and O_2 are the melatopes, and N is the point on the image due to a wave normal making angles of θ and θ' with the optic axes. Since we are taking a section of this particular surface at a distance t from its origin

$$\theta = r/t \text{ and } \theta' = r'/t$$

so that the form of the equal retardation curve for a particular thickness for a particular fringe is

$$rr' = \text{constant}.$$

Such curves are called Cassini's ovals, and are well known mathematically. The general shape of retardation surfaces and various sections of them are further discussed in Wooster's *Text Book on Crystal Physics*.

A.3 The biaxial ray velocity surface

It was remarked in 4.4 that it is difficult to imagine what shapes the biaxial ray velocity surface will have. However, since we know that the biaxial indicatrix is a triaxial ellipsoid, we can reverse the procedure for the derivation of the indicatrix in A.1 to obtain some idea of the ray velocity surface.

It is simplest to consider the three sections of the ray velocity surface parallel to principal sections of the indicatrix. To illustrate the method, let us take the γ–β section shown in Fig. A.9. There are two ray directions

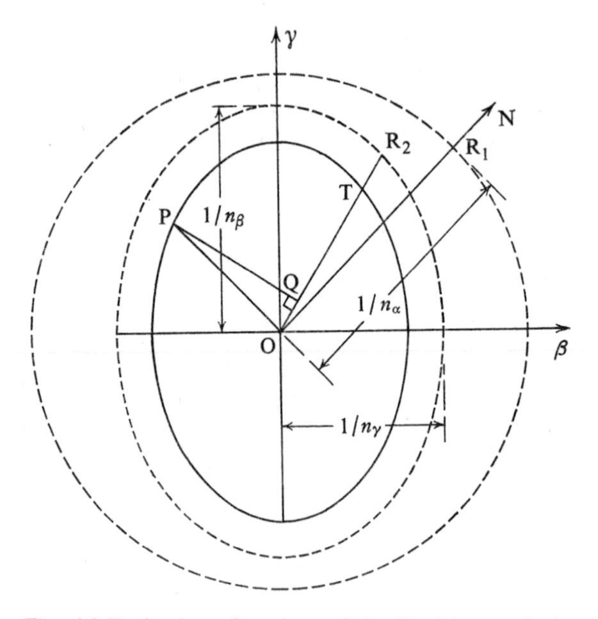

Fig. A.9 Derivation of sections of the biaxial ray velocity surface from the γ–β section of the indicatrix. The dotted ellipse and circle are the sections of the ray velocity surface in this plane.

associated with any general wave normal direction ON in this plane, and they may be obtained by the construction given in A.2. The elliptical section of the indicatrix normal to ON has one semi-axis in the plane of the diagram and the other perpendicular to it; the length of the semi-axis lying in the plane will be variable between n_β and n_γ depending on the direction of ON, but that perpendicular to the diagram will always be n_α irrespective of the direction of ON. Moreover, for this latter constant vibration direction, the associated ray direction OR, will always be parallel to ON. Therefore one sheet of the double-surfaced ray velocity figure will have a circular section in this plane with radius inversely proportional to n_α. The other sheet will correspond to rays such as OR_2 in Fig. A.9; the ray velocity will be variable depending on the direction of ON. We can deduce the form of this variation by realising that OP and OT are conjugate radii of the section of the indicatrix, and using the fact that PQ is inversely proportional to the ray velocity along OR_2, so that

$$PQ.OT = n_\beta . n_\gamma$$

and $$OR_2 = \text{constant}/PQ$$

hence $$OR_2 = \text{constant}.OT/n_\beta n_\gamma$$

i.e. the locus of R_2 is an ellipse similar to, and orientated in the same way as, the β–γ section of the indicatrix. Thus this section of the second sheet of the ray velocity surface is an ellipse with semi-axes inversely proportional to n_β and n_γ as shown in Fig. A.9. By similar arguments, the sections of the ray velocity surface in the other two principal planes of the indicatrix can be deduced; in the α–γ plane, the circular section will have a radius proportional to $1/n_\beta$, with the semi-axes of the ellipse directly related to $1/n_\alpha$ and $1/n_\gamma$, whilst in the α–β plane, the radius of the circle depends on $1/n_\gamma$, and the semi-axes of the ellipse on $1/n_\alpha$ and $1/n_\beta$. In the γ–α plane the circle and the ellipse will intersect at four points, but in the other two planes the circular and elliptical sections are independent.

Even now the visualisation of this complex surface is difficult in three dimensions. A schematic illustration is given in Fig. A.10*a*, showing the removal of the outer surface in one octant to reveal the formation of the four dimples in the α–γ plane, which are characteristic of its shape; a more detailed drawing of the formation of the dimples is given in Fig. A.10*b*. These dimples are the most interesting feature of the surface. The directions joining them to the centre of the surface represent ray directions which have the same velocity irrespective of whether the associated wave fronts are tangents to the circle or the ellipse (Fig. A.10*c*). The two directions of single ray velocity are known as *optic biradials*, or *secondary optic axes*. It is important that these directions shall not be confused with the (primary) optic axes, which are directions of single wave velocity; they are represented by the normals to the common tangents to the two surfaces across the dimple (Fig. A.10*c*). The angle between the secondary optic axes ($2B_\gamma$) can be simply evaluated as

$$\tan^2 B_\gamma = (n_\beta^2 - n_\alpha^2)/(n_\gamma^2 - n_\beta^2)$$

an equation different from that for V_γ between the (primary) optic axes; for most crystals the difference is small, less than about a degree or two.

In practice the existence of secondary optic axes has little significance, for our experimental observations are concerned with the interaction

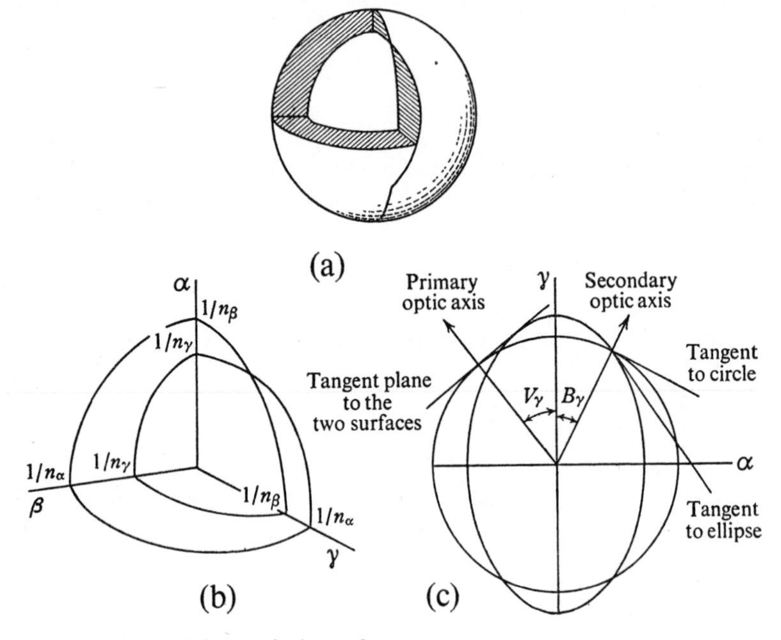

Fig. A.10 The biaxial ray velocity surface.
a. General appearance with outer surface removed for one octant.
b. Enlarged diagram of one octant showing ellipses and circles of three principal sections.
c. Section of biaxial ray velocity surface in optic axial plane, showing the difference between primary and secondary optic axes.

of waves. However, some experiments have been designed to demonstrate the existence of such directions by means of the phenomena of internal and external conical refraction. Description of these phenomena and the experiments which purport to show them will be found in more advanced texts mentioned in the bibliography; however, the attention of the reader is also drawn to the section in Wooster's *Text Book on Crystal Physics* where the validity of some of these experiments is questioned, and explanations in terms of ordinary double refraction are put forward.

APPENDIX B

THE ANALYSIS OF SIMPLE WAVES AND THEIR COMBINATION

B.1 Equations for sinusoidal waves

In Chapter 2, it was stated that the simplest waves are sinusoidal in character with a particular wavelength, linearly polarised, and travelling with a certain speed along a given direction. It was explained that representation of light by a simple continuous wave could only be an approximation to the physical reality, and that such a treatment had limitations (e.g. in the consideration of interference conditions). We can describe the continuous sinusoidal wave form by a simple mathematical treatment, in which the particles of the medium execute a simple harmonic motion at right-angles to the direction of propagation of the wave; wave equations of this kind can be used to analyse the propagation and combinations of light waves.

If such a wave is travelling in the x-direction, with the displacement of each point in the y-direction (Fig. B.1), it can be represented by the equation

$$y=a \sin 2\pi(x/\lambda-t/T).$$

As x is proportional to the time t, this represents a disturbance travelling with a velocity, v, $(=\lambda/T)$. Moreover, for a fixed value of x, the displacement, y undergoes a simple harmonic motion of amplitude, a, and period, T. At any given time t, points on the wave separated by multiples of the wavelength λ, have the same displacement y. The frequency ν, of the disturbance is the number of wave crests to pass a given point in unit time; it is therefore equal to $1/T$ $(=v/\lambda)$. Alternative forms of the simple wave equation are then:

$$y=a \sin 2\pi(x/\lambda-\nu t)=a \sin 2\pi(x-vt)/\lambda.$$

It is in terms of these equations that we can formulate a simple mathematical expression of a wave train travelling in the x-direction, with the x–y plane as the vibration plane; in the terminology of light propagation, x is the wave normal direction, while there is displacement of the electric vector in the y-direction, which is the vibration direction.

In the original equation above, the term $2\pi(x/\lambda-t/T)$ is called the phase of the motion. When we consider the effect of superposing two such identical sine waves, both with the same wave normal direction and the same vibration plane, the resultant disturbance would depend on

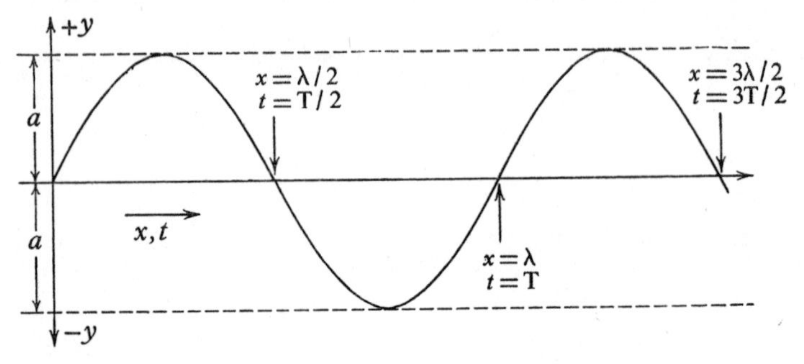

Fig. B.1 Simple sinusoidal wave motion represented by the equation $y=a \sin 2\pi(x/\lambda-t/T)$.

their relative phases. Let us suppose that there is a path difference of d between the two waves (Fig. B.2), so that their equations are:

$$y_1=a \sin 2\pi(x/\lambda-t/T);\ y_2=a \sin 2\pi[(x-d/\lambda)-t/T].$$

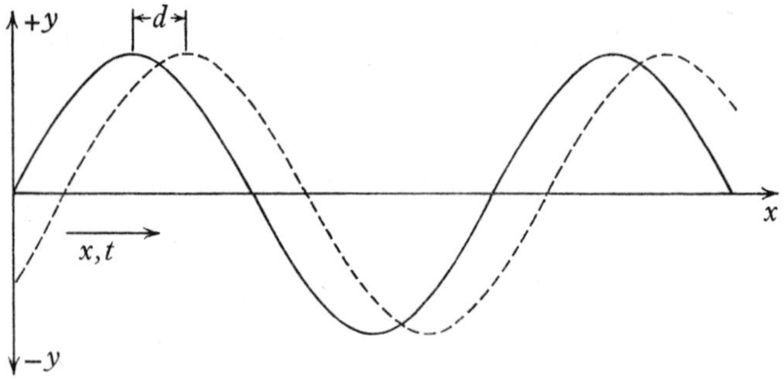

Fig. B.2 The two waves represented by $y_1=a \sin 2\pi(x/\lambda-t/T)$ (full line) and $y_2=a \sin 2\pi[(x-d)/\lambda-t/T]$ (dotted line).

(Since we can also write $y_2=a \sin [2\pi(x/\lambda-t/T)-2\pi d/\lambda]$ the path difference d produces a phase difference $\Delta=2\pi d/\lambda$, as noted in 2.2.)

Now when these two waves are combined, the displacement of any point is due to the superposition of the two motions, so that the new wave form will be given by

$$y=y_1+y_2=a \sin 2\pi(x/\lambda-t/T)+a \sin [2\pi(x/\lambda-t/T)-\Delta]$$
$$=2a \cos \Delta/2 \sin [2\pi(x/\lambda-t/T)-\Delta/2].$$

In general, this equation represents a new wave motion of the same type, with the same wavelength, period, etc. as before but with amplitude and phase different from either of the two original waves. Perhaps most important from a practical viewpoint is that the amplitude of the new wave motion ($2a \cos \Delta/2$) depends on the phase difference, Δ, between the original waves. The term $\cos \Delta/2$ can vary continuously between -1 and $+1$, i.e. it passes through zero, for which there is complete destructive interference and no transmitted wave; this occurs when $\Delta=(2n-1)\pi$, i.e. $d=(2n-1)\lambda/2$. If the intensity (measured as the square of the amplitude) is considered, the values ± 1 give maximum values four times those for each single wave; these intensity maxima are obtained if the phase difference Δ, between the original waves, is $2n\pi$, i.e. the path difference between the two waves, d, is $n\lambda$. These conditions for complete destructive interference and reinforcement were obtained in 2.2.

B.2 The phase amplitude diagram

In 2.2 it was also suggested that the resultant wave form arising from the combination of two or more co-planar waves of differing phases could be investigated using a phase amplitude diagram. The relationship of such diagrams to the simple mathematical analysis of the previous section will now be explained.

In the addition of simple wave motions, we are considering the addition of displacements at a given point in the transmitting medium, i.e. x is fixed. If the simplest case, with $x=0$, is taken, the original wave equation becomes

$$y=a \sin 2\pi(t/T).$$

Now this change of displacement with time at a given point can be set down diagrammatically. In Fig. B.3*a*, a point P rotates uniformly anti-clockwise around a circle of radius a, starting at $t=0$ from P_0; it completes a revolution in a time T. After a time t, the point will have reached a position P, having turned through an angle $2\pi t/T$. The projection of OP on to OY is

$$OQ=a \sin 2\pi(t/T)$$

i.e. OQ may be identified with the displacement (y) of the wave equation at a particular point in the transmitting medium.

Suppose the problem is that formulated in the preceding section and involves combining two identical disturbances with a phase lag Δ; to describe the resultant wave motion, it is necessary to find the total displacement $y(=y_1+y_2)$ at a particular point. Using a similar diagram

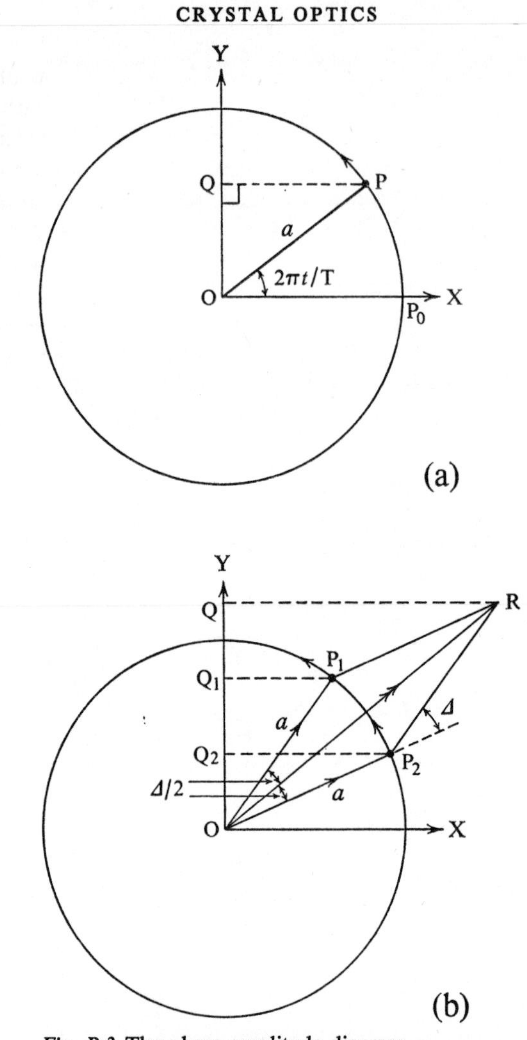

Fig. B.3 The phase amplitude diagram.
a. The projection of P rotating uniformly around the circle on to OY is $y=a \sin 2\pi(t/T)$.
b. The use of the diagram to find the resultant (OR) for two waves represented by P_1 and P_2 with a phase lag $\Delta(=2\pi d/\lambda)$.

(Fig. B.3*b*), P_1, associated with the first disturbance starts at $t=0$ from P_0. P_2, associated with the second disturbance having a phase lag Δ relative to the first wave, will be at a different position on the circle at $t=0$; it will be at the end of a radius inclined at Δ to that for P_1, for a complete revolution of the circle corresponds to $\Delta=360°$. At this instant of time, the displacements y_1 and y_2 will be given by the projection of the two vectors OP_1 and OP_2 upon OY; this will also be true at any other time, t, since the points P_1 and P_2 rotate uniformly around the circle (Fig. B.3*b*). The resultant wave motion is then obtained by vector addition of OP_1 and OP_2 to give OR, for it is clear that the projection

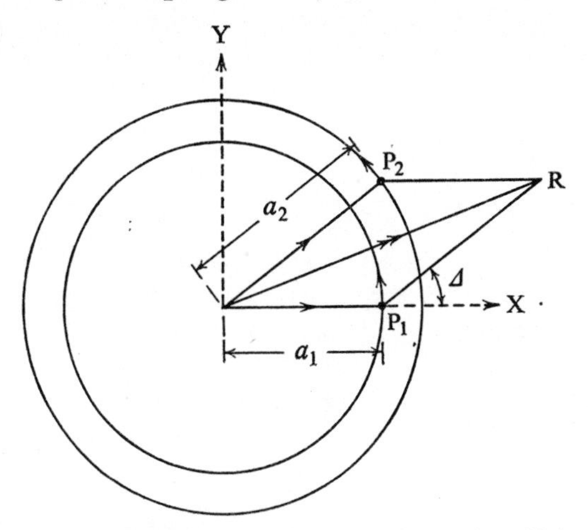

Fig. B.4 Combination of two co-planar sinusoidal waves of amplitudes a_1 and a_2, with a phase lag $\Delta(=2\pi d/\lambda)$.

of OR on to OY is always equal to the sum of the projections of OP_1 and OP_2. The amplitude of this vector sum is given by

$$OR^2=4a^2 \cos^2 \Delta/2$$

so that as before we deduce that intensity maxima will occur when $\Delta=2n\pi$, etc.; the zero resultant intensity occurs when $\Delta=(2n-1)\pi$, etc.; the phase amplitude diagram also shows that the new wave is $\Delta/2$ out of phase with either of the original disturbances.

In general, waves vibrating in the same plane with the same frequency but different amplitudes and phases can be combined by adding their respective vectors in the phase amplitude diagram. Let us take one further example relevant to the methods of optical examination in which two wave motions of different amplitudes (a_1 and a_2) with a phase lag Δ are combined (Fig. B.4). Here the resultant intensity is given by

$$a_1{}^2+a_2{}^2+2a_1a_2 \cos \Delta.$$

In this expression the third term can vary between $\pm 2a_1a_2$ as $\cos \Delta = \pm 1$. The value $+1$ will give the maximum intensity, and will occur when $\Delta = 2n\pi$, i.e. $d = n\lambda$; the value -1 will give the minimum intensity and will occur when $\Delta = (2n-1)\pi$, i.e. $d = (2n-1)\lambda/2$. Thus the conditions for maximum and minimum intensity of the transmitted wave are dependent on Δ and are still the same as they were for waves of equal amplitudes, but it is not now possible to have complete destructive interference, with no energy transmitted; there is always a transmitted wave whose amplitude and phase depends on the relative magnitudes of a_1 and a_2 as well as Δ.

B.3 Interference effects between crossed and parallel polars in parallel light

This type of wave equation can be used to analyse the interference effects observed in microscopic examination. The simplest practical arrangement is to use parallel light; let us consider first the interference conditions between crossed polars as described in 9.2.

In Fig. B.5*a*, PP and AA are the vibration directions of polariser and analyser respectively, with Ox and Oy the vibration directions of the anisotropic section set in the 45° position. The linearly polarised wave of amplitude *a* enters the section, and is resolved into the vibration planes of the crystal to give amplitudes

$$A_x = a \cos 45°; \; A_y = -a \cos 45°.$$

Now as was explained in 9.2, the passage of these two waves through the thickness (t) of the section introduces a phase lag $\delta(=2\pi t(n_1-n_2)/\lambda)$, but, of course, when they emerge from the crystal section they are still vibrating in perpendicular planes. They are resolved into the same plane at the analyser to give two waves of equal amplitude $a \cos^2 45°$ with a phase lag Δ between them; $\Delta = \delta + \pi$, for as was explained in 9.2, the analyser introduces an additional phase lag of π. The phase amplitude diagram (Fig. B.5*b*) can be used to give the resultant intensity as

$$(2a \cos^2 45° \cos \Delta/2)^2 = a^2 \cos^2 \Delta/2.$$

Under these conditions, the intensity will be a maximum when $\Delta = 2n\pi$, i.e. $\delta = (2n-1)\pi$ so that $d = (2n-1)\lambda/2$; similarly the intensity will be a minimum, zero, when $\Delta = (2n-1)\pi$, i.e. $\delta = 2n\pi$ so that $d = n\lambda$. Thus there will be complete reinforcement when the optical path difference is an odd number of half wavelengths while total destructive interference occurs when it is a whole number of wavelengths; this confirms the conditions deduced in 9.2.

If the same section is in a general orientation between crossed polars (Fig. B.5*c*), similar analysis shows that the resultant intensity is

$$(2a \cos\theta \sin\theta \cos \Delta/2)^2 = a^2 \sin^2 2\theta \cos^2 \Delta/2.$$

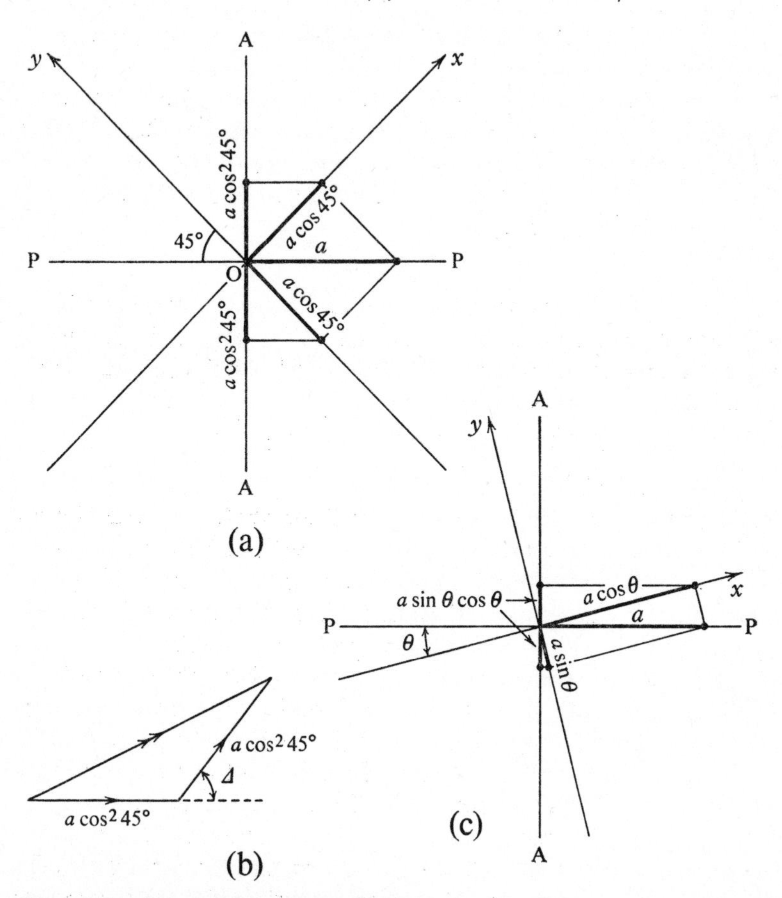

Fig. B.5 Interference between crossed polars.
a. Resolution of the light vector to produce equal amplitudes $a \cos^2 45°$ for interfering waves; section in 45° position.
b. Phase amplitude diagram for 45° position.
c. Resolution of light vector to produce equal amplitudes $a \cos\theta \sin\theta$ for interfering waves; section with x vibration direction at θ to polariser direction.

The particular value of Δ will still determine the interference conditions, but the intensity now depends on θ. If $\theta = n\pi/2$, the intensity will be zero; this corresponds to the extinction positions occurring four times in every complete revolution of the stage whenever the vibration directions for the crystal section are parallel to those of the polars. The intensity will be a maximum whenever $\theta=(2n-1)\pi/4$, i.e. in the 45° positions; so that the intensity produced by the interference conditions increases as $\sin^2 2\theta$ from each extinction position to a maximum when the stage has been rotated through 45°.

For parallel polars, the analysis is similar, except that $\Delta=\delta$, as explained in 9.2, so that the interference conditions for total reinforcement and destructive interference are interchanged. In the 45° position the interfering waves have equal amplitudes $a \cos^2 45°$ ($=a \sin^2 45°$), so that the resultant intensity is

$$a^2 \cos^2 \delta/2.$$

However, if the same section is set into a general position with one vibration direction inclined at θ to that of the polars, the interfering waves have unequal amplitudes $a \cos^2 \theta$ and $a \sin^2 \theta$. From B.2 the resultant intensity is now

$$\begin{aligned}&(a \cos^2 \theta)^2+(a \sin^2 \theta)^2+2a^2 \cos^2 \theta \sin^2 \theta \cos \delta \\ &=a^2(1-\sin^2 2\theta \,.\, \sin^2 \delta/2).\end{aligned}$$

Thus for the particular interference condition implied by a fixed value of δ, the intensity is a maximum when $\theta=n\pi/2$, and a minimum when $\theta=(2n-1)\pi/4$. The extinction positions of crossed polars are replaced by positions of maximum brightness; as the section is rotated the intensity decreases until it is at a minimum in the 45° positions.

So far we have been considering the total effect of the crossed and parallel polars and the anisotropic section. We have treated the light transmitted by the crystal in terms of the components parallel to the vibration directions of the crystal. It is instructive to consider the resultant displacements produced by the perpendicular waves and the nature of the light leaving the crystal before it reaches the analyser in the optical path in the microscope. Suppose that the normal arrangement with the crystal in the 45° position is considered. The displacement produced at a given point by the two perpendicularly polarised disturbances transmitted by the crystal can be written as

$$\begin{aligned}x&=a \cos 45° \sin [2\pi(t/T)]=A \sin \varphi \\ y&=-a \cos 45° \sin [2\pi(t/T)-\delta]=-A \sin (\varphi-\delta)\end{aligned}$$

taking $A=a \cos 45°$, $\varphi=2\pi(t/T)$ and δ as the phase lag introduced by the optical path in the crystal. Then

$$y=-A(\sin \varphi \cos \delta-\cos \varphi \sin \delta)$$

from which φ may be eliminated in terms of x and A to give

$$x^2+y^2+2xy\cos\delta=A^2\sin^2\delta.$$

This expression gives the general displacement produced by the waves transmitted by the crystal, and represents in general *elliptically polarised light*. The form of the ellipse depends on δ; it is always circumscribed by a square of side A, but its inclination within the square and the lengths

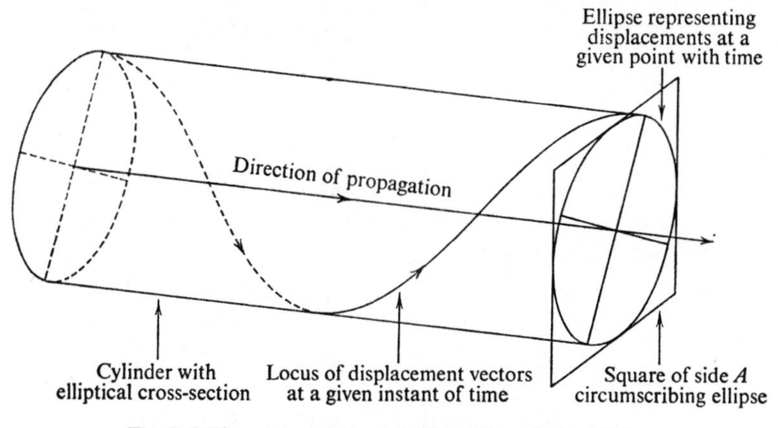

Fig. B.6 The representation of elliptically polarised light.

of the semi-axes are variable. From a physical viewpoint we can understand what is meant by elliptically polarised light from the diagram in Fig. B.6. This shows a cylinder parallel to the direction of propagation whose normal cross-section is an ellipse whose form is determined by the particular value of δ. As the light advances, the displacement (or electric) vector traces a periodic path around the surface of the cylinder; at a particular point, the displacement varies in amplitude and direction around the elliptical section of the cylinder, completing a revolution in the period of the motion. However, for certain special values of δ, the motion will be reduced to a simpler form, so that

when $\delta=0$, $x=-y$, and we would expect linearly polarised waves transmitted unchanged by the crystal;

when $\delta=\pi$, $x=y$, and the crystal transmits a linearly polarised wave with a vibration direction perpendicular to that of the light entering the crystal;

when $\delta=(2n-1)\pi/2$, $x^2+y^2=A^2$, and circularly polarised light is transmitted.

In terms of this treatment, the nature of the light transmitted by a wedge (providing a continuous variation of δ) set in the 45° position can be deduced. Fig. B.7 shows the sequence for a wedge as δ changes from 0 to 2π; this sequence will be repeated along the wedge. If the analyser is now introduced in the crossed position, the intensity maxima for the wedge will appear when the wedge transmits linearly polarised

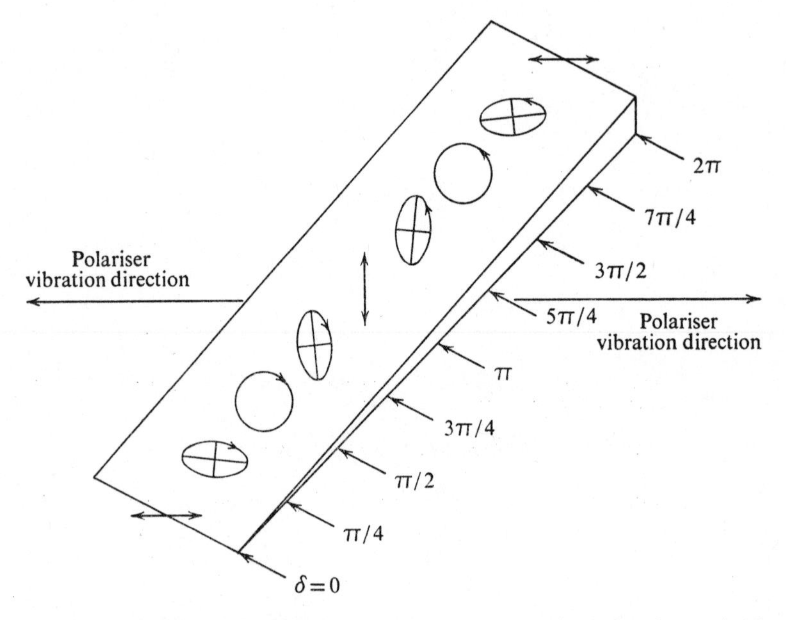

Fig. B.7 The nature of the light transmitted at various points of wedge set in the 45° position with respect to the polariser.

light parallel to its vibration direction, i.e. when $\delta=(2n-1)\pi$, i.e. $d=(2n-1)\lambda/2$; by a similar argument the black bands of zero intensity will appear whenever the wedge transmits linearly polarised light vibrating perpendicular to the vibration direction of the analyser, i.e. when $\delta=2n\pi$, i.e. $d=n\lambda$. In all other positions, the intensity will be intermediate depending on the resolution of the elliptically or circularly polarised light by the analyser. This diagram also clearly shows that when the analyser and polariser are parallel, the conditions for maxima and minima are interchanged, so that the light and dark bands on the wedge change places.

B.4 Interference effects in parallel light with general orientations of polars and crystal section

To complete this analysis of interference effects between polars in parallel light, we can treat the most general case in which the polars are in any general orientation with a general anisotropic section in any position on the stage.

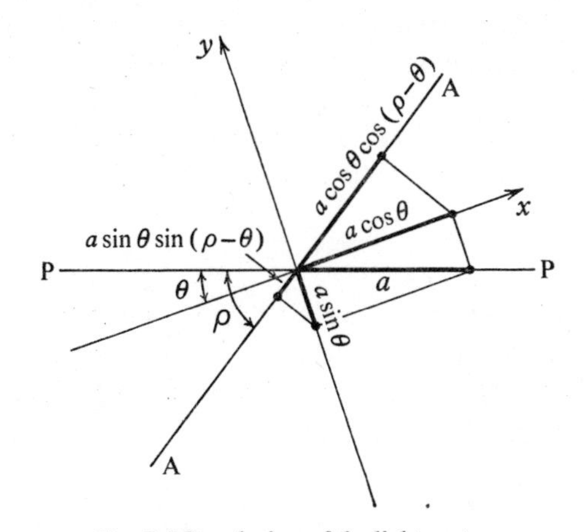

Fig. B.8 Resolution of the light vector to produce amplitudes $a \cos\theta \cos(\varrho-\theta)$ and $a \sin\theta \sin(\varrho-\theta)$ for interfering waves; section with x vibration direction at θ to polariser direction, with analyser and polariser inclined at ϱ.

The vibration directions of the polariser and analyser are inclined at an angle ϱ, with one of the vibration directions of the section inclined at an an angle θ to that of the polariser (Fig. B.8). Light waves of amplitude a enter the crystal to give two plane polarised disturbances of amplitudes $A_x = a \cos\theta$, $A_y = -a \sin\theta$. After travelling with different speeds through the crystal, these are resolved into the plane of the analyser with amplitudes $A_1 = a \cos\theta \cos(\varrho-\theta)$ and $A_2 = a \sin\theta \sin(\varrho-\theta)$. We are again concerned with the combination of two waves of unequal amplitude with a phase lag δ between them, so that from B.2 the resultant intensity is

$$A_1{}^2 + A_2{}^2 + 2A_1A_2 \cos\delta$$
$$= a^2[\cos^2\varrho - \sin 2\theta \cdot \sin 2(\theta-\varrho) \cdot \sin^2 \delta/2]$$

after substitution for A_1 and A_2 and subsequent trigonometrical manipulation. This expression shows that there can never be complete extinction unless $\varrho=90°$, and we have crossed polars. In any other setting even if the path difference ensures that $\sin^2 \delta/2=0$, some energy will still be transmitted. For general values of ϱ and $\sin^2 \delta/2$, the intensity will be a maximum whenever the second term is a minimum, i.e. when either of the permitted vibration directions of the crystal are parallel to the vibration directions of analyser or polariser; midway between these positions will be the intensity minima.

Apart from such general considerations, this expression can be reduced to give the conditions for crossed and parallel polars evaluated separately in the preceding sections. For example, with crossed polars, the intensity becomes

$$a^2 \sin^2 2\theta \,.\, \sin^2 \delta/2,$$

i.e. the interference conditions are modulated by the term $\sin^2 2\theta$. The conditions themselves are identical to those deduced before; for example for complete reinforcement $\delta=(2n-1)\pi$, i.e. $d=(2n-1)\lambda/2$ and so on.

APPENDIX C

THE MEASUREMENT OF REFRACTIVE INDICES BY NON-MICROSCOPIC METHODS

C.1 The minimum deviation method

THIS method requires that the crystal specimen shall be of sufficient size to be easily handled, and has two faces of good quality inclined to form a prism of moderate angle; alternatively it must be large enough to allow such a prism to be cut. When light passes through a prism of

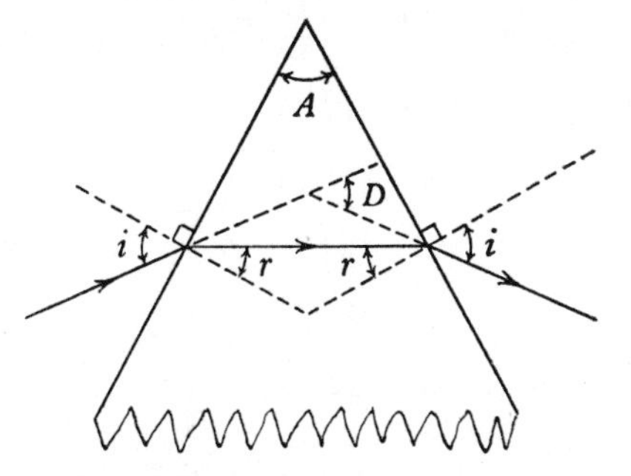

Fig. C.1 The wave normal directions for light passing symmetrically through a prism at minimum deviation.

moderate angle, the total deviation is not independent of the angle of incidence; for one particular angle of incidence, the deviation is a minimum. For a given prism, at the position of minimum deviation the light waves pass symmetrically through it (Fig. C.1). We see from this diagram that

$$D=2(i-r) \text{ and } A=2r$$

where A is the angle of the prism, D, the angle of minimum deviation, and i and r, the incident and refracted angles at the air-prism interfaces. Thus

$$n=\sin i/\sin r=\sin(A+D)/2/\sin A/2$$

so that measurement of D for a prism of known angle allows the determination of the refractive index n for the specimen; the method is well known in elementary isotropic optics. The crystal is mounted on a spectrometer so that the planes of the prism faces are parallel to the axis of rotation for the instrument. Light from a collimator passes through the prism, and the refracted image observed through a telescope. Adjustment of the crystal and telescope allow the position of minimum deviation to be determined; light can then be reflected from the prism faces to obtain the angle of the prism. Under optimum conditions, the accuracy in the determination of n is about $\pm 0{\cdot}001$. Apart from limitations set by the difficulty of obtaining crystals of a suitable size, there are some restrictions on the angle of the prism. Since $n \sin A/2 < 1$, for a particular substance this imposes an upper limit on the value of A; on the other hand, if the value of A is small, the angle of minimum deviation must also be small, with some loss of accuracy in its measurement. For the majority of substances, values of A of about 60° are most suitable. To avoid any difficulties due to dispersion, it is best to use a monochromatic light source.

So far we have been discussing prisms of isotropic material. With anisotropic prisms, the incident light will be doubly refracted on entering the prism to give, in general, two wave normal directions within the crystal. There are two refracted images to be observed through the telescope, each of which may be set in turn to its position of minimum deviation; the two values, D_1 and D_2, can then be used to calculate two refractive indices n_1 and n_2. The question now arises as to the significance of n_1 and n_2, and this must be considered in terms of the light path through the specimen at the minimum deviation positions. If we remember that at minimum deviation, the wave normal for each disturbance is symmetrically disposed with respect to the prism, the appropriate section of the indicatrix perpendicular to this common direction can be used to evaluate the significance of n_1 and n_2. As an illustration, let us consider experiments on a uniaxial crystal of quartz. A prismatic crystal (Fig. C.2*a*) is set on the spectrometer so that light enters and leaves the crystal through two of the prism faces enclosing an angle $A = 60°$. Two minimum deviation positions are found to give the angles $D_1 = 41°\ 04'$ and $D_2 = 41°\ 54'$, so that n_1 and n_2 are 1·544 and 1·553 respectively. For each of these disturbances, the wave normal at minimum deviation is in the same direction, parallel to another prism face (Fig. C.2*b*, *c*). We can then locate the appropriate section of the indicatrix, and deduce that n_1 and n_2 are n_o and n_e (Fig. C.2*d*). If there is any doubt as to which value corresponds to which principal refractive index, the vibration directions for the two refracted images can be

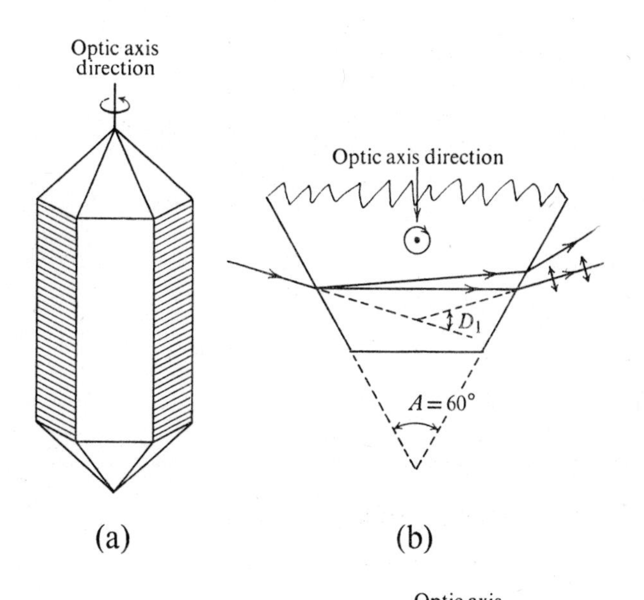

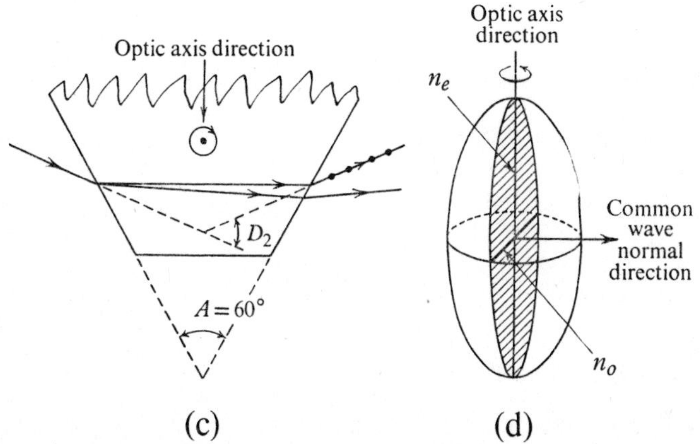

Fig. C.2 The minimum deviation method using a prismatic quartz crystal.
a. Quartz crystal with the faces used to define a 60° prism shaded.
b. Section through crystal at position of minimum deviation for light vibrating perpendicular to optic axis.
c. Section through crystal at position of minimum deviation for light vibrating parallel to optic axis.
d. Section of indicatrix perpendicular to common wave normal direction.

investigated using a polar; that which is found to be vibrating perpendicular to the optic axis direction must be due to the ordinary waves so that n_o=1·544 and n_e=1·553. This example shows that in uniaxial crystals it is possible to find the two principal refractive indices provided

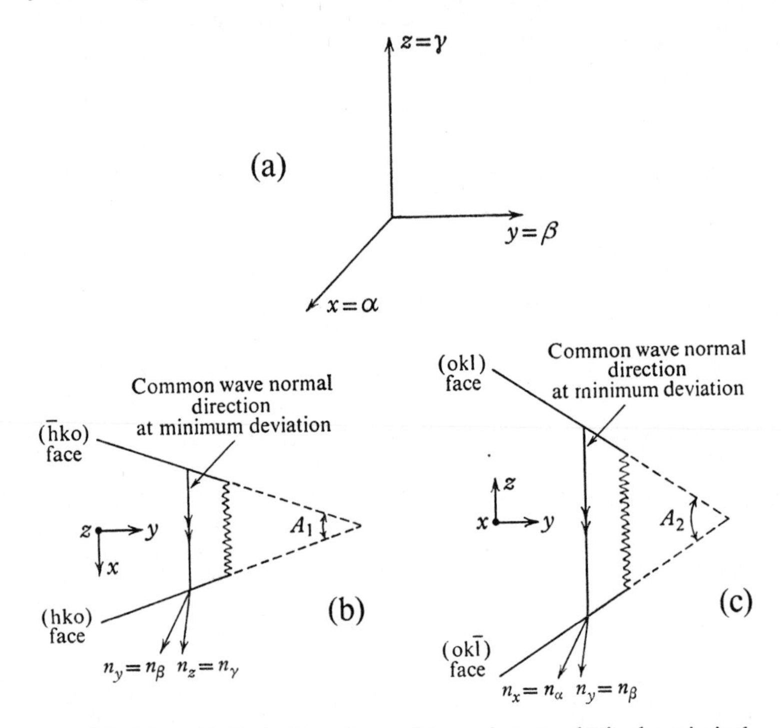

Fig. C.3 Schematic illustration of use of two prisms to obtain the principal refractive indices of an orthorhombic crystal using minimum deviation methods.
a. Orientation of the indicatrix relative to the crystallographic axes.
b. Use of the prism of acute angle formed by (hk0) and (h̄k0) to obtain $n_y=n_\beta$ and $n_z=n_\gamma$.
c. Use of the prism of acute angle formed by (0ki) and 0kī) to obtain $n_x=n_\alpha$ and $n_y=n_\beta$.

that the wave normal direction at minimum deviation is perpendicular to the optic axis; otherwise values of n_o and $n_{e'}$ will be obtained.

The same principle can be applied to the interpretation of investigations of biaxial crystals. If the common wave normal direction at minimum deviation is parallel to one of the principal axes of the indicatrix, we shall obtain the refractive indices associated with the other two principal axes (see the example in Fig. C.3); to get the value of the third principal refractive index, we must use a second acute angled prism of the same specimen orientated so that the common wave normal direction is parallel to a different principal axis of the indicatrix (again see Fig. C.3).

We see that within the practical limitations, unfortunately considerable, this simple method for determining principal refractive indices is most powerful. From a few measurements it can not only give values with an accuracy higher than that of all but the most refined immersion techniques, but also we can get valuable data about the orientation of the indicatrix.

C.2 The critical angle method

The second method commonly employed requires that the crystal specimen shall be large enough to cut a polished plate of reasonable size. The plate is immersed in a bath of refractive index liquid whose index is higher than that of the plate, and the critical angle measured. From 3.1 we know that

$$\sin i_c = {}_l n_c = n_c / n_l$$

where i_c is the critical angle, ${}_l n_c$ is the refractive index at the liquid-crystal boundary, and n_c, n_l are the refractive indices of the crystal and the liquid respectively. The measurements of i_c for a crystal plate immersed in a bath of known refractive index n_l allows the determination of the refractive index of the specimen, n_c.

These measurements are conveniently made with a form of Kohlrausch refractometer; fuller details of these instruments are given in Wooster's *Experimental Crystal Physics*. The essentials of a simple apparatus are shown in Fig. C.4. Light from an extended source is incident on the polished plate immersed in the liquid; the plate is mounted so that it can be rotated about an axis normal to the diagram. The orientation of the plate and the position of the light source are adjusted until the normal to the plate is inclined at the critical angle to the axis of the telescope. In this setting, the field of the telescope shows a boundary between a lighter sector, in which light is reflected from the plate, and a darker sector, corresponding to light being transmitted through the crystal. With this boundary on the crosswires of the telescope, the setting of the crystal plate is read on an engraved scale around the axis of rotation. The light source is then placed on the other side of the telescope, and the experiment repeated with the rotation of the crystal.

The angular difference between the two positions of the plate at which the boundary is on the telescope crosswire is a measure of $2i_c$. The liquid in the bath is usually of known refractive index, though to obtain the highest accuracy it is necessary to record the temperature of the liquid and the wavelength of the monochromatic light to permit any

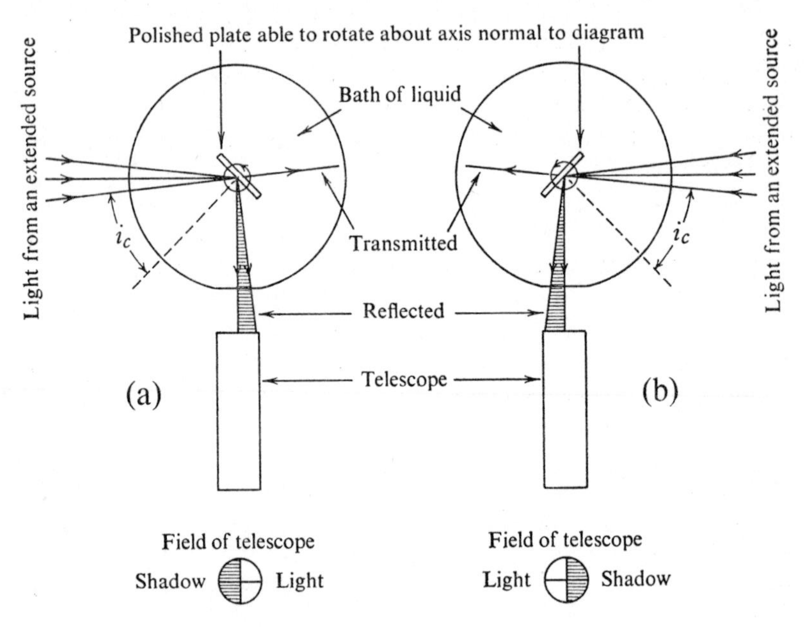

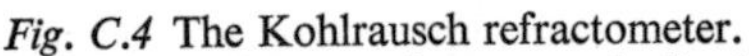

Fig. C.4 The Kohlrausch refractometer.
(*a*) and (*b*) illustrate diagrammatically the two settings of the crystal plate with the boundary on the telescope crosswires; the angle turned through by the plate measures $2i_c$.

correction for dispersion. Under optimum conditions, an accuracy of $\pm 0{\cdot}001$ is obtainable with this refractometer. It is essential that the surface of the crystal plate is flat otherwise the boundary will be indistinct and difficult to detect; it is rare for any natural crystal face to have such perfection, and plates invariably require polishing.

While for isotropic specimens there is only one boundary to be located, general plates of anisotropic crystals show two boundaries; these divide fields, in one of which both double refracted disturbances are reflected, in another, one disturbance is reflected and the other transmitted through the plate, and a third field in which both disturbances are transmitted. Measurements of both critical angles lead to two refractive indices n_1 and n_2, but again the significance of these values must be determined for the particular experiments with a particular plate. Light waves which are transmitted into the crystal plate for angles of incidence just less than the critical angle are refracted so that they

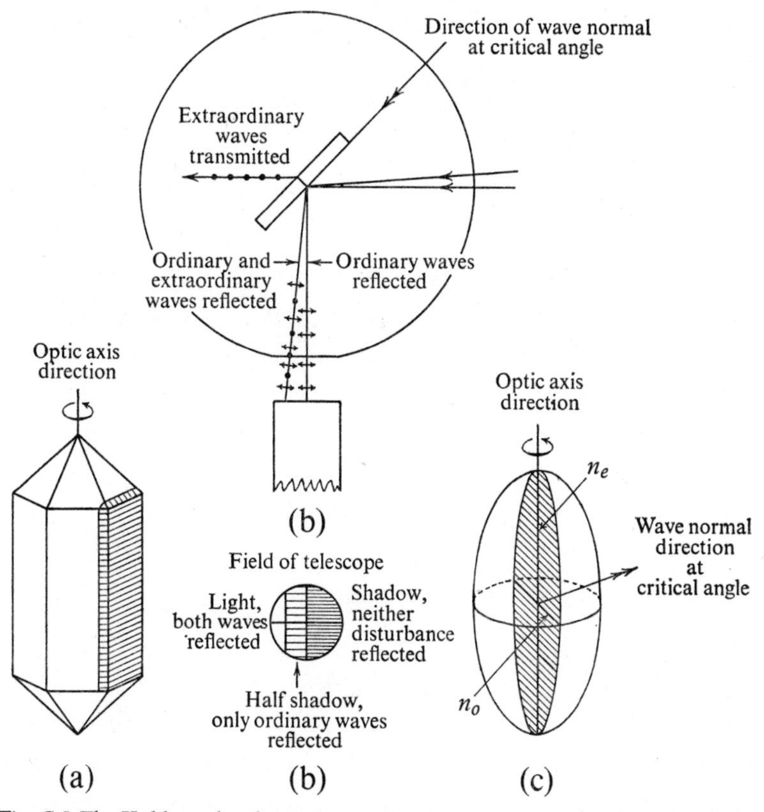

Fig. C.5 The Kohlrausch refractometer using a prismatic quartz plate.
a. Quartz crystal showing the plate.
b. The quartz plate, with optic axis direction vertical, set so as to record the critical angle position for the ordinary disturbance.
c. Section of indicatrix perpendicular to wave normal direction in crystal at critical angle.

travel parallel to the surface of the plate. Their wave normal direction is parallel to the surface of the plate and perpendicular to its axis of rotation; it is this direction within the crystal which determines the boundary marking total reflection. We can use this direction to fix the section of the indicatrix to interpret the significance of n_1 and n_2. As before we can illustrate this argument by experiments with a prismatic section of a quartz crystal inserted into the refractometer so that the axis of rotation of the plate is the optic axis direction (Fig. C.5*a*); the

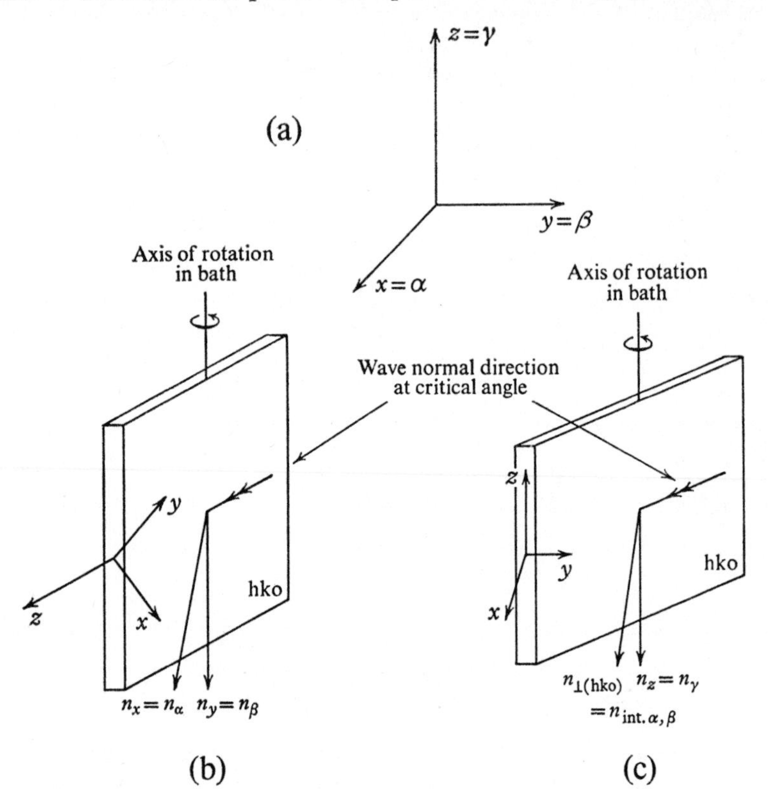

Fig. C.6 Schematic illustration of use of a section to obtain the principal refractive indices of an orthorhombic crystal using the Kohlrausch refractometer.
a. Orientation of the indicatrix relative to the crystallographic axes.
b. Use of an (hk0) section set so that *z*-axis is wave normal direction at critical angle to give $n_x=n_\alpha$ and $n_y=n_\beta$.
c. Use of the same (hk0) section turned through 90° to give $n_z=n_\gamma$ and $n_{\perp\,(hk0)}$ =value intermediate between n_α and n_β.

bath is filled with α-monobromonaphthalene (a refractive index liquid often used in this work) at 20°C when $n_l=1{\cdot}6582$ for NaD light ($\lambda=$ 589mμ). Critical angles of 68° 36′ and 69° 28′ are recorded giving $n_1=$ 1·544 and $n_2=1{\cdot}553$ respectively. The common wave normal is now parallel to the prism face and normal to the optic axis direction (Fig. C.5*b*); it is perpendicular to a section of the indicatrix whose semi-axes are n_o and n_e (Fig. C.5*c*). We can determine which boundary is due to the ordinary waves by using a polar to ascertain the vibration direction of the light arriving at each sector of the telescope field; the results confirm that $n_o=1{\cdot}544$ and $n_e=1{\cdot}553$ for quartz. Again this result may be generalised for uniaxial crystals, whose principal refractive indices will only be obtained if the wave normal parallel to the surface at the critical angle is perpendicular to the optic axis.

For plates of biaxial crystals the same treatment can be applied to evaluate the significance of n_1 and n_2 obtained for a given setting of a particular polished section. To obtain two of the principal refractive indices, the wave normal must be parallel to one of the axes of the indicatrix, i.e. one of the axes of the indicatrix must lie horizontally in the plane of the plate (see the example of Fig. C.6). The orientation of the other two axes does not affect the positions of the boundaries, though it will obviously determine the vibration directions of the reflected light. To obtain the third principal refractive index either another plate with another axis of the indicatrix horizontal must be used, or the experiment can be repeated with the original plate turned through 90°; in this latter case, n_1 and n_2 will correspond to the third principal refractive index and a value intermediate to the other two principal values (again see the example of Fig. C.6).

The Kohlrausch refractometer has some advantage over the minimum deviation method in that it is more often possible to obtain a suitable crystal plate than a prism of moderate angle; moreover, for biaxial crystals, the use of the same plate in different orientations can obviate the necessity for a second specimen of different orientation. The practical difficulties of the experiments lie in the preparation of the surfaces of the plates and the adjustment of the apparatus to give clearly resolved boundaries. If these can be overcome it can provide an accurate and rapid method of refractive index determination, and can also give useful data on the orientation of the indicatrix.

APPENDIX D

OPTICAL ACTIVITY

D.1 Description of phenomena

ONE of the features of a so-called isotropic direction is that there is no double refraction and light is transmitted unchanged along it; linearly polarised light with any vibration direction travels within the medium in this direction without resolution into two permitted vibration planes. For a few substances, however, there is a change in the vibration direction of linearly polarised light as it travels along isotropic directions; the orientation of the light vector changes continuously as the waves advance. For example, $NaClO_3$, a cubic material, shows this rotation of the plane of polarisation for any direction of propagation; another well-known example of rotation of the light vector occurs when light travels along the optic axis direction of a quartz crystal. The phenomenon, known as *optical activity* or *rotary polarisation*, is commoner for crystalline forms of organic substances than for inorganic ones. Its simplest manifestation is in the failure of a normally isotropic section to extinguish in any position in parallel light between crossed polars.

The angular rotation of the vibration direction of polarised light passing through an optically active material depends on the thickness of the crystal and the wavelength of the light; the sense of the rotation can differ in various isotropic sections of the same substance. The size of the effect is usually defined in terms of the *specific rotation* (ϱ), the rotation of the vibration direction measured in degrees per mm thickness. The dependence of the specific rotation upon wavelength is expressed in the form

$$\varrho = A/\lambda^2 + B/\lambda^4 + \ldots$$

where $A, B, \ldots$ are constants, λ, the wavelength; only the first two terms of this series are usually significant. Sections are said to be righthanded or lefthanded depending on whether the rotation of the light vector is clockwise or anti-clockwise.

It is well known that optical activity associated with isotropic light propagation occurs in non-crystalline solids and liquids, e.g. in solutions of some sugars. Indeed optically active substances are of two types; there are some which are only active in the crystalline state, and there are others which remain active in a fused or dissolved state. For the latter, the specific rotation of the non-crystalline form may be quite different from its value for the crystalline modification, which suggests that the origin of the activity may be different in the two states. In fused materials or solutions, optical activity derives from the existence of asymmetric molecules; in crystalline solids, the activity is due, at least in part, to the nature of the atomic arrangement. Thus fused quartz is not optically active, for the essential features of the crystalline atomic arrangement have been destroyed; on the other hand, cane sugar solutions remain active for they still contain the essential asymmetric molecular complexes. Our concern is with crystalline solids, and in these optical activity is associated with the enantiomorphous crystal classes, i.e. classes in which, owing to the absence of certain kinds of symmetry elements, right- and left-handed forms can occur; these right- and left-handed crystalline forms can produce optical rotations of right- and left-handed senses. Not all substances crystallising in these classes show the phenomenon for the essential structural arrangement for activity depends on more stringent criteria. The essential structural condition requires that the atomic arrangement shall have screw axes parallel to one another with the same sense so as to produce helical distributions of atoms; whilst enantiomorphism is a necessary condition, it is not sufficient. Clearly the hand of the optical activity depends on the sense of the helical atomic distribution. In biaxial crystalline substances, the specific rotation for the two optic axis directions is controlled by the symmetry of the crystal; thus for orthorhombic crystals it must be the same for plates cut perpendicular to either optic axis, though this does not necessarily hold for similar sections of monoclinic and triclinic crystals.

A theory of optical activity for isotropic sections was proposed by Fresnel. In this, the essential development rests on the resolution of linearly polarised light into two circularly polarised disturbances of equal amplitude but with opposite senses of rotation; it can be shown by elementary analysis that any simple sinusoidal wave form can be resolved in this way. Fresnel proposed that the two circularly polarised components travel with different speeds in an optically active substance. The resultant motion at any point is linearly polarised, but the vibration direction rotates as the light advances through the crystal in the same sense as the faster circularly polarised component. In effect, in isotropic directions in optically active crystals, circularly polarised light components of opposite hands have different refractive indices,

n_R and n_L. We can easily work out a relationship between the birefringence $(n_R - n_L)$ and the specific rotation for a particular wavelength. By analogy with the argument of 9.2, the phase difference after passing through a plate 1 mm thick is

$$2\pi(n_R - n_L)/\lambda.$$

If we now examine Fig. D.1*a*, which shows the orientation of the electric

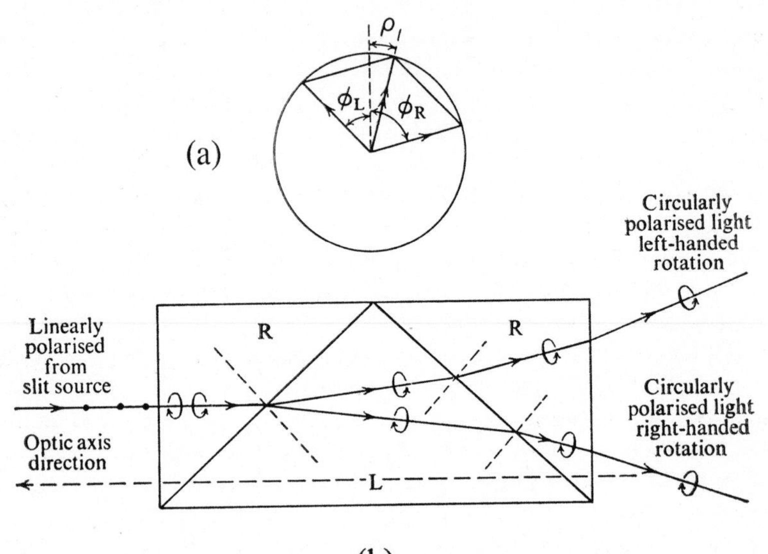

Fig. D.1 Fresnel's theory of optical activity for quartz.
a. Combination of displacement due to two circularly polarised components travelling with different speeds after unit distance; $\varrho = (\varphi_R - \varphi_L)/2$.
b. Experimental confirmation of the theory using a multiple quartz prism; the angular deviations due to refraction at the interfaces are greatly exaggerated.

vectors for the two circularly polarised components after this unit distance, it is clear that the vibration direction of the resultant linearly polarised light has rotated through an angle equal to one half this phase difference, so that

$$\varrho(\text{radians/mm}) = \pi(n_R - n_L)/\lambda.$$

The specific rotation for quartz for yellow light (589 mμ) is 22·1°/mm, so that $n_R - n_L \sim 7 \times 10^{-5}$, a small value typical of this birefringence for optically active substances.

Some confirmation of Fresnel's theory can be obtained by a simple experiment. The multiple prism shown in Fig. D.1*b* is made of two pieces of quartz of one hand together with a third piece of opposite hand; they are cut and cemented together so that the optic axis direction is accurately parallel to the length of the prism in all three sectors. A very fine slit is illuminated by monochromatic linearly polarised light. When the slit is observed through the prism two images of the slit are seen, neither of which will extinguish for any setting of a polar. If a quarter wave plate is inserted, however, each image can be extinguished separately, with the polar turned through 90° between extinction positions; this demonstrates that the light forming each of the two images is circularly polarised but one wave train has the opposite sense to the other. These observations confirm Fresnel's hypothesis concerning the passage of linearly polarised light along the optic axis direction of quartz. Light waves enter the first sector of right-handed quartz without refraction and, according to the theory, right-handed circularly polarised light travels faster than a left-handed circularly polarised component. The two components then pass through the interface into the second sector of the prism; since this is made from left-handed quartz, the relative speeds of the light components are interchanged. They are therefore refracted on entering the left-handed prism so that while the right-handed component is bent towards the normal, the left-handed component is bent away from it. Further separation of the two circularly polarised disturbances takes place at the next interface with the third sector before the two beams leave the prism to form the two separate images of the slit.

In a sense this theory implies that in directions described as isotropic for non-active crystals, an optically active crystal shows double refraction for circularly polarised light. Since we know that unpolarised light may be analysed into a succession of linearly polarised pulses, it follows that these linearly polarised pulses may be resolved into circularly polarised components. This means that the whole of the Fresnel prism experiment could be carried out with unpolarised light with similar results. More importantly it implies that the representation surfaces for optically active crystals are not exactly the same as those described for non-active crystals. For example, it suggests that the two sheets of the ray velocity surface for quartz will not touch along the optic axis direction; in fact, the outer ordinary surface is slightly bulged in this region, while the inner extraordinary surface is slightly flattened, so that they do not have their normal spherical and ellipsoidal shapes. However, the deviations are very small, and, even for substances with greater birefringences than quartz, they can be neglected for nearly all practical purposes. Nevertheless, anyone who is interested in the detailed study of light propagation in different media will realise that the phenomenon of optical activity and the double refraction of circularly polarised light normal to isotropic sections is only one facet of the more general problem of light propagation in optically active media; in more general directions in quartz, say, there will be double refraction of the elliptically polarised vibrations produced when light travels through the crystal. The pursuit of this complex problem for uniaxial and biaxial crystals is beyond the scope of this book, and reference must be made to other works mentioned in the bibliography.

D.2 Experimental observations

For most optically active materials, microscopic examination of normal thin sections or grain preparations does not allow the effects of the phenomenon to be detected, for the specific rotation is too small to allow significant rotation of the vibration direction within the thickness of the specimen. Occasionally one finds crystalline substances with particularly large specific rotations; for example, a standard 30μ section of cinnabar, HgS, rotates the light vector through about $10°$. But generally the effects of optical activity are not noticeable in microscopic work unless we use thick sections at least of the order of a few mm. Thick sections of this magnitude are employed to study activity for a particular crystalline substance; the basic experiments are designed to determine the hand of a section and the specific rotation at particular wavelengths for the material.

We need several sections of differing thicknesses within a range of several mm. Let us suppose that the sections are cut from several quartz crystals, exactly normal to the optic axes. When the thinnest of these sections is placed on the microscope stage between crossed polars in parallel monochromatic light it will not extinguish at any position of the stage due to rotation of the vibration direction in passing through the crystal; however, it is possible to obtain extinction if the analyser is rotated from its crossed position (Fig. D.2*a*) (in practice it will usually be necessary to rotate the polariser, for the analyser cannot be rotated in the microscope tube). The angle, θ, turned through by the analyser, is a measure of the rotation produced by this quartz section, but we do not know in which sense it should be measured, i.e. whether the crystal is right-handed or left-handed, so that the rotation of the light vector can be either θ or $180°-\theta$. We started with the thinnest of the sections to ensure that the rotation was not greater than 360°, a possibility that can arise with thicker sections so providing further ambiguity so long as the hands of different sections are unknown. However, the ambiguities can be resolved by using measurements for several different thicknesses

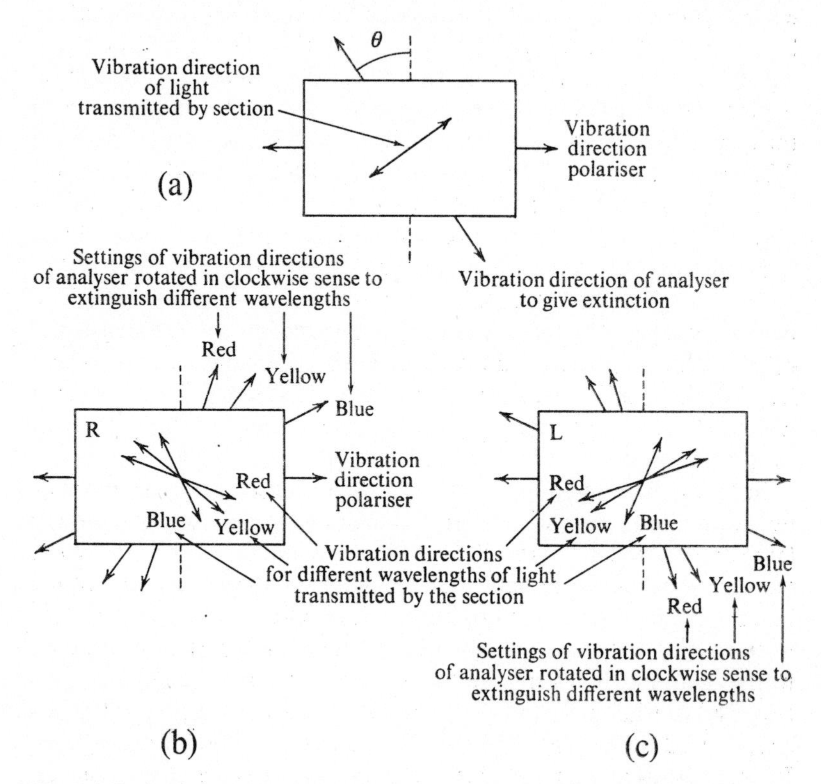

Fig. D.2 Extinction positions for quartz sections normal to an optic axis.
a. In monochromatic light, complete extinction after analyser rotates through θ.
b. In white light, right-handed section appears coloured, with sequence of colours due to extinction of different wavelengths as analyser is rotated clockwise.
c. In white light, left-handed section of the same thickness as (*b*) shows opposite sequence of colours due to extinction of different wavelengths as analyser is rotated clockwise.

of quartz, and analysing the results in terms of the various possibilities until a self-consistent specific rotation is obtained for all thicknesses; a table of typical results is analysed in this way in Wooster's *Experimental Crystal Physics*. The experiments can then be repeated with monochromatic light sources of different wavelengths to obtain the dispersion of the specific rotation; in colourless transparent materials, the specific rotation is greater for blue light than for red. Experimentally to obtain reliable accurate results, it is essential that the sections shall be cut accurately, and that the monochromatic light has only a small wavelength spread, otherwise the extinction positions will be difficult to locate. Incidentally, the dispersion of specific rotation provides an alternative method of confirming the hand of the thinnest section. When this section is illuminated by white light, the field is coloured and rotation of the analyser will never produce complete extinction; at various settings, different wavelengths will be eliminated, and the transmitted light will be coloured. If the section is right-handed, the vibration directions for different wavelengths can be as shown in Fig. D.2*b*; when the analyser is rotated in a clockwise direction, the colours are eliminated in the order red-yellow-blue through the spectrum giving a characteristic colour sequence. On the other hand if this section is left-handed, the optical activity produces the vibration directions for different wavelengths shown in Fig. D.2*c*; rotation of the analyser in a clockwise sense will now give the characteristic colour sequence but with the colours in the reverse order.

In 10.2 we referred briefly to the effect of optical activity on an interference figure in convergent light. Unless the specific rotation is very large or a thick section is used these effects are not noticeable. However, thick sections normal to optic axis directions show that the centre of the interference figure from an optically active crystal is different from that from normal materials; in uniaxial crystals, the isogyres do not extend to the centre of the figure and are replaced by a bright circular region (Fig. D.3*a*), while a similar bright region surrounds the point of emergence of an optic axis direction on the brushes for biaxial figures. Between crossed polars in white light, this region of the figure has the same colour as the section shows in parallel light; as the analyser is rotated from the crossed position, this colour changes in the same way as it does in parallel white light. In monochromatic light this bright central region of the interference figure can be extinguished when the analyser is rotated from the crossed position through the appropriate angle. These abnormal interference figures can also be used to confirm the hand of a section. If the interference figure from a thick section of quartz has a quarter wave plate superposed and is observed in monochromatic light, its appearance is shown in Fig. D.3*b*. The fringes are known as *Airy's spirals*, and their sense is the same as that of the hand of the quartz plate; with the quarter wave plate inserted below the same

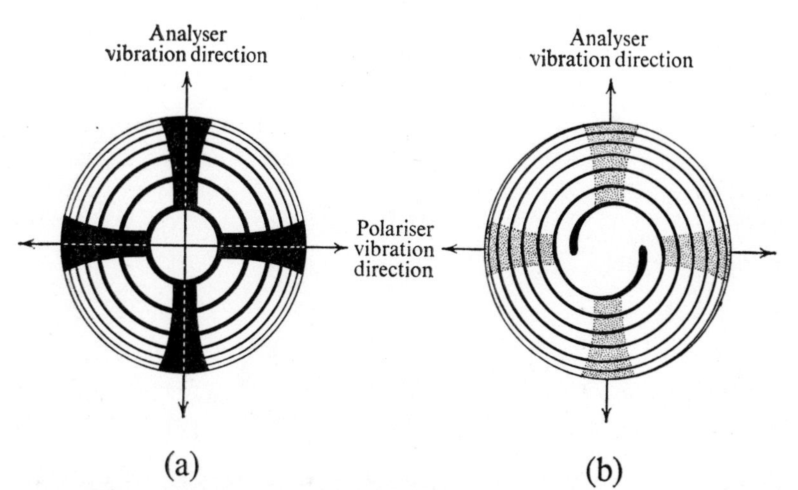

Fig. D.3 Interference figures from thick basal section of quartz.
a. In monochromatic light; note light centre of field.
b. In monochromatic light with quarter wave plate superposed; note that Airy's spirals are right-handed as is the quartz plate.

section, the sense of the spirals is reversed. Analogous effects are observed for similar plates of other uniaxial and biaxial crystals. The explanation of the origin of these spirals need not concern us here but may be found from references in the bibliography.

BIBLIOGRAPHY

THE lists under the various sub-headings do not attempt to be exhaustive but aim to give a representative selection from which the reader can supplement the present text.

1. Reading list for related fields

Crystallography

BRAGG, W. H. and BRAGG, W. L. *The Crystalline State*, Vol. 1. Bell, London, 1933.

BUERGER, M. J. *Elementary Crystallography*. Chapman and Hall, London; Wiley, New York, 1956.

BUNN, C. W. *Chemical Crystallography*. Oxford University Press, 1961.

PHILLIPS, F. C. *An Introduction to Crystallography*. Longmans, London, 1963.

Optics

DITCHBURN, R. W. *Light*. Blackie, London, 1963.

JENKINS, F. A. and WHITE, H. E. *Fundamentals of Optics*. McGraw-Hill, New York and London, 1957.

PARTINGTON, J. R. *An Advanced Treatise on Physical Chemistry*, Vol. 4: *Physico-Chemical Optics*. Longmans, London, 1953.

STRONG, J. *Concepts of Classical Optics*. Freemans, San Francisco, 1958.

2. Sources of data and materials

Crystallographic constants

Apart from the descriptions of materials which appear in professional journals, collections of data have been published in:

DONNAY, J. D. H., DONNAY, G., COX, E. G., KENNARD, O. and KING, M. V. *Crystal Data*. American Crystallographic Association, Monograph No. 5, 1963.

GROTH, P. *Chemische Krystallographie*, Vols. 1–5. Engelmann, Leipzig, 1906–19.

PORTER, M. W. and SPILLER, R. C. *The Barker Index of Crystals*, Vols. 1–2. Heffer, Cambridge, 1951–56.

Optical constants

Apart from the descriptions of materials which appear in professional journals, tables of physico-chemical constants, etc., collections of data are available in:

DEER, W. A., HOWIE, R. A. and ZUSSMAN, J. *Rock forming Minerals*, Vols. 1–5. Longmans, London, 1962–63.

KORDES, E. *Optische Daten* (inorganic substances). Winter, Heidelberg, 1960.

TRÖGER, W. E. *Tabellen zur optischen Bestimmung der gesteinsbildenden Minerale*. Schweitzerbartsche Verlag, Stuttgart, 1959.

WINCHELL, A. N. and WINCHELL, H. *The Microscopic Characters of Artificial Inorganic Solid Substances or Artificial Minerals*. Academic Press, New York and London, 1964.

WINCHELL, A. N. *The Optical Properties of Organic Compounds*. Academic Press, New York and London, 1964.

Immersion Liquids

Apart from the liquids supplied by chemical companies, standard sets can be obtained from the mineral dealers below and:

R. P. Cargille Laboratories, Inc., Cedar Grove, New Jersey, U.S.A.

Minerals and thin sections of rocks and minerals

Most of the materials mentioned in the text may be obtained from:

Gregory, Bottley and Co., 30 Old Church Street, Chelsea, London S.W.3.
Ward's Natural Science Establishment Inc., P.O. Box 1712, Rochester, N.Y., 14603, U.S.A.

3. List for further reading on particular topics mentioned in the text

The optics of highly absorbing and opaque materials

CAMERON, E. N. *Ore Microscopy*. Wiley, New York and London, 1961.

DRUDE, P. *Theory of Optics*. Longmans, London, 1922.

HALLIMOND, A. F. *Manual of the Polarising Microscope*. Cooke, Troughton and Simms, York, 1956.

SCHNEIDERHÖHN, H. and RAMDOHR, P. *Lehrbuch der Erzmikroskopie*, Vol. 1. Borntraeger, Berlin, 1934.

The indicatrix and other representation surfaces

FLETCHER, L. *The Optical Indicatrix and the Transmission of Light in Crystals*. Oxford University Press, 1892, reprinted from the *Mineralogical Magazine*, No. 44, 1891.

JOHANNSEN, A. *Manual of Petrographic Methods.* McGraw-Hill, New York and London, 1918.

SHUBNIKOV, A. V. *Principles of Optical Crystallography*, translated from the Russian. Consultants Bureau, New York, 1960.

Polars and polaroid

HALLIMOND, A. F. *Manual of the Polarising Microscope.* Cooke, Troughton and Simms, York, 1956.

JOHANNSEN, A. *Manual of Petrographic Methods.* McGraw-Hill, New York and London, 1918.

SHURCLIFF, W. A. *Polarised Light.* Oxford University Press, 1962.

Microscope design and the polarising microscope

HALLIMOND, A. F. *Manual of the Polarising Microscope.* Cooke, Troughton and Simms, York, 1956.

PAYNE, B. O. *Microscope Design and Construction.* Cooke, Troughton and Simms, York, 1954.

Preparation of specimens for microscopic work

CHAMOT, E. M. and MASON, C. W. *Handbook of Chemical Microscopy*, Vol. 1. Wiley, New York and London, 1958.

HARTSHORNE, N. H. and STUART, A. *Practical Optical Crystallography.* Arnold, London, 1964.

JOHANNSEN, A. *Manual of Petrographic Methods.* McGraw-Hill, New York and London, 1918.

Immersion Liquids

JOHANNSEN, A. *Manual of Petrographic Methods.* McGraw-Hill, New York and London, 1918.

LARSEN, E. S. and BERMAN, H. 'The Microscopic Determination of the Non-opaque Minerals', *Bulletin of the Geological Survey, U.S.*, No. 848, 1934.

MEYROWITZ, R. 'A Compilation and Classification of Immersion Media of High Index of Refraction', *American Mineralogist*, Vol. 40, 1955, p. 398.

Variation methods

HARTSHORNE, N. H. and STUART, A. *Crystals and the Polarising Microscope.* Arnold, London, 1960.

WINCHELL, N. H. and WINCHELL, A. N. *Elements of Optical Mineralogy*, Part I. Wiley, New York and London, 1948.

Interference phenomena

PÖCKELS, F. *Lehrbuch der Kristalloptik*. Teubner, Leipzig and Berlin, 1906.

WOOSTER, W. A. *A Text Book on Crystal Physics*. Cambridge University Press, 1949.

WRIGHT, F. E. *Methods of Petrographic-microscopic Research*. Carnegie Institute of Washington, 1911.

Compensators and other similar auxiliary devices

JOHANNSEN, A. *Manual of Petrographic Methods*. McGraw-Hill, New York and London, 1918.

PÖCKELS, F. *Lehrbuch der Kristalloptik*. Teubner, Leipzig and Berlin, 1906.

Subsidiary stages

EMMONS, R. C. *The Universal Stage*. Geological Society of America, Memoir No. 8, 1943.

HARTSHORNE, N. H. and STUART, A. *Crystals and the Polarising Microscope*. Arnold, London, 1960.

NIKITIN, W. *Die Federow Methode*. Borntraeger, Berlin, 1936.

REINHARD, M. *Universaldrehtischmethoden*. Wepf, Basle, 1931.

ROY, N. N. 'A modified spindle stage permitting the direct determination of 2V', *American Mineralogist*, Vol. 59, 1965, p. 1441.

Non-microscopic methods for refractive index determination

WOOSTER, W. A. *Experimental Crystal Physics*. Oxford University Press, 1957.

Optical activity

SHUBNIKOV, A. V. *Principles of Optical Crystallography*, translated from the Russian. Consultants Bureau, New York, 1960.

WOOSTER, W. A. *A Text Book on Crystal Physics*. Cambridge University Press, 1949.

WOOSTER, W. A. *Experimental Crystal Physics*. Oxford University Press, 1957.

ANSWERS TO EXERCISES

Chapter 3.5

1. (i) $\lambda_{\text{glass}}=3545\times10^{-8}$ cm; $\lambda_{\text{liquid}}=3790\times10^{-8}$ cm;

(ii) $n_{\text{liquid}}=1{\cdot}503$;

(iii) $i_B=42{\cdot}2°$.

Chapter 4.6

2. For (110) section, $n_o=1{\cdot}590$, $n_e=1{\cdot}556$; for (101) section, $n_o=1{\cdot}590$, $n_{e'}=1{\cdot}580$; for (111) section, $n_o=1{\cdot}590$, $n_{e'}=1{\cdot}584$.

3. (i) $n_\alpha(=1{\cdot}520)$, $n_\gamma(=1{\cdot}529)$;

(ii) $V_\gamma\sim30°$;

(iii) $n_{\alpha'}=1{\cdot}523$, $n_\beta(=1{\cdot}522)$.

Chapter 6.4

1. (i) 16·3°;

(ii) 8·8°;

(iii) 25·1°.

Chapter 7.9

2. (i) Sodium nitrate is trigonal; potassium chlorate is monoclinic;

(ii) The initial crystals of potassium nitrate are trigonal, the later crystals are orthorhombic.

Chapter 8.5

3. For KCl, $n=1{\cdot}490_5$.

Chapter 9.6

4. (i) Slow vibration direction: edge of rhomb$\sim$51°.

Chapter 11.4

1. For some varieties of apophyllite, the birefringence dispersion is such that (n_e-n_o) is approximately proportional to the wavelength.

3. (i) The difference is $\sim$4°;

(ii) The difference is $\sim\frac{1}{3}°$, and unlikely to be noticed in routine examination.

Chapter 12.5

2. $NH_4H_2PO_4$ commonly crystallises as tetragonal prisms, capped by small pyramidal faces. It is optically negative with $n_o=1{\cdot}52_5$, $n_e=1{\cdot}48_0$.

3. Scapolites are uniaxial (tetragonal), optically negative. Birefringence variable from about 0·010 to 0·040, principal refractive indices in the range from about 1·54 to 1·66. Good cleavage (100), imperfect cleavage (110).

5. The principal refractive indices of X are $n_o = 1{\cdot}378$, $n_e = 1{\cdot}396$.

7. Tremolite asbestos has monoclinic symmetry. The maximum angle from the slow vibration direction on to the z-axis is likely to be ~10°–20°, depending on the variety.

8. For aragonite, $x = \beta$, $y = \gamma$, $z = \alpha$; $n_\alpha = 1{\cdot}530$, $n_\beta = 1{\cdot}681$, $n_\gamma = 1{\cdot}686$, optically negative with $2V_\alpha \sim 20°$.

9. 675μ.

10. For diopside, the optic axial plane is parallel to (010), i.e. $y = \beta$; $n_\alpha = 1{\cdot}680$, $n_\beta = 1{\cdot}685$, $n_\gamma = 1{\cdot}707$, $Bx_\alpha = \gamma$, $z:\gamma \sim 40°$.

13. The optical properties of Y are $n_\alpha = 1{\cdot}586$, $n_\beta = 1{\cdot}592$, $n_\gamma = 1{\cdot}617$, $y = \alpha$, with γ almost parallel to (100), i.e. optic axial plane perpendicular to (010), with $2V_\gamma \sim 27\frac{1}{2}°$; the symmetry is monoclinic.

14. $KClO_3$ is monoclinic; $y = \gamma$, $z:a = 56°$ in the obtuse $x - z$ angle; optically negative, $n_\alpha \sim 1{\cdot}41$, $n_\beta \sim 1{\cdot}51_5$, $n_\gamma \sim 1{\cdot}52_5$, with $2V_\alpha \sim 25°–30°$.
Occasional lamellar twinning on (001).

INDEX